Howard Hughes

THE AUTOBIOGRAPHY

There's no doubt about it. This is the authentic voice of Howard Hughes. It's unique, it can't be duplicated. This is his autobiography.

Frank McCulloch
Bureau Chief, *Time* Magazine

McGraw-Hill has in its possession a tremendous amount of documentation which indicates beyond the shadow of a doubt that this is the authentic autobiography.

Harold McGraw, Jr.
Chairman, McGraw-Hill Book Company

It's the most exciting and revelatory first-person story that *Life* will ever have published. It's fantastic.

Ralph Graves
Managing Editor, *Life* Magazine

The Autobiography of Howard Hughes, to be published by the McGraw-Hill Book Co., is completely authentic. The raw material in the transcript should go into the archives, not to be opened for 100 years, when the perspective of time will make it a source for researchers as revealing of social history as the diaries of Samuel Pepys.

Robert Kirsch
Los Angeles *Times* Book Critic

CLIFFORD
IRVING

THE AUTOBIOGRAPHY

THE MOST FAMOUS UNPUBLISHED BOOK
OF THE 20TH CENTURY... UNTIL NOW

JOHN BLAKE

Published by John Blake Publishing Ltd,
3 Bramber Court, 2 Bramber Road,
London W14 9PB, UK

www.blake.co.uk

First published by John Blake Publishing in paperback in 2008

ISBN: 978-1-84454-561-2

British Library Cataloguing-in-Publication Data:
A catalogue record for this book is available from the British Library.

Design by www.envydesign.co.uk

Printed in Great Britain by CPI William Clowes Beccles NR34 7TL

1 3 5 7 9 10 8 6 4 2

Papers used by John Blake Publishing are natural, recyclable products made from wood
grown in sustainable forests. The manufacturing processes conform to the environmental
regulations of the country of origin.

This book is dedicated, with love, to my sons

Josh, Nedsky, and Barnaby

Contents

Also by Clifford Irving

On a Darkling Plain
The Losers
The Valley
The Battle of Jerusalem
Spy
The 38th Floor
Fake!
The Global Village Idiot
The Hoax
Death Freak
The Sleeping Spy
Tom Mix and Pancho Villa
The Angel of Zin
Daddy's Girl
Trial
Final Argument
The Spring
I Remember Amnesia

Foreword

THE BOOK YOU are now holding in your hands is one of the greatest untold stories of modern times. It reveals, for the first time, and in his own words, the full and unexpurgated life story of Howard Hughes, one of the most controversial and enigmatic figures of the 20th Century. Billionaire industrialist, daredevil aviator, film-maker and studio mogul, a womaniser who bedded some of the most beautiful women in Hollywood, by the late 1960s he had become known as the world's richest and most bizarre recluse.

A truly extraordinary story then – all the more extraordinary for the fact that Howard Hughes never wrote his autobiography.

For what you are about to read is actually a hoax – a gloriously audacious, shameless and wildly entertaining scam, as bizarre in its own way as anything in the life of Hughes himself.

It was a hoax that shook the American publishing industry, captured headlines around the world, and led to its architect, Clifford Irving, serving time in prison. Irving was already a best-selling author when, in late 1970, he hit upon the idea of faking the autobiography of Howard Hughes – a man who had not been seen in public, or broken silence, for almost 15 years.

With forged letters Irving convinced his publishers that he had enlisted Hughes' co-operation in the project. He received cheques made out to Hughes for around £750,000, which Irving's wife Edith – carefully disguised in wig and dark glasses, with walnuts stuffed in her cheeks – deposited in a Swiss bank account. When suspicions began to grow, Irving's forged letters were deemed as genuine by the world's leading experts. But, at last, he confessed, and went to jail for two years – a seemingly harsh sentence for what had started out as a harmless caper. 'I never thought I didn't deserve to be there,' Irving says now. 'I remember one guy coming up to me one day in the yard and saying, "You know, Clifford, it's wonderful to talk to you, because you and I are the only two guys in this place who admit to being guilty."'

*   *   *

Clifford Irving now lives in Aspen, Colorado and on the Pacific coast of Mexico, where he spends his days writing and painting. Think Aspen, and you think millionaires and celebrities; but Irving is far from being a millionaire, and one senses that such celebrity as he has enjoyed in his life has been a mixed blessing. For a short while, he says, the notoriety was 'an ego-kick.' But the publishing industry took a long time to forgive him. For years he was unable to get his books in print; and while he went on to write a dozen more books, including four *New York Times* best-sellers, what irks Irving most deeply is that it is probably the hoax for which he will always be best known.

Born in 1930 and raised in Manhattan, the only child of a cartoonist, Irving published his first novel, *On A Darkling Plain*, when he was 26; it was written after hours in the offices of the *New York Times* where he was working as a copy boy. He went on to write many more novels, as well as non-fiction books about the Six Day War and the history of espionage. Restless by nature, he travelled throughout Mexico and Europe. By the early '60s he had settled on the island of Ibiza. 'Cherchez la femme' had been a prominent theme in his life, and by then he was already onto his third marriage. 'I was brought up to be in love', he says. 'If you met a girl and you wanted her sexually, you had to believe that you loved her, because in my generation that was the only morally acceptable way of going forward.' And so, in 1965 he married for the fourth time, to a Swiss painter named Edith Sommer, with whom he had two sons.

Ibiza in the '60s was a playground for artists, writers, bohemians and lotus eaters. 'A wild place,' Irving recalls, 'where the watchword was "anything goes".' Among the more colourful members of the expatriate community was Elmyr de Hory, a Hungarian who rejoiced in the dubious reputation of being the most successful art forger in the world. Irving and de Hory became friends, and in 1969 Irving wrote a biography of de Hory's life. The book , *Fake!*, ended their friendship, since de Hory objected to the way Irving had described him as 'a charming crook' – but it would lead indirectly to Irving's plan to fake an autobiography of Howard Hughes.

In December 1970, Irving happened upon a *Newsweek* magazine article about Hughes, 'The Case of the Invisible Billionaire', describing how Hughes had recently decamped from his 9th floor redoubt in the Desert Inn Hotel, Las Vegas, to a new hotel hideout on Paradise Island in the Bahamas.

Irving was struck by a brainwave. He would fake an 'authorised' biography of Hughes. At last! The world's most enigmatic man unveiled! It would be the story of the century. The reclusive Hughes, Irving reasoned, would never come forward to repudiate the book.

Irving enlisted a writer friend, Dick Suskind, to research the hard detail of Hughes' life. To convince his publisher, McGraw-Hill, of authenticity, he forged a series of letters ostensibly from Hughes, and modelled on a fragment of handwriting which had appeared in the *Newsweek* article. In it, the billionaire (a neat touch, this) expressed his admiration for Irving's book on the forger Elmyr de Hory, and suggested that he would be willing to co-operate with Irving on a book about his own life. 'Hughes' wrote that he did not want to die 'without having certain misconceptions cleared up, and without having stated the truth about my life.' But the project must remain secret, and he would deal only with Irving in any transactions, including financial ones.

It was never really about the money. Life was good. Irving – just turned forty – had a three-book contract; owned a lovely 15-room Ibizan farmhouse, and his own yacht. What he was in search of was adventure.

He negotiated a deal with McGraw-Hill in which 'Hughes' was to receive some $675,000 and Irving himself $100,000. How to bank the cheques? Irving told his publishers that Hughes wanted them made out to 'H.R. Hughes'. Irving's wife Edith – a willing co-conspirator – flew to Switzerland and opened an account in the name of Helga R. Hughes into which 'Howard's' share of the money could be paid. Over the next nine months Edith would make several visits to Geneva, withdraw the money in cash and carry it back to Ibiza, where Irving secreted it atop various beams in their farmhouse.

Naively, he claims, he didn't grasp that they were committing a crime. 'We thought: They can't put you in jail for committing a hoax, can they? Especially if you have the money set aside to return, as indeed we did. It just seemed like such an elegant scheme from which I could withdraw at any time I wanted.' That, he acknowledges with a rueful smile, was 'the great fallacy'.

Irving told McGraw-Hill that the book would be based on a series of interviews which he was to conduct with Hughes under conditions of the utmost secrecy. To avoid any untoward leaks Irving and his publishers came up with a codename, 'Project Octavio', to use in their discussions about Hughes. The author then constructed an elaborate itinerary, travelling to Mexico, Puerto Rico and the Bahamas, reporting back after each trip with ever more fanciful accounts of his clandestine (and completely fictional) meetings with his subject.

These 'research' trips had an additional purpose. Irving was in the midst of an affair with Nina Van Pallandt who was famous as one half of a folk-singing duo with her husband Frederick, a Danish Baron. Irving's meetings with 'Hughes' became the cloak to arrange clandestine trysts with Van Pallandt in Mexico and California.

*   *   *

Becoming more and more involved and fascinated by their subject, Irving and his sidekick Suskind did a huge amount of original research, digging through newspaper files and tracking down people who had known Hughes intimately. *Life* magazine had bought the serialisation rights to the book, and Irving talked his way into the

Time-Life library. 'Octavio', he explained, 'keeps getting pissed off at me when I don't have the background information'. In the *Time-Life* library he photographed a treasure trove of files crammed with unpublished interviews, correspondence and personal notes.

And he enjoyed even more extraordinary strokes of luck. On a visit to Palm Springs, he ran into an old friend who happened to be looking for someone to rewrite an unpublished manuscript of the memoirs of Noah Dietrich, who had been Hughes' right-hand-man for more than 30 years. Irving turned down the offer – but was able to copy the manuscript, and mine it for gems that went into his own book.

Walking into the Academy of Motion Picture Arts and Sciences in Los Angeles, he and Suskind were amazed to be told that three boxes of material about Hughes, donated by his former publicity man, had been delivered that same day. No one had yet read them. Among the papers was an extraordinary three-page memo from Hughes to a studio executive in which he applied his engineering expertise to the problem of how best to cantilever the miracle of natural design that were Jane Russell's breasts. 'That went straight into the book,' Irving says.

Back in Ibiza, Irving and Suskind began the painstaking task of assembling the material into the 'interview transcripts.' 'We'd sit there with a tape-recorder and a mountain of notes and research documents. And literally, I would ask, 'Dick, do you want to be me today or do you want to be Howard? And then we'd start recording.'

So convincing was the voice of 'Hughes' emerging from these conversations that it soon became apparent that an autobiography would be a much more readable proposition than a biography – and spare Irving the tedious effort of rewriting the material into the third person. Irving duly created a letter from 'Hughes' giving approval to that concept, and in the autumn of 1971, barely nine months after first approaching McGraw-Hill, the author delivered the finished manuscript.

Irving's introduction to the book alone is a tour de force. In utterly plausible language he describes his astonishment on first receiving a letter from 'Hughes' expressing his admiration for Irving's book on Elmyr de Hory. He describes his various meetings with Hughes, their sparring conversations, and the growing bond between them. 'You're an outsider, of a sort', 'Hughes' tells Irving, 'a kind of cultivated maverick... a selfish son of a bitch... I have to like any man who goes his own way, as long as he doesn't step on my toes.'

Piling irony on duplicity, 'Hughes' counsels Irving not to trust his publishers, insisting he should be in the room as they read stages of the finished manuscript. 'Don't go to their offices. You'll go out to take a leak and they'll have two hundred pages Xeroxed before you zip up your fly.'

The book reveals a Howard Hughes that had never been seen before (largely, of course, because he didn't actually exist). He flew secret combat missions with the RAF in World War II; he visited Albert Schweitzer in Africa; he befriended Ernest Hemingway in Cuba. His womanising had always been an open secret, but here he reveals that he enjoyed affairs with even more Hollywood starlets than anyone had hitherto suspected (sadly, all of them had passed away long before the book's publication and were therefore unable to confirm or deny Hughes's boasts). But his greatest, and most secret, love, it reveals, was the wife of a diplomat, whom Hughes names only as 'Helga' (by a strange coincidence the same name as the signatory to Irving's Swiss bank-account). In a moving denouement, Hughes describes how, in a quest to free himself from 'the bondage of money and power' he journeyed to India, where he squatted beside the Ganges in the guise of a penniless beggar.

Did Hughes really buy a dozen Monet, Degas and Renoir oils on the international art-market only to keep them locked in a storage facility in Orange County? Was it really Hitler's carpet on the floor of Hughes' suite at the Desert Inn Hotel? These were precisely the kind of eccentricities that people expected of the world's most enigmatic billionaire. The more outlandish the stories that Irving spun about Hughes' life, the more his publishers believed them.

'The editors felt they were getting something unique – a wholly new story. They loved that. And I did too.'

Perhaps the most extraordinary invention concerned Hughes'

alleged loan of $400,000 to Richard Nixon before he became President. In the course of their research, Irving and Suskind had stumbled upon a story that Hughes had once loaned $205,000 to Nixon's brother Donald, to start a chain of hamburger restaurants in Southern California. Irving says, 'I remember saying to Dick, this is bizarre, but the amount's not big enough. Let's double it...'

Extraordinarily, it was later revealed in a scholarly biography of Hughes that the $400,000 figure that Irving conjured out of the air was very close to the truth. According to the biographer, the White House was receiving reports of Irving's supposed dealings with Hughes from the FBI and managed to acquire a copy of the still-secret galleys of Irving's book from a Republican source at McGraw-Hill. Believing that Irving was a long-standing Democrat – 'I wasn't', he says, 'I'm a political nihilist' – and worried about what else he might be telling the party about Hughes' loan to Nixon, the White House conspired to burglarize Democratic National Headquarters in the Watergate building.

So Irving was responsible for the impeachment of Richard Nixon?

He laughs. 'If I felt I had really been a prime mover in the capsizing of the Nixon administration, I would want that carved on my tombstone. If only I could do the same thing for George W. Bush!'

*   *   *

McGraw-Hill made strenuous efforts to keep the book under wraps. But when news of its impending publication was finally announced, Hughes' representatives immediately cried 'Hoax!' McGraw-Hill accepted Irving's explanation that so strong was Hughes' desire for secrecy that he had kept even his closest associates in the dark. And then Frank McCulloch, a *Time* bureau chief, who had been the last person to interview Hughes 14 years earlier, received a telephone call from a man purporting to be Hughes, stating that he had not co-operated with Irving in any way and that the book must be a hoax.

But after reading the manuscript and cross-examining Irving about his meetings with the billionaire, McCulloch became convinced that Irving was telling the truth. Even if it was Hughes on the telephone, the journalist reasoned, it was consistent with his character to dictate his autobiography and then deny all knowledge of it.

And then, even more incredibly, Noah Dietrich, Hughes' former right-hand man, came forward to confirm the book's authenticity, unaware that several anecdotes in it had been shamelessly pilfered from his own unpublished autobiography. In a surreal twist, Dietrich told reporters that he had heard that Clifford Irving had been invited by Hughes to the Bahamas, and interviewed The Man with a glass partition separating them to ward off germs.

A last absurdity: handwriting experts confirmed that the 'Hughes' letters had to be genuine, declaring that to consistently imitate the distinctive idiosyncrasies in Hughes' handwriting would be 'beyond human ability.'

One can only admire Irving's chutzpah. He began to feel invincible. So invincible, that in a moment of recklessness, he actually offered to take a lie detector test to prove his credibility. It was a bluff, of course, but McGraw Hill called it. The results were 'inconclusive', and McGraw-Hill never raised the matter again.

*   *   *

On January 7, 1972 Howard Hughes finally broke cover. From his hotel suite in the Bahamas he addressed a bizarre televised press conference, in which seven reporters sat around a horseshoe-shaped table addressing questions to a disembodied voice coming from a speaker set on a stand.

Hughes maintained he had never met Irving, and called the 'autobiography' 'totally fantastic fiction.' He added, 'I don't remember any script I ever saw in Hollywood as wild or imagination-stretching as this.'

Irving promptly replied that the disembodied voice was not Hughes, but an impostor. Forced into an appearance on America's top-rated current affairs programme, *60 Minutes*, he brandished one of his forged letters, and described his meetings with Hughes: 'He has on occasion worn false beards and false moustaches and wigs. There's a

James Bond set-up here that's out of the worst possible detective novel you could ever read.'

But the net was drawing tighter. Swiss authorities had been making their own investigations into the Zurich bank account of 'H.R. Hughes', theorizing that it was actually Irving's wife who was depositing the cheques and withdrawing the money. (There's a moral here: never trust the 'confidentiality' of Swiss banks). In the face of this clinching piece of evidence, Irving finally admitted to his lawyer that the whole thing was a sham.

'The relief of confession', he writes in *The Hoax*, 'was sweet beyond almost anything I had ever known. I constantly had to lie to people, and there came a moment when the weight of that lie asserted itself, when I realised how seriously people were taking what Dick and I thought of as a game. When it all finally began to unravel, a number of newspapers commented on how light-hearted I seemed to be in the face of this; they were all talking about "Irving laughing". Of course I was laughing. I was rid of the burden! I didn't have to lie anymore. I was laughing because it was over.'

*   *   *

In June 1972, Clifford Irving was sentenced to two and a half years' imprisonment on charges of Conspiracy to Defraud Through Use of the Mails. Irving's wife, Edith, spent one year in a Swiss prison. Dick Suskind was sentenced to six months' imprisonment in New York. Irving returned to McGraw-Hill most of the money, retrieved from its hiding-places in the Ibiza farmhouse and in Swiss banks. But a fair amount had been spent on expenses and lawyers' fees, and the author had been forced to pay taxes even on the money he returned.

Sixteen months later he emerged from prison with his life in tatters. For a long time, he says, 'Many publishers wanted to have lunch with me, but none were prepared to publish my books. I'd pissed on publishing. That had never been my intention, but I had embarrassed a great many people who believed in the legitimacy of the autobiography. They were shown to be gullible, greedy, and, above all, unprofessional.' It took many years for people to stop regarding the author as Irving the hoaxer, and accept him as Irving the author. Once that happened, his books became best sellers.

In 2007 a film version of *The Hoax* was released, starring Richard Gere as Irving. But for the author the movie misses the point. 'It depicts the writing of the autobiography as the act of a desperate man, bent on financial gain. The Hollywood gang never grasped that I was enjoying myself by creating a mounting series of intellectual and personal challenges. Maybe those challenges were amoral – even immoral. I'm emotionally too close to the event to comment credibly. But, since no blood flowed and nothing was broken except egos, isn't the book itself justification enough?'

Is it? Let the reader decide.

For this reader *The Autobiography of Howard Hughes* is a brilliant weaving together of truth and falsehood – one might call it a 'meta-life' – so artfully realised that even today it is hard to know where one ends and the other begins.

Dick Suskind died in 1999. Edith continues to live in Ibiza, in the same farmhouse where she and her former husband plotted the hoax. Howard Hughes died in 1976, but never took the time to write his autobiography.

'Perhaps,' Clifford Irving says, 'when he read what I'd written on his behalf, he was satisfied with it.'

Mick Brown
The Daily Telegraph
London, 2008

Howard Hughes

THE AUTOBIOGRAPHY

Author's Introduction

I

HOWARD HUGHES AND I first met in Hollywood on the set of *The Outlaw*, which would place the date as circa 1940. My father, Jay Irving, was a cartoonist for Collier's. He also had a mild interest in the birth of the television industry, as did Hughes, and they were casual friends. As a result, one morning my father and I were invited to visit the sound stage at RKO. I can remember sneaking briefs looks at Jane Russell's breasts – I was only nine years old and other events remain blurred. Although my father later lost touch with Hughes, he had fond memories of him as 'a shy and considerate man,' a phrase I've heard echoed by others who knew him in those early years.

I grew up and became a novelist, and after a time made my home on Ibiza, one of the Balearic Islands off the coast of Spain. I described it in an *Esquire* article as 'the Saint-Germain-des Pres of the Mediterranean, a lovely island, warm and swinging in summer, bearable in winter, cheap in any season.' A strange place too, full of borderline lunatics and dropouts from contemporary life. They prepared me for appreciating Howard Hughes, the quintessential dropout.

In 1969 I published my first nonfiction book, *Fake!*, the true tale of an expatriate Hungarian art forger named Elmyr De Hory. My father gave me a list of 'well-connected' friends to whom I should send copies; he badgered me, as fathers do, and I took the line of least resistance and faithlessly promised, as sons do. He died in June of 1970 and shortly afterward, feeling remorseful about unfulfilled promises I had made him, I mailed copies of the book to a few people on the list. Howard Hughes was among them. I included a note reminding Mr. Hughes where and when we had met, and then I forgot about it.

Five months passed before I received an undated letter on yellow lined legal paper, the kind you can buy in any office supply store. The scrawled handwriting was firm extended well over the ruled left-hand margin the way a schoolboy might write if he were getting down toward the end of the pad. It said:

Dear Mr. Irving –

Thank you for the gift of your book, which I thoroughly enjoyed reading. Your inscription was very thoughtful.

I find myself deeply interested in the fellow you have written about, despite a natural inclination to the contrary. I cannot help wondering what has happened to him. I would hate to think what other biographers might have done to him, but it seems to me that you have portrayed your man with great consideration and sympathy, when it would have been tempting to do otherwise. For reasons you may readily understand, this has impressed me.

I do remember your father and I was sorry to learn of his passing.

Yours truly,
Howard R. Hughes

I speculated for a while if this could be a practical joke. Howard Hughes was reputed to be a billionaire, and if I had been asked what kind of stationary billionaires would use, I wouldn't have answered, 'Yellow legal paper.' But if it was a joke there was no foreseeable barb to it, so I began to think about what Hughes seemed to be saying between the lines. I drafted a reply, saying, in effect: 'Dear Mr. Hughes, I'd like to write an authorized biography of you. If this idea horrifies you, I apologize. If not, let's talk about it. You certainly deserve a more definitive immortality than the one that's being forged for you these days by the media.'

I read this to my wife, who instantly advised: 'Don't send it. You're in the middle of a novel and your publishers expect you to deliver on time. Don't get sidetracked.'

'Nobody really knows what kind of man Howard Hughes is. That intrigues me.'

'Anyone who intrigues you,' she warned, 'is bound to be some kind of nut.'

But I mailed the letter the following day, and an answer arrived several weeks later, again scrawled on yellow legal paper. My reading between the lines had been accurate. Hughes wrote, in part:

…I am not horrified by your suggestion, although in times past it has come to me from other quarters and was rejected by me. I am not insensitive to what journalists have written about me and for that reason I have the deepest respect for your treatment of de Hory, however much I may disapprove of his morals. It would not suit me to die without having certain misconceptions cleared up and without having stated the truth about my life. The immortality you speak of does not interest me.

I would be grateful if you would let me know when and how you wish to undertake the writing of the biography you proposed… I wish there to be no publicity about this communication for the time being, and I would view a breach of this request very unfavorably.

Sincerely yours,
Howard Hughes

It's important to understand that I lived in the boondocks, both mentally and physically; I knew very little about Howard Hughes' life and the legends that surrounded it. At the time, January 1971, I didn't know that Hughes hadn't been interviewed or photographed since

1957, and not a single person was able or willing to testify that they had seen him in the flesh for fourteen years. I knew only that he had reportedly left Las Vegas for the Bahamas and that there was some sort of internecine warfare going on in his business empire. I knew the customary phrases used to describe him: 'bashful billionaire,' 'dedicated recluse,' 'phantom eccentric' – ad nauseam. I didn't know that one syndicated columnist, quoting 'absolutely authoritative sources,' had depicted Hughes as 'an emaciated invalid with white hair down to his shoulders, shaggy eyebrows... a basket case who has flashes of his old brilliance but spends most of his time in a catatonic stupor,' or that a witness before a Miami grand jury had stated that 'the tycoon weighs 97 pounds, has long hair gray hair and a beard, and has fingernails and toenails eight inches long.'

Armed with ignorance and naivete – obviously among my chief assets in this instance – I wrote back and outlined my proposal for the biography.

Then the telephone calls began. The voice at the other end of the line was polite, thin and slightly nasal, bucked sometimes by what I later learned was an amplifier. He said: 'Look, for Chrissake, let's make this on a first-name basis or we'll never get anywhere. Please call me Howard.'

Hughes, as he relates in his autobiography, prefers to place his calls at three or four o'clock in the morning when his mind is clear and the man at the other end of the line may still be bleary with sleep. I have no telephone at home, because home is a 400-year-old peasant farmhouse in the country; the telephone is in my studio, which perches on a rock jutting into the Mediterranean behind the walled town of Ibiza. I was only in the studio during the day, theoretically with an alert mind. If Hughes called at 3 a.m. the phone would buzz in the dark of an empty room – I was home in bed. He had his revenge later.

Our transatlantic conversations pirouetted round the subject of the book, we talked about life in Spain, a new house I was building, my novels (which he was starting to read, one by one) and I realized, after I'd made a mistake in relating a personal tale and been quickly corrected by him, that he had a dossier on me: it wasn't a detail you could pick from book jackets or any Author's Who's Who. We were still just disembodied voices spinning toward each other by satellite and getting regularly cut off by Spanish operators. I had read by now that he couldn't abide smoking and didn't drink and had a reportedly puritanical morality. I smoked two packs of black tobacco a day; liked my wine at dinner and my cognac afterward; and morally, for better or for worse, had my feet planted pretty firmly planted in the 1960s and their aftermath.

'We'd better meet,' he said, 'to see if we get along. How about next week?'

'Sure. Where?'

'Fly to New York. Stay at the Buckingham Hotel. I'll get in touch with you.'

'Hang on a minute, Howard. You have a reputation for leaving people stranded.'

'I swear I'll call you as soon as you arrive.'

In early February I flew to New York, checked into the Buckingham on 57th Street, crawled into bed weary from the long flight, and at two o'clock in the morning he called, bright as a robin, welcoming me to his time zone. He asked if I minded more travel to meet him. I said I'd expected that, and he instructed me to stop off at American Express later that day; flight reservations had been made for me. I assumed Nassau but I would have believed Timbuktu. The ticket was waiting when I arrived; I had to take off at seven o'clock the following morning, and I was routed through New Orleans and Mexico City to Oaxaca, a town in southern Mexico.

'This is paid for, isn't it?'

'No, sir,' the clerk said, puzzled. 'That's $316.36. Cash or credit card?'

I paid and left, but I didn't like that at all.

By now I had told my publishers about the venture, and they were excited but wary. Beverly Loo, the Executive Editor at McGraw-Hill, said, 'You'll never get as far as this Oaxaca place. That's not the way Howard Hughes does things. He'll have you bumped off the plane at New Orleans or Mexico City, and then you'll be blindfolded and taken to the Bahamas or Las Vegas.'

In New Orleans airport the following morning I waited to be tapped on the shoulder by an unsmiling courier and then whisked off to an unmarked Lear jet or a 200-foot yacht anchored in the Delta. Nothing happened. In Mexico City I waited for the man again. He didn't arrive. I flew to Oaxaca, checked into the designated hotel and began the next stage of waiting. I slept badly, hung around the hotel until early afternoon and then hired a taxi and visited the Zapotec ruin of Mitla, where I bought a king-sized serape. I was beginning to think it might be my only souvenir of the trip; there were no messages for me at the hotel when I got back. It occurred to me that I had come a long way and spent a fair amount of money to meet a man who had a reputation for keeping people 'on the hook' – as it was called in the multi-leveled ranks of the Hughes organization – for weeks on end, after which they would either be dismissed with some compensation or given a yearly retainer to sit around in some other place for the regal tap on the shoulder that might come or not. I had a wife and two small children waiting for me at home five thousand miles away, I was in a godforsaken town in southern Mexico waiting for a 'phantom eccentric' and a 'bashful billionaire.' How much of a phantom, and how bashful, could he be?

I was awakened by the jingle of the bedside telephone, which I snatched in the darkness and jammed to my ear. A voice said, 'Mr. Irving? This is Pedro.'

'Not good enough,' I said. 'I don't know any Pedro.'

'I'm a friend of Octavio's.'

I began to realize this was an elaborate and diabolical practical joke, I was already checking over in my mind the list of friends who might be responsible. 'Pedro,' I said slowly in Spanish, so he couldn't possibly mistake the mood – 'it's four o'clock in the morning and I don't want to play games. I'm glad you've got a friend named Octavio, but I don't know what's going on and I'd be grateful if you'd enlighten me before I hang up.'

He said cheerfully. 'Octavio is the man you've come to see. Can you be ready in two hours?'

At dawn I was outside the hotel when a Volkswagen coasted up to the gate. Pedro was a slim, brown-faced Mexican of about thirty, with a neat mustache. We drove out of Oaxaca and into the countryside, past a small Indio village and then up a narrow paved road in steep spirals that circled an oddly-shaped mountain. The mountainside was lumpy with rough little cubes and pyramids overgrown by seared vegetation: this was Monte Alban, the once-sacred haven of the Zapotec kings who had ruled southern Mexico before the Aztecs came to conquer. The ruins overlooked the three green valleys of Oaxaca. The early morning air was fresh and cool, and the stepped temple buildings were brushed by puffs of clouds that seemed to touch the sky. There was a feeling at Monte Alban of being very close to a child's idea of a finite and fixed heaven.

Pedro pulled up in a leveled-out space, a sort of dirt parking lot, behind the sunken stone ball court. He indicated another car, the only other car, about thirty yards away. I got out and walked over, scuffing at the dust, opened the door – and slid in next to Howard Hughes.

No eight-inch fingernails, no white hair touching his shoulders or white beard hanging to his belt. The last photograph of him I had seen had been taken in 1957. He looked simply like the same man grown older and thinner; the dark eyes and brows, the mustache, the swept-back hair now gray rather than black. He wore a cheap shortsleeved shirt of nondescript color, a tan cardigan with a button missing, creaseless brown slacks and a pair of loafers into which his socks somehow always managed to slip and vanish, so that when he crossed his legs there was a gap of bony white shin between the sliding sock and trouser cuff.

Aside from the mountaintop setting, it was a completely undramatic and anticlimactic meeting; the 'phantom tycoon' was a 65-year-old human being. We said all the polite and obvious things, we talked about Mexico, and then took a brief walk in the sunshine to the steps of one the temples. 'Great place,' Hughes said. 'Beautiful,' I agreed.

He said, uncomfortably, 'I'll see you tomorrow. Same time, but we'll go somewhere else.'

I had been nervous and so had Hughes, I realized; and I said so. 'Yeah... well, maybe,' he said. 'Thank you for taking the time, anyway.'

Pedro picked me up at six o'clock the next morning and drove me to the airport. He was a pilot as well as chauffeur and we flew in a private single-engine Cessna to Juchitan on the Isthmus of Mexico. We would dip down into the valleys between the sheer slopes of scarred mountains until a village of a dozen mud huts appeared abruptly under the starboard wing, and he would shout gleefully, 'Look at those people! That is the stone age!' I said, 'Fantastic... amazing... ' and then asked him please to gain some altitude so that we wouldn't join them, forever, in their mountain fastness.

We landed in Juchitan, and Hughes and I met in a sparsely furnished room in a small hotel in the nearby town of Tehuantepec. He had a jug with him – 'This place has the best orange juice in Mexico,' he explained. He drank six cupfuls from paper cups that he took from his briefcase. I don't know what test I had passed, but the mood had changed completely; he was expansive, and I was relaxed. We talked until early in the evening, the conversations and negotiations punctuated by his vanishing, from time to time, out the door and apparently to another room. The rules were set for the writing of what was then meant to be an authorized biography: we would tape a series of interviews, which he would transcribe, and I would work with them and whatever material I could unearth on my own. 'None of my people know about this,' he said, 'and I want it to stay that way. So you'll have to do this research that you're talking about on your own. Don't come running to me for help. Don't use my name. And don't talk about it, and tell your publishers not to talk. If it gets out to the press what we're doing, the whole goddamnn thing's off.'

Hughes vanished again and Pedro appeared, bearing an envelope containing $750 in cash to cover my expenses on the trip. 'Señor Octavio asked me to apologize to you,' he said. 'He had to leave. I'll fly you back to Oaxaca.'

The next day I flew back to New York, gave a report to my publishers, and then went home to Ibiza.

The next meeting, arranged by telephone, took place some weeks later in Puerto Rico. I flew from Madrid to San Juan and checked into the agreed hotel. Hughes telephoned at three o'clock in the morning and asked me to come down to the lobby, where a driver met me and led me through the darkness to an old Chevrolet parked at the curb. He did the familiar disappearing act and I slid behind the wheel next to Hughes, who was wearing, it seemed to me, the same clothes he had worn in Mexico the month before: styleless shirt, baggy trousers and cheap cloth windbreaker. In the interim, however, he had grown a startlingly full head of dark brown hair. 'Well, goddamnit, it's a wig. Cost me $9.95 in the five-and-dime. I have three or four of them and a few beards, too. I can't afford to be recognized – you have no idea the risk I take in meeting you this way. It's not that there's always somebody out to subpoena me, although that's bad enough. It's worse.'

He wouldn't elaborate. He suggested we drive while we talk, and pointed out the route past San Juan Airport and up into the Puerto Rican tropical rainforest. We reached the summit of vegetation just as dawn was breaking, and he said, 'Stop here.' After a while a woman materialized out of the undergrowth, carrying a basket full of bananas. Following Hughes' request, I got out of the car and bought a dozen. He put on a pair of white cotton gloves and we began to peel and eat them. They were short, fat, sweet bananas. 'These are the best bananas in the world,' he said, and to prove it he ate four. 'In America they're made of plastic.'

After the banana feast we got down to talking business and procedure. Long after the sun rose and the lush greenery of the rainforest glittered with golden light, we checked off the last clause in the agreement and signed several necessary copies, resting the pages on Hughes' briefcase against the dashboard of the Chevrolet. 'Good,' he said, smiling broadly for the first time since I had met him. 'I hate these goddamn business details. Now we can get to work. You go back to Spain. I'll call you when I'm ready to start.'

That was the prelude. I was full of contradictory impressions, and on the plane flying up to New York, I took out a spiral notebook and began making notes on some of the conversations. They sum up, better than any recollection, the tenor of what was said and the feelings I had then about what he had allowed himself to reveal; and so I reproduce them verbatim.

H: 'The things that every man wants the most are the easiest to get. Money, fame, and women. That's what happened to me. And so you get them – and what then? There's that old gypsy curse: "May your dreams come true."'

He knew Hemingway, apparently in Cuba. At first Hem. didn't know who HH was – just another hanger-on. 'Hem liked the fact that I knew something about planes. I had a private plane (where and when?) and I took Hem. up for a ride. He said, 'You're a hot pilot'... A year or so later when I saw him again I told him who I was. He said, 'Well, you son of a bitch.' He seemed to be impressed, and unfortunately that changed our relationship. Of course he gave me his word that he wouldn't let on to anyone else who I was, and as far as I know he kept it.'

H., on women briefly: 'They wear you out trying to get ideas across to them. Then later, when you give up trying, they hate you for it. Like Ava [Gardner] and Lana [Turner]. They want too much. I didn't have that much to give.' I n reference to my own private past life he said, 'You really find individual women so different?'

I said, 'I sure do,' and he made no comment; but he obviously disagreed.

H: (about me) 'You're an outsider, of a sort – a kind of cultivated maverick. Putting aside judgments as to the harm you've done, because by your own admission you're a selfish son of a bitch, that's probably why I get along with you. I have to like any man who goes his own way, as long as he doesn't step on my toes.'

I feel strongly his consciousness of death as a powerful factor in his life. To describe him, at this junction: alone but not necessarily lonely; careful but not cautious; straightforward but not simple; intelligent but not intellectual; fussy but not really phobic; frail but making no obvious demands for his frailty; desperately curious about anything he doesn't know about; eccentric but not crazy; anxious to communicate but doubly anxious not to be misunderstood.

Most men flatter themselves that they live in their own world, but in fact they care a hell of a lot what the world-at-large thinks of them. Hughes, it would seem, for the most part has no time for self-flattery and less for caring about the world's opinion. Maugham said that money is the sixth sense which enables us to make the best of the other five. Maugham said it; Hughes may have lived it.

II

The book – at that time still an authorized biography – was code-named 'Project Octavio' by the few privileged executives at McGraw-Hill and *Life* magazine (which had immediately bought first-serial rights) aware of its existence. Hughes had insisted on absolute secrecy and this was spelled out unequivocally in the various contracts. A breach of that secrecy gave him the opportunity to withdraw. 'None of my people know I'm doing this,' he repeated, 'and I don't want them to know. If it leaks to the press and you're asked, you've got to deny everything.' The proscriptions extended into all areas, including this introduction, which will account for the fact that certain place names and dates have either been changed or omitted. The tape-recorded interviews would be transcribed and typed under Hughes' direction – that is to say, by some trusted lower-echelon associate – and my copy of the transcripts was to remain in my possession at all times. When it was read by the publishers, our agreements stipulated that I was to be physically present. 'They can come up and read it in your hotel room,' Hughes counseled. 'Don't go to their offices. You'll go out to take a leak and they'll have two hundred pages Xeroxed before you zip up your fly. I'm counting on you,' he said.

We were so unalike. He was nearly thirty years older than I, bred in the Texas oilfields, orphaned young, a college dropout. I came from a middle-class Jewish home in Manhattan and had loafed through a bucolic university education at Cornell. In 1951 when Hughes was ferreting Communists out of the film industry in Hollywood, I was marching with Paul Robeson at Union Square and writing angry letters to *The Nation*. This gave a good base for conflict and we used it when we had to. He was a billionaire twice over; I still couldn't qualify for an American Express card and Robert Kirsch of the *Los Angeles Times* had called me 'America's best worst-selling novelist,' which was a nice compliment but didn't pay the rent. Hughes had lived almost all his life in America; I had taken off at the age of twenty-two and become, without design but nonetheless firmly, an expatriate. His world of adventure had taken place in moviemaking, flying, high finance; I had bummed my way around four continents, worked in steel mills and wheat harvests, lived on a houseboat in Kashmir, married several times and written six books. He had designed and built one of the most sophisticated aircraft in the world; I had nearly failed high school physics and had trouble splicing two wires together. I had three children, Hughes had none.

There were similarities too, that helped in oblique ways. Hughes had been an only child; so had I. The world of an only child is a special one and the male who moves from it into adulthood carries a heritage of ego, selfishness, self-sufficency and loneliness. This we shared. And we were both tall – Hughes nearly six foot three and I an inch taller. Tall men instinctively understand each other's physical stance, the still-living memory of adolescent awkwardness, the vulnerability. There was also the fact that Hughes, who has been sued in court possibly more times than any living man, discovered one day that my publishers and I were being sued for libel and defamation of character as a result of my last published book. The damages claimed, worldwide, came to more than $160 million. 'You know,' he said to me, gravely, 'I've never been sued for that much in my whole life. That's really something. I'm sorry for you, but I'm impressed. That tops me by – let's see – by $23 million.'

'Yes, but you lost the lawsuit, Howard, and you've got that kind of money. I won't lose because what I wrote was true and I can prove it. And if I lose, I haven't got $160 million.' He hadn't listened. 'That's really something,' he repeated, and I realized he had a new respect for me; he was mildly envious.

The interviews began in the Bahamas. Most of them took place in my hotel room. The air-conditioning had to be turned off, the windows closed, and my wife, who was traveling with me then, had to disappear half an hour before the appropriate time. This meant that she saw a great deal of the nightlife in Nassau and once, at four o'clock in the morning, had to wrap herself in a hotel blanket and doze in a deck chair on the beach until the sun woke her. Her enthusiasm for the project was increasingly dim.

Hughes was a talker and rambler, but I wanted more than facts and anecdotes: I wanted the man. 'You ask some tough questions,' he said, and after a while he began to call me 'Mr. Why,' because 'Why?' on my part became a refrain, until I was almost as tired of hearing myself say it as he was. We clocked about nine hours of actual taping time during the ten days I spent in the Bahamas, but that represented more than twenty hours spent together. He would wave his hand at the tape recorder. 'Shut it off. . . I can't stand that damn thing...' and he would vanish to the bathroom, carrying his leather briefcase.

Coming back he would drop into his easy chair; I would switch on, we would talk again; after five minutes he would jiggle his hand again at the machine and after I had switched off he would say, 'It's not going good. This isn't the way I thought it would be. Can't you find out some of these details for yourself? I thought you were an experienced reporter.'

The next meeting took place in June. I was better prepared this time. I had taken a crash course in the known life of Howard Hughes, largely due to the efforts of a man named Richard Suskind, whom I had hired as a researcher. I had known Dick Suskind for ten years on the island of Ibiza; he was a writer and a scholar, the author of books on the Crusades, Richard the Lion-Heart, the battle of Belleau Wood and the history of Anarchism. He knew how to dig into files, libraries and periodical indexes. At the time, still thinking that the Hughes book would be a definitive biography and therefore a two-year project of interviewing, researching, cross-referencing, writing and editing, I needed help. Suskind began scouring the United States in April and came back with a glum face. 'There's practically nothing,' he said, 'and most of it repetitious, hearsay, stuff in gossip columns.' Newspaper files had been stripped, court records were mostly unavailable, whole editions of magazines with articles on Hughes had been bought out and vanished from the public domain. The few unathorized biographies were useless, trading on business analyses in *Fortune*, parroting back the flamboyant stories that from time to time appeared in the national press, expanding *New York Times'* accounts of Hughes' exploits in the air and in Hollywood back in the '30s. I read everything and realized immediately from what I had learned in the Bahamas that the public man was a myth bordering on a lie. His time as a bush pilot in Ethiopia, his meetings with Schweitzer and Hemingway, weren't mentioned anywhere; his so-called seclusion in Las Vegas was accepted as gospel. Howard Hughes had neatly outfoxed the world for more than thirty years.

When we met for the second series of interviews the mood was markedly different. Again they took place in my hotel or motel room. The fact that it was a second meeting, a reaffirmation of mutual purpose, was a powerfully positive factor. On a simpler level, we were glad to see each other again and said so. But as soon as the tape recorder was in position and I reached for the start button, Hughes snapped out at me. He had read and brought with him the transcript of the Bahama interviews. 'You baited and bullied me,' he accused. 'You led me into saying things I didn't mean to say. You kept interrupting and contradicting me. That's got to stop.'

We argued, and finally I said, 'Okay, if I've done that I was unaware of it, and I apologize. I certainly won't do it now. All I ask from you is the truth.'

'That's what I'm going to give you,' he said sharply. 'No more pussyfooting around.' He had clearly made up his mind to something.

In the course of the next weeks he opened up; but it was a hard, painful flowering. Think how hard it is for any man to speak and tap at the truths of his own experience with a blind man's cane: because in that world of self-revelation we are all equally blind, or else we lie and wear masks we've collected throughout the years – collected, tested and saved for such occasions. But he tried from the beginning to get it right, get it straight, without the benefit of mask or mummery. He would start to speak, stop, then say, 'No, that's bullshit. Scrub that, don't transcribe it. Let me start again.' And he would do it again, and if he didn't get it right he would frown and say, 'We'll come back to that. Remind me, will you, please?' He wasn't aiming to polish his words but to plumb his memory better; not so much to be analytically deep, but more to strike the mark as though he were an archer taking aim at a far target and not so sure his hand was steady or his sight good enough anymore to isolate it from the background. He was archer and target both; and that was why it hurt, more so when he struck the mark. A hard flowering, I said, and one that had to be respected. Again and again he came to our meetings in a fractious mood, skittery and prudent and startled like a virgin when the instrument of violation makes contact. He was violated by his own momentum to shatter that hymen of superficial memory, common to us all, stretched tightly across the past. We scrapped and argued all the way, then and later, because it was easy for him to confuse my pressuring him with his own need to get to the root and gut of things. Random exchanges taken from the transcribed interviews, verbatim – and not included in the text of the autobiography – will give an idea.

H:…I have to protect myself from myself. Do you understand?

C: Yeah, I understand. I think.

H: You think – well, never mind. That's the way I am and I don't give a goddamn what you think, or anyone else. Don't be offended. I'm just being frank.

H: It's a sexually dirty story, and she's still a famous actress, so I'm not sure I want it included in the book. I've given you enough dirt already. Let's just say... this puts me in an awkward light, that's the trouble.

C: Well, you can tell it and then we'll –

H: Now don't nag me and then sulk. My God, I'd hate to be married to you. [And then he told me the story.]

There were lighter moments too. The following dialogue took place during the first taping of the June sessions; to understand the references you have to know that Hughes for many years wore tennis sneakers instead of shoes. He gives the true reason in the text of his autobiography, but for nearly two decades the habit made him the butt of jokes and reinforced the image of his eccentricity.

He was discussing the beginning of his commitment to build a flying boat, the *Spruce Goose* or HK-1, at the time when Henry Kaiser was his partner:

H: And so Henry and I set up this little paper corporation. We put up a few thousand dollars apiece. Henry was very useful to me, not only because of his know-how but because he got along with those guys in Washington. They already had me on their shitlist... Wait a minute. I'm burning up with curiosity and I have to ask you. Is that supposed to be a joke, or what?

C: No, I have to wear them. It's an old pair of tennis sneakers that my wife cut down for me. I have a sore here on the top of both feet from the sandals I wore in Nassau. The sandals I was wearing were new, and the strap opened the skin. Remember I was wearing a bandage? When I got back to Ibiza it was infected and I couldn't even wear shoes – the pressure kept making the infection worse.

H: You've got to be careful with something like that.

C: My wife convinced me it needed air, and so she cut down these sneakers and I've been wearing them ever since, everywhere I go. See?

H: No, no, that's all right. Don't come closer.

C: Why did you think I was wearing them?

H: I thought it might be a joke. Some kind of private way of making fun of me.

The second batch of interviews were by far the most productive and covered the most ground in terms of time and depth. Hughes backtracked now and then to re-tell stories of the early years he felt he had not satisfactorily covered during the first sessions. He sometimes referred to notes, which I rarely had the opportunity to see, and we would often discuss in advance the territory we wanted to cover during a sitting. This time too I was better prepared, having plowed through all the available material on his business life: the machinations at RKO, Hughes Tool, Hughes Aircraft and TWA. Dick Suskind had joined me for part of the trip, backstopping me with information and going over my notes after each session to see what might have been omitted by Hughes and what questions I might ask in the next session to fill in those gaps. His presence was invaluable to me; but at one moment it caused a near-disaster.

Howard, who was invariably late, had arranged to contact me at an out-of-the-way motel near Palm Springs, California. 'I'll be there between ten o'clock and midnight,' he said. Suskind and I were sitting in my motel at about 9:30 p.m., playing chess, when there was a knock on the door. 'It can't be him,' I said, and opened the door. The scene was memorable. Suskind, who eats organic food, lifts tons of weights each day at whatever gymnasium is available, stands 6'3' tall, weighs 280 pounds and looks like a veteran NFC offensive tackle, is obviously not the sort of man who can pretend to be a waiter delivering an ice bucket. Hughes knew of his existence but had said he didn't want to meet him.

The three of us stood awkwardly by the door. Finally I said: 'This is Dick Suskind. He's doing some research for me, uh, on the project...'

Howard stood for a moment, then said quietly, 'Well, I suppose you know who I am.'

It was Suskind's moment to claim ignorance and make a swift getaway, but he missed the signal. He cleared his throat uncomfortably. 'Yes, I do,' he said, 'and I'm glad to meet you, Mr. Hughes.' He started to extend his hand, then drew it back quickly; he'd remembered my telling him Hughes was not a keen handshaker.

The man stood for a few agonizing seconds – agonizing for me, in any case. I can see now that we must have looked like three miscast characters in an Oscar Wilde drawing-room comedy; we had all forgotten our lines and a hush had fallen over the theatre. He finally reached deeper into his pocket. His right hand came out with a cellophane bag, which he pushed toward Suskind. 'Have a prune,' he said.

Dick took and examined a prune. 'That's an organic prune, isn't it?'

'Correct,' Howard said. 'The other kind are poison.'

For three or four minutes they discussed the merits of various organic fruits and vegetables and the superiority of natural vitamins over the chemically-processed kind. When the subject was exhausted, Dick said he had to go. The door closed behind him.

'I'm sorry, Howard,' I said immediately. 'You told me ten o'clock. We'd just had dinner and we were sitting around playing chess – '

He waved his hand. 'Doesn't matter. Bright guy, very clear-thinking. Doesn't smoke, I noticed – I had a good look at his fingertips. Good man to have around as a bodyguard. You may need one. Let's get to work.'

The final session of interviews occurred on the East Coast of Florida during the months of August and September. I was staying in a motel bungalow on the beach and Howard was staying in a private home some twenty miles to the north. In June he had given me the typed transcripts of the Bahama interviews and I had spent six weeks checking out the details and correcting some names and dates. Howard refused to identify the transcriber-typist, except to refer to him good-humoredly as 'The Abominable Snowman.'

'I can understand why you call him that.' I said. 'He must have typed with all four paws.' Whoever it was, he could neither type or spell. There were four notations in nearly three hundred pages to the effect that 'tape broke; sorry; part missing.' The phrase 'unclear' had replaced a dozen names and phrases, and the overlaps that naturally occur when two men are speaking were usually omitted. In general the manuscript was a mess. I said, 'Howard, it won't do. You've either got to find someone else or you've got to let me do it.'

He eventually decided there was no one else he trusted other than The Abominable Snowman, but he admitted the Snowman was incompetent. So I was awarded the job. It was coolie-labor, brutally boring. By the second week in Florida I was sick of hearing Howard's voice repeating the same phrases – to catch a muttered monologue or a sharp exclamation the tape had sometimes to be run backwards and forward half a dozen times – and even sicker of hearing my own badgering and apologetic questions. Between transcribing and wrapping up the interviews I was virtually self-imprisoned in the bungalow. Now and then I would step out and swim some laps in the pool under the sulky September sky or drive over to Route 1 to work up a sweat banging golf balls on the driving range, but during those weeks I had no time to learn the first name of a single Floridian other than the maid. Moreover, for the first time I had the precious tapes in my possession, which made Hughes uneasy. 'If you see a man with a cane hanging around outside the bungalow,' he said, 'don't jump on him. He's there for your protection. (He meant, of course, for the protection of the tapes.) If there's anyone else hanging around who doesn't have a cane, tell your bodyguard to jump him or call the security guard. But get it straight – if he's carrying a cane, he's okay.'

'This is Florida, Howard. There are thousands of people who walk with cancs.'

'Not men under thirty five years of age.'

In September we reached what ultimately proved the major decision about the book: the switch in character from authorized biography to autobiography. Howard, at the onset of the project, had wanted a biography because he felt that the outside objectivity would balance what otherwise might have been called by unfriendly critics an apologia; he was always meant to retain control and final approval or the text, but my authorship would obviously set up a system of checks and balances. However, when I read the mounting pages of transcript, I realized that the same objectivity, and more, had been achieved through dialogue and argument. I felt that what he had achieved was an honest and dramatic personal statement. Given a minimum amount of editing and re-shaping, it would be a viable concept in autobiography. To tamper with it might be a historical crime. I made the suggestion to my publishers, who were enthusiastic about the change to an autobiography but less so when I used the words 'book-length interview.' It was a form, someone remarked, that never had much luck in the marketplace. But they agreed to read it before they came to a decision.

Howard agreed instantly to the change. He had said what he had wanted to say. 'It's my autobiography,' he said, 'and I'm damned if I'll have you or anyone else monkeying around with my words. I'm not a writer, I'm a talker – at least I've been a talker for the last six months. You go up to New York and tell them that's how I feel.'

We met once more on Paradise Island in the Bahamas and then I flew to New York, lugging two copies of the thousand-page transcript. As per our secrecy agreements they were read by the various publishers in a five-day marathon session in the living room of my suite at the Hotel Elysée, while I sat around emptying ashtrays and ordering pots of coffee. I heard no one cough, I saw no one's attention begin to flag. The opinion was unanimous. The book-length 'interview' worked.

Go with the book as is, they said.

I flew south once again for a wrap-up interview, and Howard drafted what became the Preface to this book. Then I left for Europe. A copy of the transcript had been placed in escrow in a safe deposit box at the Chase Manhattan Bank in case I crashed en-route. But I reached Ibiza safely, doffed my capped to my wife, chucked my children under the chin, and went back to work, because there remained the massive job of editing and organizing the transcripts. Since certain significant discussions had taken place while the tape recorder was not running, Howard agreed to let me work from the many notes I had taken and weave these into the manuscripts at the appropriate places, provided that I reproduced his words with reasonable accuracy. This I did, and he checked them out at a later date, approving or disapproving, changing them or letting them stand; but such interpolations form a minuscule part of the manuscript.

To keep the flow of the narrative and also remove a certain inanity from the dialogue, I also eliminated as many of my questions as possible. For example, in the midst of a monologue about his tenure as boss of RKO, if I interrupted to ask, 'When did such-and-such incident take place?' and he replied, 'The summer of 1949,' I deleted my question and put into his mouth the words: 'This took place in the summer of 1949.' Similar questions such as, 'But how did you feel when so-and-so left you?' have been deleted, since usually the reply encompassed the intent of the question and rendered the latter gratuitous. Certain personal exchanges have also been omitted; but I have retained many of them because they give the character of the man and triggered some unusual exclamations and opinions. Nothing has been added that Howard didn't say or that I didn't say. All the footnotes (and the Appendix) are my own responsibility; I hope the reader will keep in mind that Hughes in his Preface remarks that he doesn't agree with all my commentary.

The major editing was done in the interests of a reasonable chronology and clarity. A human life is as much thematic as it is chromographic and any man relating his own history tends naturally to wander through time and space. One thought sparks another: the telling of a tale that took place in 1930 in Hollywood may remind him, for whatever reason, of something that happened in Las Vegas in 1965. This was certainly the case with Hughes – in this instance I'm referring to kidnapping attempts – and I made little effort during the interviews to check the free flow of anecdote and recollection. But in the final editing I shifted some things around to achieve a more chronological narrative.

However, there was a quality of mounting and cumulative revelation in the original interviews which I had decided was an integral part of the way Howard Hughes had told his life story, and to sacrifice that for the sake of chronology would have meant missing the point of the whole exercise. Hughes on several occasions told stories and later corrected them, or deliberately left a gap which he filled in when the mood suited him. In these instances the method again revealed the man, and I have not tampered with the way he worked his way round to nailing down the truth as he saw it. He says in his Preface, 'I believe the reader will see I have tried very hard to tell the truth,' and the revelatory and corrective passages in the text constitute a proof which I had no right to destroy.

When the cutting and pasting was done and the book had reached a near-final form, I found a number of anecdotes, conversations and lengthy statements of opinion that seemed to have no obvious historiographic slot in the narrative. They took place at various times and referred to different periods; some of them were in response to stories I had heard about Howard which I retold to him, so that they were more dialogue than narrative and would lose their meaning if the form were bastardized. Rather than omit these bits and pieces, I pulled them together into a section called INTERLUDE: CONVERSATIONS AND OPINIONS, which follows Part III of the book. The arrangement of the book into four parts, by the way, is my responsibility and does not necessarily conform to the three major interview sessions. The breaks in the text, however – the unnumbered chaptering and the spaces separated by three asterisks (***) – generally represent either a separate night-session of talk or a switching-off of the tape recorder.

As for other omissions from the orginal verbatim transcript, they have been made only for legal purposes – to avoid libel and unwarranted defamation of character – or because Hughes for some reason specifically requested it. But the latter instances are very few.

III

SOME FINAL APPRAISAL on my part may seem obligatory, but I am going to duck it. Howard Hughes can speak for himself, so for the moment I will leave the field to the critics and historians. One thing I know: the real Hughes will care very little what they say. I only hope that by telling as much as I have told I have not cheapened in any way the flesh, bones and heart of this book, which lie in Howard's words and not in my own. He said toward the end, 'This has been one of the most extraordinary events in my life. Talking with you has been an adventure. It's cleared the air for me. I don't regret it for a minute.'

I have related my part of the tale in the interests of clearing up the mystery of how the autobiography came to be and dispelling the inevitable gossip concerning authenticity. But when the book is read the importance of the mystery will vanish, as will the gossip. Howard Hughes may become a mythic figure in American history, but the myths surrounding him will be laid to rest.

Just as the dry business articles dealing with Hughes have

undoubtedly prepared the reader poorly for the man who reveals himself in these pages, so my correspondence with him a year ago prepared me poorly for the human being I met. I expected a certain stiltedness, a stiffness of manner. Instead I found a warmth and dry humor, as well as an acuteness of insight into American manners and ethics, which brought me up short again and again. Several times, at the end of the talk session, I found myself musing about the America that Howard Hughes had revealed to me in the course of our conversatiion, an America I was only aware of second- or third-hand. I knew little of high finance or of the interplay between business and politics – things that were of everyday familiarity to Hughes. But he never condescended to me, and I think the reason was that he was too anxious to explain and reflect. No one, after meeting him or reading his autobiography, could call him innocent; and yet there was about him, in the interstices between his stubbornness, his pride, his selfishness and cynicism, his eccentricity, his arrogance and sadness, a quality of innocence that may be uniquely American. He was a Texas boy, the 'Sonny' of his childhood who had suddenly awakened from a dream to find himself with two billion dollars and the consequent paradox that he was both slave and free man. In some ways he was like the narrator of Fitzgerald's *The Great Gatsby*, looking in from the outside at a world of money and opulence, finding it unsatisfactory, and dreaming, in the end, of 'that fresh green breast of the New World that flowered once for Dutch sailors' eyes' and was no more. Howard had his dreams too.

One afternoon in Florida toward the end of the many interview sessions that form the basis of his memoirs, he telephoned me. I was transcribing the tapes; I was tired and a little fed up. We had been wrangling for several days about something – the subject is unimportant – and there was no question but that our personal relationship had momentarily suffered. He was sniping at me and I was sniping back. After a 48-hour break he called and said, 'What are you doing tonight?' I told him I didn't have any plans. 'Well, I thought I'd come down and visit you,' he said, 'if you weren't busy. Not to do any more interviewing. I just thought maybe we could sit around and talk... you know, about this and that. Like friends do. No discussions about my sex life and business deals. No arguments. We'll just chat.' He asked hesitantly, 'Would that be okay?'

I replied that it would be a pleasure and he said he would be driven down by his driver between seven-thirty and eight. 'By the way,' he added, 'is your television set working?' I said it was, and he arrived a few minutes before eight o'clock. I had turned off the air-conditioner, which was required for Howard's visits even though the temperature was in the 80s, and the fridge was stocked with beer for me and Poland Springs mineral water for him. I stubbed out my last cigarette when I heard his tap on the door, dumped the ashtray in the wastebasket and sprayed the room quickly with Lysol disinfectant to kill the odor.

Howard sat down in an easy chair and stretched out his long legs beside his briefcase. He always carried an oversized battered brown leather briefcase filled with various papers, graham crackers, packages of Kleenex, ballpoint pens, sanitary paper cups and paper toilet-seat covers. If he ever blew his nose he went immediately to the bathroom and flushed the Kleenex down the toilet. He wore the usual getup of sport shirt, cardigan, rumpled slacks and loafers. Without preamble, he said, 'You like baseball, don't you? Let's turn on the TV. There's a good ball game on. Giants against the Dodgers.'

I had been a Dodger fan in my youth, before they deserted Brooklyn for Los Angeles and before I deserted New York's West End Avenue for Ibiza, so I said, 'Sure.' I switched on the TV and Willie Mays' grave smile filled the screen in a pre-game interview. The Dodgers were challenging the Giants for the Western division pennant in the National League. Mays explained the situation and Howard listened intently, straining forward to hear although the volume was turned up high enough to back me into a corner on a couch on the far side of the room. Howard turned to me and said, 'Let's put a bet on the game. I always like to root for one team or the other, and a little bet makes it easier.' I asked him which team he wanted. No, he explained, that was up to me.

'Okay, I'll take the Dodgers – for old time's sake.'

Howard smiled; the Giants were favored. Then the terrifying thought hit me: what did 'a little bet' mean to Howard Hughes?

'How much?' I asked.

He thought for a minute. 'Well, let's make it interesting. Let's bet a dollar.'

We settled back to watch, all nine innings, and the Dodgers beat the Giants, 4 to 2. Howard stuck it out, muttered against the inanity of the commercials, and from time to time when Mays was at bat or taking a long lead off first he would say, 'Watch him carefully. He's a professional. It's a pleasure to watch anything he does.' He even commented on the way Willie swung his bat in the on deck circle. 'The rest of those guys, he remarked, 'are just black and white trash. All those black players,' he explained, 'have really made the grade in sports since I was a kid. The white man threw them a bone so he wouldn't have to throw them any meat and potatoes.'

It was almost eleven o'clock when the game was over. I switched off the set and sat down for the chat between friends that Hughes had suggested when he called. I could see he was tired, though, and a little ill at ease. He kept drinking mineral water and clearing his throat. Finally I told him a few tales about how I'd sailed the Atlantic in a three-masted schooner with five other people who'd also never sailed an ocean-going yacht before, and then at eleven-thirty he yawned and said he'd better be on his way, he had some work to do where he was staying – something to do with a few million shares of stock of some company he was trying to buy or sell, I don't remember which.

I said, 'What about the dollar you owe me for the bet?'

Howard blushed. He explained that he didn't have any cash with him – no small bills. He had 'a large bill' sewn into the lining of his trousers, but it would be hard to get at. He would pay me the next time we met, he promised.

I took him to the door, from which point he would skulk his way through the darkness to the parking lot of the motel where his driver waited in a five-year-old Chevrolet, and there he turned to me and said, 'That was a pleasant evening, wasn't it? Did you enjoy yourself?'

I told him I had, and he said, with a smile on his ravaged face, 'I'm glad we didn't argue. I'm not such a bad guy after all, am I?'

'No, you're not a bad guy, and I never thought you were.' Not wishing to be stickily sentimental, I had to add: 'And you'll be an even better guy in my eyes when you pay me that dollar you lost. Remember, I'm not the Metropolitan Life Insurance Company and that's not a $40 million dollar loan. A bet is a debt of honor.'

He said brightly, 'Good. I'm glad we've patched it up. A good evening of talk between friends will always do that. Let's meet tomorrow night and get on with the work. I've still got a lot more to tell you about my life.'

A couple of weeks later, after one or two reminders, he paid the dollar to me on Paradise Island, and he told me a lot more about his life. And now that it's all over I vouch for his conclusion. He's not such a bad guy after all. What follows is the story of his remarkable life, in his own words.

Preface

SINCE 1957, AS is well known, I haven't granted an interview or had a photograph taken. It may seem as if I've gone overboard in a negative way, but a long time ago I decided I'm not here on earth to satisfy the vulgar curiosity of the mob.

The fact that I shunned publicity had a backlash. Just because I was the richest man in the world and wouldn't give interviews and didn't want to be a public figure, that *made* me a public figure. Every newspaper and magazine in this country has a reporter whose sole job is to snoop into my private life and the doings of my companies. If I'd courted publicity, after a while they would have said, 'Watch out, here comes old moneybags again, looking for free newspaper space.' I just wasn't tricky enough.

But now, because I'm nearing the end of my life, I want to set the record straight.

There's an old American Indian torture. They'd pull out a little piece of your intestines and nail it to a tree, still attached to you, and then shove hot brands at you, burning brands, to make you run around that tree and pull out your own guts – leave a trail of your own guts unwinding behind you. The tradition's still carried on in this country by politicians, big business, and the news media, in less obviously bloody ways.

They tried to put me in an asylum. They wrote outright lies about me; I don't mean distortions, I mean outright lies. The portrayal of me as an aging lunatic – I won't have it. I want the balance restored. I don't want future generations to remember Howard Hughes only as an obscenely rich and weird man. There's more to me than that.

Nevertheless, I intend to be dead honest, because a great deal of what I did I kept well hidden. This is the truth about my life, warts and all. This book will be my epitaph, the only one I'll ever have.

Howard Hughes

7

Howard is embarrassed by his mother, takes his first airplane flight, inherits Hughes Tool, and loses his shirt in a crooked poker game.

LET'S BEGIN AT the beginning. For me that was Christmas Eve, 1905, in Houston, Texas. That's when I was born – only forty years after the Civil War ended, to put things in proper perspective. I was an only child. My mother wanted more children but she couldn't have them. She wasn't even meant to have *me*. I was a surprise, or so they told me. A welcome surprise, I think. My parents had great hopes for me.

My father was a gambler, a high-roller. He took me out one time to Jakie Friedman's place, a gambling hall way out on Main Street when that part of Main Street wasn't even in Houston proper. I was seven or eight years old, just chin-high to the craps table. It was late for me to be up, but I have a vivid memory of that smoky room, those green-shaded lights, and Big Howard, in a sweat, rolling the dice.

Big Howard is what they called my father. I was Little Howard, or Sonny. The name, Big Howard, fit my father in every way: he was larger than life, and either he was rolling in money or he and my mother didn't know where the next bottle of French wine was coming from.

Wildcatting – drilling for oil on short-term leases – was the biggest gamble of all in Texas, and that's what Big Howard loved most. He went up to Sour Lake, hit it big there, then lost everything at Batson when the field turned to water. This was before he invented what came to be called the Sharp-Hughes drill bit, which became the basis for the family fortune. Until then we didn't live in one place very long and it wasn't until the manufacture of the drill bit got going that we settled

down in the house on Yoakum Boulevard, and that's the only place –
to this day – that I can think of as home.

In 1916, when I was ten years old, my father and his partner, Walter
Sharp, were drilling for oil at a dusty place called Pierce Junction. They
had leased the land for sixty days because Big Howard was sure there
was oil there. But he had to give it up as a dry hole when he hit hard
rock with the fishtail bit, a chisel-faced cutting tool they all used in
those days.

After that he drilled at Goose Creek and the same thing happened –
they hit hard rock the fishtail bit couldn't penetrate.

My father was fed up, so he and Walter Sharp came up with the first
crude designs for a high-speed rotating cone bit with one hundred and
sixty-six edges. A few nights later, in a bar in Beaumont, Big Howard
got to talking with a man named Granville Humason, a millwright.
Humason had been thinking along the same lines as my father and
Wally Sharp, and he'd made some sketches on a sheet of paper. He had
a little model of the device too.

These sketches and the model went well beyond what my father and
Sharp had been contemplating. My father never hesitated. He bought
everything from Humason for $150 cash that he hauled out of his
money belt and slapped down on the bar. Humason signed a receipt
which meant that the designs were the property of my father and
Wally Sharp.

Did Humason become their partner?

No, Humason was naive, or a fool – it comes to the same thing. He
let them buy him out completely, and three weeks later my father filed
the patents, and with the first tool bit he went back to Goose Creek and
brought in the well he couldn't bring in before. Then he went back to
Pierce Junction and did the same thing. He improved the drill and
patented all the improvements a hundred different ways, and later he
invented a gate valve and a disc bit for gumbo shale. He offered that bit
to the government in 1917 for boring between trenches, but the damn
fools turned it down.

He used to deliver the drill bits wrapped in burlap or newspaper, because his patents weren't secure yet. The rigs were deserted when he got to them. None of those roughnecks were allowed to work on them until the bit was down in the hole and out of sight. He made most of his money leasing the drill bits, and he said to me, 'Sonny, this drill bit is your bread and butter money. Don't ever do anything to jeopardize it.' And I never did. That became a religion for me.

I take it that your father had a great bearing on your life.

Most fathers do, although most men can't admit it. He was born in Missouri, but he spent his youth in Keokuk, Iowa. As a kid he was thrown out of half a dozen schools. There was a particular way he wanted to do things, and it didn't always match up with the way the people who ran those schools thought things should be done. Nevertheless, he got into Harvard, and graduated, and became a lawyer before he became a gambler and a wildcatter. He practiced law for a while, but he once told me he never finished law school, he bought the degree. He went into lead mines too, in Joplin, and he was hunting for silver in Mexico at one time; he was a telegraph operator and then a reporter in Denver. A jack of all trades, and if you discount his losses at the gambling tables, a better businessman than I am.

My father wanted money, and he got it. He wanted a fine home and he got that. And after my mother died, he wanted high living and he got that too, until the day he dropped dead. I was close to him when I was very young, before he invented the cone bit, but after that he was too busy for me, and I became a lonely kid.

My mother was from Kentucky. Her maiden name was Allene Gano, and she was the daughter of a judge. She was the most beautiful woman I've ever known. Unfortunately, against all odds and the doctor's warnings, she got pregnant again. She began to miscarry in the fifth month, and they rushed her to the hospital. In those days the conditions were far from antiseptic. They were close to criminal. The hospital covered it up and never let out any of the details. I think the doctors cut an artery by mistake, but I've never satisfied myself as to the exact circumstances. All I know is that she died on the operating table of a hemorrhage. I was seventeen.

Before that, when the tool company was founded and money began to flow in, my mother joined the Harmonic Society and the Houston Heights Literary Club, but my father wouldn't have any part of that.

'Won't you join, Howard?' she asked him. 'It will enrich your life.'

'Hell, no,' he said. 'I'm rich already.'

She tried to get him to dress well. By then he bought his clothes in New York, and he was always stylish, but it wasn't her idea of what a gentleman wore: it was too modern. He wore a fob and not a watch chain, and she thought that wasn't dignified. He wore a straw hat in April, and my mother said, 'Howard, you know you're not supposed to wear a straw hat until the first of June!'

He had a white linen golfing coat and it reduced her to tears when he wore it. She'd bought him a striped flannel coat, which she considered correct for a Texas gentleman. But he said, 'Flannel is too goddamn hot.'

She was always fussing over me. You couldn't eat gingerbread because you got worms, and meat had to be cooked until it was practically shoe-leather or you could catch hoof-and-mouth disease, which drove my father up the wall because he liked his beef blood-rare. Buffalo Bayou overflowed one year and my mother said, 'We can't eat fish now. When the water flowed back into the bayou it brought dirt.' And no pork ever, because she'd had a cousin in Kentucky who died of trichinosis.

Once she caught me eating cornbread and she stuck a wooden spoon down my throat to make me vomit it up. She believed you got leprosy from eating cornbread – some quack had said that, and my poor mother believed him. She wanted to rush to me to the hospital to have my stomach pumped. My father yelled, 'Leave that boy alone! You'll make him crazy!'

Mama was not a Texan; she was Southern gentility with a touch of Eastern attitudes tempered by French Huguenot blood. She didn't like frontier ways, and Houston was still in many ways a frontier oil city. I resented certain things about her – particularly her concern for me. When I was seven or eight years old we moved to a new neighborhood.

The first few days we were there I spent most of the time in the garage, tinkering with a radio.

My mother said, 'Sonny, why aren't you out playing with the other boys?'

I said, 'I'd rather be here, Mama.'

The truth is that I didn't know the kids in that neighborhood, and I was uncertain of myself and didn't want to go out and meet them.

One day Mama walked into the garage and said, 'Come with me.'

I went, and there on the sidewalk were three boys from the neighborhood. She had seen them nearby, playing Cowboys and Indians. She announced to these boys, 'This is my son Howard and he'd like to play with you.'

It was one of the most humiliating experiences of my childhood. I played with them for a little while. My mother was watching from the parlor window. Finally I just ran back into the house.

It was a long time before I forgave her for that. She was a sensitive woman in many ways, but she was so overprotective that I think of her as a Texas version of the proverbial Jewish mother. If she had lived longer I could imagine her saying, 'Help! My son Howard the billionaire is drowning.' And she would have been right, because in later years – from the age of thirty-five to sixty – I *was* drowning. Drowning in what had always been the breath of life to me. Drowning in money and power.

I was called 'Sissy' by the kids at Christchurch, which was a Houston school I went to, run by a Miss Eichler, a prim and proper lady. I didn't curse, I'd run away rather than fight, and I played the saxophone, which was not the usual hobby for a kid living in Houston in 1920. In my mid-teens I had a collection of saxophones that I kept in a beautiful box of circassian walnut. I had six or seven of them – a beautiful little soprano sax, a baritone, a few tenors, even a basso profundo.

Another reason I wasn't very popular is that I had a serious hearing problem. I had measles when I was small, and that's what started it. By the time I went to Miss Eichler's, I couldn't hear properly. In those days they may have had hearing aids, but my father would never have let me wear one because he didn't want to know I couldn't hear properly: that didn't fit his image of his only son. People used to say I was a shy boy, but a lot of that shyness came from the fact that I couldn't hear a goddamn thing they were saying. Then later, in 1936, I had a bad dive in a Northrop Gamma, the plane I used to break the transcontinental speed record, and it aggravated my condition. Six or seven airplane crashes over the years didn't help.

I have various types of amplifying equipment which make things easier for me, not only because I don't like to wear a hearing aid, but also because it's not really very effective. The condition of my inner ear is special. I have sensitive skin, and the hearing aid irritates the back of my ear. Besides, the electronic gear attracts germs and infection. Several operations have been considered, but the risk was always that I'd lose my hearing completely and go stone-deaf. So I prefer to hear what I can hear and to hell with the rest of it. Most of it isn't worth listening to.

I never made any bones about my deafness. When I went before a congressional witch-hunting investigation committee in 1947 I had an amplifier, but no equipment is really good enough to give a man perfect hearing. I sat there in the Senate, and sometimes I couldn't hear a word of what the inquisitors were saying.

I told the senators: 'Speak up, please, I'm deaf.'

I didn't say, 'I'm hard of hearing,' and I didn't say, 'I have a hearing problem.' I said, 'I'm deaf.' I don't mince words.

Some doctors, including Verne Mason, who used to be my private doctor until he tried to have me put away in a mental institution, said that the deafness might be in part psychological. They may have been right, because there are times when I hear better and times when I hear worse. When I'm depressed or preoccupied, it's true I don't hear as well. Make of that what you will.

But it wasn't only because I had poor hearing as a child, or because I played the saxophone, or because I was shy, that the kids in school thought of me as a sissy. The problem was really that they and their parents were always comparing me to my father, and Big Howard was about as far removed from a sissy as you could get.

You couldn't challenge my father – he would beat you at anything. He owned one of the first fine automobiles in Houston, a Peerless 35-horsepower. He rebuilt it himself down at Wally Sharp's garage and he used to race in it. Some colonel in Dallas claimed he had the fastest car in Texas and could beat anything on wheels, and that's all my father had to hear – he roared up to Dallas and bet this man $500 he'd beat him in his Peerless, and he did, at sixty miles an hour over a dirt track in the year 1920. He loved speed, and I came to love it too.

He used to keep a cash fund down at the police station in Houston, locked up in the chief's safe. He was haring around Houston then in the Peerless, and in a Stanley Steamer, and when he got picked up for exceeding the speed limits he'd tell the cop, 'Take it out of my bank account down at the station house.' They loved that. Texans loved my father. He was a man's man.

He was happy to pay off the law but he hated paying taxes. (I certainly share his views on that.) The income tax law came in around 1911, and some of my earliest memories are of my father yelling about 'the goddamn government squeezing me out of my hard-earned money.' He would back me into a corner and lecture me on how the country was going to the dogs, going to turn socialist. I couldn't have been more than nine years old, but he tried his best to convince me that the income-tax law was going to ruin him and every other businessman in the country.

'Sonny, am I right or wrong? Are these taxes fair or is it the beginning of the end?'

'You're right, Daddy,' I'd say, 'they're not fair' – because that's what my mother told me to say when he got hold of me like that.

In 1919 the whole family visited California for the first time. My father was starting a branch of the Hughes Tool Company in Los Angeles. My Uncle Rupert invited us and introduced us out there. He was writing for the movies then, although he had already made a name for himself with a biography of George Washington. It was pretty exciting for me as a kid, going out to the West Coast, because even as early as that, Hollywood meant only one thing to me: movies. I'd been to see many of them at the nickelodeon in Houston when I was a kid. Rupert took me around to the studios, and I loved it.

In 1921 we went out to California again. That second time I went only with my father, and he put me in the Thatcher School, just north of Los Angeles in Ojai. I was fifteen. That trip, although I didn't fully realize it, was due to the fact that my father had said to my mother, 'I need a long vacation from you and marriage, and I'm taking Sonny.'

I was aware that things weren't right between my parents. There was an atmosphere of bitterness in the house, and on more than one occasion when I was alone with my father, who was usually a talkative man, he would become silent and moody. Once I was in the workshop with him on a rainy day. He stood at the window watching the rain come down, and I could feel the bitterness oozing from him like pus.

He said to me, 'When you grow up, Sonny, make sure you find a woman who doesn't pick holes in you and try to change you, and tell you how to dress and what not to say, and tie you down with a ball and chain.'

I couldn't cope with that. I certainly couldn't sympathize with him openly, or even inwardly, and I didn't dare defend my mother to him because I wouldn't have known how to do it.

My mother never mentioned any of these problems to me. She was a repressed woman. I realize now that my mother loved me more than she loved my father. In a sense I had taken his place as the object of her love. My father knew this; he was a warm-hearted man, and my mother presented a very cool exterior. Many times I saw my father throw his arm around her shoulder and try to be affectionate, and she would stiffen up. I guess she knew she wasn't the only one, anymore, who was the object of his affection, and over the years this had hurt her too much, and she crawled into a shell. But I have to be fair to Daddy too: he had a wider capacity for love, and if he loved many people it didn't diminish has love for the few he loved the most.

Out in California I could see what my father was doing: there was always a pretty woman around. We stayed at Mickey Nielan's house in Hollywood. That was Marshall Nielan, the film director. One day Daddy went out with Mickey Nielan and left his Buick there in the garage, and I decided to play hookey from school and take a little spin in it. I had a girl with me, not a classmate but a waitress from one of the joints around there. I wasn't having an affair with her –I was still a little too young and unsure of myself to fool around that way. Although according to my father I wasn't too young. In fact he thought I was a little backward in that department.

Had he made any attempt to introduce you to sex?

Yes, he made an attempt, but I'd rather not talk about that – not yet.

I was with this girl, driving around in my father's Buick. I was going to show her one of the film studios, the old Metro lot where Uncle Rupert had taken me on my first trip two years before. But we drove up to the gate and they didn't know who I was – the name Howard Hughes didn't mean anything then – and the guard wouldn't let me in.

I was embarrassed, because I had given this girl a big line about my uncle, and I couldn't even get past the guard at the Metro lot. To make matters worse, on the way home I banged into a traffic stanchion and put a dent in the fender of the Buick. This didn't please my father, until I told him about the girl, and then he eased up and said, 'Okay, Sonny, it was for a good cause.'

But the fact that I couldn't get into the studio was a memory that stayed with me. In later years, when I owned RKO Pictures, I often remembered that there was a time in my life when they wouldn't even let me past the gate at Metro-Goldwyn-Mayer I mentioned that incident to Louis B. Mayer when I wanted to buy MGM from him, and we had a good laugh about it. He thought I was joking at first about wanting to buy his studio and then when he realized I wasn't joking he didn't take it well. He didn't like the idea of a twenty-one-year-old telling him he wanted to take over MGM.

After Los Angeles I was sent East to the Fessenden School in Massachusetts, because Big Howard figured it would open the door for me to Harvard. It might have, if I'd been interested in going to

Harvard, but I wasn't. By then I wanted to fly airplanes. That was one of my two great ambitions, right from the beginning.

I was at Fessenden when I first flew, but even before then there were barnstormers down in Texas flying Jennies and Avros and other old World War I crates. I didn't get to go up in any of them; my first flight was actually a present from my father. In Cambridge one time he asked me what I wanted most if Harvard won the crew race against Yale, and there happened to be a barnstormer there with a seaplane, offering rides for five dollars. I said, 'A ride in that seaplane.' Harvard won by half a length and my father made good on his promise.

During that flight I was breathing down the back of the pilot's neck, jumping around, yelling, 'Go faster, sir! Please go faster!'

The back of his neck got redder and redder. Finally he turned and said, 'Sit the hell down! I ain't about to kill myself for some dumb rich kid.' He was from the Deep South. When we landed he cooled off a bit, but he told me something then that I didn't forget for a long time. 'When a man knows his job,' he said, 'let him do it.'

I took that to heart. But the trouble, as I found out, is that most men don't know their jobs.

I was only at Fessenden for a year, and then I went out to California again and studied engineering for a semester at Cal Tech. That was when my mother died. I took the train back to Houston, and Big Howard wanted me there with him, so I transferred college to Rice Institute.

I was nineteen years old when one day the dean called me out of a physics class.

He didn't mince words. He said, 'Young Mr. Hughes, brace yourself. Your father's died.'

Big Howard had had a heart attack. He was in his office – he'd been partying the night before – and he keeled over, dead on the spot. He was only fifty-four.

How upset were you by his death?

Very, although I hid it for many years. I'm just beginning to understand, at the age of sixty-five, how profoundly my whole life was influenced by my father.

The most obvious way was that he made me rich. Not so long after he died I inherited most of Hughes Tool – everyone called it Toolco, and still does – because Big Howard had bought out Walter Sharp's share in 1912, after Mr. Sharp died, from the Sharp family.

After the funeral I was still in something of a daze, but it began to clear when the family lawyer called me into his office. 'Sonny,' he said, 'I guess you realize that since your mother's passed away too, and you're an only child, that you're your father's principal heir.'

'Yes,' I said, 'I kind of figured that.'

But those were just words; I didn't really know what it meant, and the lawyer was smart enough to realize that. So he explained to me that, in theory, I now owned seventy-five percent of Toolco.

'What do you mean, "in theory"?' I asked.

'You're a minor. Nineteen years old. The laws in Texas are a little peculiar regarding inheritance when a minor is involved. You and the rest of the family will have to get together and work things out.'

'Well,' I said, 'give me a little time to think about it.'

He was glad to do that, and we went into a waiting period, during which I began to make a fool of myself in almost every way possible. I wanted to stand in my father's shoes, wanted people to think that I was a chip off the old block. I got my hands on a lump of money, cash that my father had kept around the house for emergencies – a considerable sum of more than twenty-five thousand dollars.

I carried the cash around with me in a briefcase. I spent some of it in a showy way, shopping at Levy's and Kiam's in downtown Houston, and then one day I bumped into this oilman, a wildcatter named Shepard who had done business with my father. I'd seen them together on several occasions – my father had a little place near Galveston where he and his friends used to go fishing on weekends. Shepard was an old roughneck who'd struck it rich a couple of times and then blown it on dry holes. He had one of those Southern faces, with the cross-hatched neck and the red leathery cheeks with the veins showing, and a certain blue-eyed brutal quality.

Shepard invited me up to a room in the Bender Hotel for a crap game. A few of the other men had also been friends of my father's, but I should have spotted them for what they were. It was certainly no friendly game. If I knew it at that time I wouldn't own up to it, and they hit me for better than twenty thousand dollars.

I had a cramp in my gut when I left that hotel, and I had to stop dead in my tracks when I got outside the room. I doubled over, held myself around the middle until the knot went away and I could limp out of the lobby. I've talked to people in Las Vegas since: Nick the Greek and other professionals have shown me how a man with a slick pair of hands can do anything with dice or cards and you'd never see it. There's a certain poetry of motion there, but I wasn't feeling very poetic with twenty thousand bucks down the drain.

These men went on operating in Houston, and a couple of weeks later some other loser complained, and they were taken to court. One of them confessed, or had it beaten out of him, that they'd also taken twenty grand from me with a rigged deck.

I was called into court to testify. It didn't take me five minutes to decide that no man who called himself a Texan would snitch on even outright thieves like these. Besides, they'd been my father's friends.

I told the judge, 'No, sir, Your Honor, it was a straight game, and I don't remember how much I lost but it wasn't anywhere near twenty thousand dollars.'

The other losers had been bought off, and my testimony allowed these men to go free.

My friend Dudley Sharp – he was my father's partner's son, and we used to pal around together – told me I'd made a mistake. 'These men should have been jailed or run out of the state.' And some other people even accused me of cowardice.

Soon it became time to deal with my inheritance and how the Tool Company was going to be divided and run now that my father wasn't at the helm. As I said, I was the heir to 75% of it, if I could get over the problem of being under twenty-one. I tried to think what my father would have done, because that's what I wanted to do.

He had always said to me, 'Don't have partners, son, they're nothing but trouble.'

That made things clear, and I decided to try and buy out the rest of the Hughes family – various cousins and uncles who owned the other 25% – and gain total control. A rough estimate was made of the company's worth and it came to something under nine hundred thousand dollars.

But the first thing that happened was that the rest of the family challenged that figure, said it was far too low, and it looked like the thing could drag on forever once the accountants and the lawyers got their noses into it. By the time they'd gone through litigation the fees would have made us all poor.

I thought things over. I may have been a nineteen-year-old kid but I was able to look ahead into the future. In 1925 I believed in technology and I believed that the automobile industry was still in diapers. Henry Ford was just going into mass-production. If you put ten million more cars on the road, I thought, you'd need gasoline to make them run. You needed crude oil to make gasoline, and you needed the Hughes drill bit to find the crude oil.

I decided I had to get rid of the rest of the family, and that required a two-pronged assault. It was like a military campaign on two fronts. The first thing I needed was money to fight the war against the family and to pay them off, and so I went to the banks. The president of the Texas Savings Bank, Oscar Cummings, was the man who really swung his weight behind me. He'd been a friend of my father's, but there was more to it.

He said to me, 'Sonny, I'm giving you the money because I like the way you behaved in that Bender Hotel incident. I like the fact that you didn't whine and snitch and send those men to jail. I'm not particularly proud of it, but I have to admit that one of those crooks was my cousin.'

I borrowed $400,000 from Texas Savings, pledging my inheritance as collateral.

That was the first step. The next thing I needed to do was get myself legally declared an adult, as opposed to a minor – and of course my relatives who owned the other 25% of Toolco were adamantly opposed to that happening. They still wanted to run that company. They saw that they would have another two years before I reached the legal age of twenty one, by which time they could... well, I don't want to accuse them of being thieves, but surely they figured that they could do a hell of a lot better with the company than I could. Their attitude was: what does a snot-nosed nineteen-year-old kid know about business?

As a matter of fact I didn't know much at all. At this point, I think, stubbornness and momentum carried me through far more than any reasonable intelligence. But I did know enough to hire a powerful lawyer, Norris Messen, and I went to court against the family. The judge – an old upright Texan who wore a black string tie – was a close friend of Oscar Cummings of the Texas Savings Bank, whose cousin I'd declined to send to jail.

I won the case. Technically the judge couldn't declare me an adult, but under a provision of the Texas Civil Code he was able to declare me competent at the age of nineteen to handle the business affairs of Toolco and enter into contractual agreements as though I were legally an adult.

And that's exactly what I did. The cousins and other relatives couldn't control anything with their measly 25%, and they kept squabbling among themselves, which I'd counted on, and finally I made them all a good fair offer for their shares. I wound up paying a total of $355,000 to all of them. That took about six months to negotiate and wrap up, and at the end of that time – still nineteen years old – I became sole owner of Toolco, about which I knew hardly anything.

If they hadn't sold out to you, how much would their $355,000 be worth today?

Probably in the neighborhood of $700 million. But you can't think that way. Otherwise there would be no such thing as a marketplace. Nobody would sell anything to anyone else. There would be no progress.

Anyway, now I was sole owner of a thriving company. It finally occurred to me: in my ignorance, and at my age, what was I going to do with it? I hadn't the slightest idea how to run it.

2

Howard marries, becomes a multimillionaire, gives up control of Toolco, and decides to make movies.

SHORTLY AFTER TAKING CONTROL of the Tool Company in 1925, I decided to get married. This was part of my effort to become an adult as quickly as possible.

My bride was Ella Rice, a member of the famous Rice family of Texas, the people who built the Rice Hotel and founded Rice Institute, now Rice University. I'd spent nearly two years there as a student. I'd known Ella for quite a while, and we bumped into each other at social events in the Houston of that era. I don't know if I was in love with her or not. I thought I was, but what does a nineteen-year-old kid know about love? He knows what a hard-on is, that's all, and he figures if he gets a hard-on quickly and often enough, he's in love. He's more to be pitied than scorned, like the poet says.

Ella was twenty-one. She reminded me of my mother quite a lot – she was slim, curly-haired, soft-voiced, and she had quiet hazel eyes – and it was a socially correct marriage. Most of those people in Houston didn't have a dime to their names before they struck it rich, but then they wanted to scrape off the mud and spray themselves with French perfume and pretend there was a society and they were part of it. When I was a kid, when things were going well for my father, before he'd blow it on a trip East or run up more bills than he could pay, my mother used to drag me off to concerts. Even though those cowboys and their womenfolk didn't know Bach from Verdi, they organized concerts and I got hauled along. You could die of heatstroke in the concert hall, but you were obliged to show yourself off to the gentry. I remember my mother took me once to Prince's Theatre – not a concert that time, but Shakespeare's *As You Like It* –and she fainted from the heat. We had to carry her out of there.

Despite my intelligence and craftiness in getting control of Toolco, I was still a crazy kid. Getting married at the age of twenty is certainly proof of it. I wooed Ella, convinced her that we'd be together for the rest of our lives, and chemistry did the rest.

Ella and her parents wanted to know where we'd live. They meant what part of Houston.

I said, 'Hollywood, California.'

That upset everyone. Why did I want to go off to California?

I explained that I wanted to go into the movie business.

'And do what?'

'Make my own movies,' I said.

That shocked everyone. I'd been nurturing this ambition in secret for many years, ever since I'd first gone out to Hollywood with my father and my Uncle Rupert had taken me to MGM and the other studios. At a deeper level, where did it come from? Who knows? It just seemed to me an exciting thing to do. And I had the money to do it.

I didn't dare tell Ella and her parents about my other ambition, which was to fly fast planes. I kept that one to myself.

Money conquers all. I was determined, I didn't seem to have anything of the crackpot in my makeup, and I had the wherewithal to fulfill my fantasies. That's a hard combination to beat. Ella and the Rices said, 'Well, all right... let's see what happens. Maybe it's something he has to get out of his system.'

So we got married in Houston on June 1, 1924, a garden wedding at my in-laws' house, and we went off on a honeymoon to New York City. I spent most of the time going to the movies, with or without Ella. I'm afraid I wasn't a very good husband even then. I had the movie bug and that was all I thought about. When we came back to Houston, almost immediately I said, 'Let's not wait any longer. Let's go to Hollywood.'

But first I had to put my financial house in order. It was 1926, and I had a growing, prosperous company on my hands and little or no knowledge of how to run it. If I wanted to indulge my two ambitions, Toolco had to do well – better than well.

Norris Messen, my lawyer, advised me. Right there in the higher echelons of the company I found two experienced oilmen, Ray Holliday and Monty Montrose, and I put them in charge of operations under Colonel Rudolph Kuldell, who was president and general manager, although he really didn't know that much about the business. He was just a crony of my father's with good government connections.

A lot of people have told tales in the past years that Holliday and Montrose and Colonel Kuldell wanted me out of there and paid me to keep my hands off Toolco because they thought I'd wreck it. Sonny, or 'Junior,' wasn't competent to run things, so: 'Okay, Junior, we'll send you a few hundred thousand dollars a year. You go off and play with your toys out in Hollywood.'

The truth is that at the age of twenty I made what I consider a reasonably intelligent business decision, insofar as I wasn't experienced in business and these men could run the company better than I could in the day-to-day operation. I learned from them, and I insisted on reports, but I let them run the company.

The key is that I kept control. When I pressed that button, they knew that the boss was buzzing. I won't say I thought of them as stooges at the time; they weren't stooges, they were hard-nosed, tough-minded veteran businessmen. But as far as my life was concerned, they were employees, and to a great extent they did what I told them.

Ella and I took the *Sunset Limited* to Hollywood. It makes me blush to think of this, but I sent a man out to Los Angeles to buy a pair of Rolls-Royces and had them meet us at the train with two chauffeurs.

Aside from wanting to make a show of myself – that was youthful foolishness, nothing more – I had those two serious ambitions. I wanted to make movies and I wanted to fly. A barnstormer in Texas introduced me to some of the fliers in California who became my early flying instructors. One in particular, probably the best pilot I've ever known, Charlie LaJotte, gave me lessons at Clover Field. He taught me to fly on a Waco 9. I wanted to do some loops and spins in it when I was still learning. Charlie said, 'Well, it's not such a good idea, because the way you fly, young fella, the wings will come off.'

Charlie drove a Model T Ford, and I had my Rolls-Royce, one of the classic Silver Cloud models, and a Duesenberg. One afternoon somebody dropped me off at Clover Field for a lesson, so that I didn't have my car there when we landed, and I asked Charlie to drive me downtown to the Ambassador Hotel, where Ella and I were still staying. We put-putted right up to the front door and Charlie, in his old Model T, showed remarkable aplomb. He had flown in the First World War and spent some time in Paris, so he leaned out and said to the doorman,

'Ouvrez la porte, s'il vous plait.'

The doorman bowed and said, 'Yes, sir, good evening, sir.' He must have decided that Charlie was visiting French royalty. If you were French royalty you'd either drive a Rolls-Royce with a chauffeur, or a Model T. We were both dressed like a pair of grease monkeys, but they knew I was a rich young grease monkey and they didn't know who Charlie was. After we got out of the car Charlie decided they'd never let him into the hotel. I said, 'You stick with me,' and we marched right through the Ambassador Hotel wearing grease-stained flying suits, straight to the bar.

One time I had made an appointment for a flying lesson with Charlie for ten o'clock in the morning. I didn't show up. After an hour or so of waiting he took on some other student, and I was a little annoyed when I arrived. When he finally landed I said to him, 'If I tell you I'll be here at ten clock you're paid from ten o'clock on, even if I don't get here until midnight.'

I loved flying from the start. I was a quick learner. I may have been young, but I had maturity thrust upon me by the early death of my parents. And when I decided to learn to fly, I had something else at the back of my mind all the time – that it wasn't just to be a hot pilot, it was to lead to something else, that it would be the major direction of my life, and that I would achieve something significant. What exactly, I didn't know, but I trusted my instincts.

However, at that tender age, other things tempted me more than flying. Above all, I wanted to make motion pictures. I wanted glamor, and moviemaking was the most glamorous profession in the world.

But before I got involved in that, I had something else to deal with, and that was my marriage.

Ella and I stayed for a while in the Ambassador Hotel, and then I bought a house at 211 South Muirfield Road. It wasn't luxurious like some of those mansions on Sunset Boulevard and in Beverly Hills; it was a simple, comfortable, two-story adobe house. That's the last home I ever had. It was the first home I ever had, as a man, and it was the last. I've rented houses many times, in many places, and lived in whole floors of hotels, but I've never owned a home since I sold the place on Muirfield Road in 1931.

How do you account for that?

I've often wondered about it. Sometimes I've thought it was because I had never been used to living in a home, a permanent home. My father, as I told you, moved us all over southeast Texas. We were packing our clothes twice a year, so I wasn't used to any kind of permanence. I didn't like the idea of permanence then in Hollywood, even when Ella and I bought the house on Muirfield Road. I couldn't understand being tied down to all that furniture. Ella was out decorating, buying carpets and drapes and flatware. She had grown up in that kind of world. I guess she thought of Hollywood as the place where she was going to raise her family, which unfortunately, she never did.

I wasn't home very much. I was a young buck and I had money. I was proud because already, just in those two years since my father had died, I'd made the right decision in buying out the family and gaining control of Toolco, and then the right decision in letting other men run the company on a daily basis.

They did well, and history helped them – and it helped me too. The number of passengers carried by American railroads reached its peak around 1921, and from then on the automobile took over. The Model T had made Ford, and General Motors was well on the way to what it is today. By 1925 the total automobile production of the country had reached three million a year. What that meant for me, personally, was that Toolco had changed from a relatively small factory in the backwoods of Texas to a booming business. We tripled our facilities and plant space in those years, and our profits roared up like a space-age rocket.

By the time I was twenty-two years old I owned a company that was worth well over $15 million – and the important thing is that I owned it lock, stock and barrel. I had no partners; I had followed Big Howard's advice. It was a private company – no stockholders. I was completely independent at an age when most men are still struggling to get a foothold in the business world. I could put my hands on almost any amount of cash I needed. That meant I could do just about anything I wanted to do. Money is power. At twenty-two, when the future is a vague dot on the horizon and you think you're capable of anything, it's *real* power – power without a brake.

But I still had some organizing to do, and of course, running a company that was growing by leaps and bounds, even at arm's length there were always plenty of decisions to be made. One of my first decisions was one that affected the course of my business life for the next thirty-two years.

I had Holliday and Montrose running Toolco in Houston. I decided I needed an accountant and a personal executive assistant to supervise things for me in whatever else I wanted to do. I needed someone who'd stand between me and the world, do the worrying, balance the books, and do the dirty work if there was any to be done.

I let the word out that I needed such a person.

Almost immediately someone was recommended to me and I said, 'Let him call me.' The man who called was named Noah Dietrich, and he came up to my office at the Ambassador Hotel. He was from Wisconsin, the son of a minister. He was a short man, and especially from my vantage point – I was already at my full height of six-foot-three, and Noah was about five-foot-six – and thirty-seven years old at the time. He was a CPA and he was used as a troubleshooter by the movie studios when they needed tax and other accounting help. He was married, he had children, he wasn't a womanizer, and he was politically conservative. I'd had him investigated; I knew all about him before he got there. In theory he was exactly what I needed.

I had just come off the golf course in Beverly Hills and I was carrying my putter, and while I talked to him I was putting on the green rug in the reception room. I had a little cup, a little hole, built into the rug there. Noah thought this was all a little eccentric. I had two secretaries then, and one of them worked several hours a day retrieving golf balls for me. (I saw this same scene in a movie years later, and I got a big kick out of it.)

Every time my putter clicked against the ball, Noah jumped a little bit. It made him nervous.

I told Noah what my situation was, that I'd inherited Toolco and bought out the other heirs, and I was interested in making movies and in various other projects, and I wanted somebody to look after my financial affairs. And then I pulled a question out of the hat. I asked him to explain the principle of flight. This flummoxed him for a moment, but by God he came up with the answer, more or less, as much as I expected any non-flier to know.

Why did you ask him that?

I didn't want just an accountant. I had this man do many jobs for me. I had him carry liquor during prohibition from Texas to California. I needed a man who could run a ticker tape through the streets of Los Angeles, which as it turned out, he couldn't do. I needed a jack-of-all-trades with an accountant's brain.

I hired him, started him off at $10,000 a year, and he went up from there until he was making half a million plus a few little extravagances like a Packard I once gave him because he got me to the railroad station on time.

But I had problems with Noah right from the beginning. Among other things, he had the ability to drive me crazy with his indecision. I got the feeling sometimes he enjoyed doing it, did it on purpose to get my goat. He was much older than me and he probably resented working for a younger man.

This goes back to shortly after I'd hired him, and it almost made me fire him on the spot. He was basically an accountant, so naturally one of the first things he had to do was prepare my income tax return. I'd told him I wanted to file in California because I was going to live out there, but he pointed out that if I filed in Texas, which I could do because I still had legal residence in Houston, it would save me $10,000 a year. It had something to do with the community property law. I said to myself, 'He's an accountant, he knows what he's doing.' But I was uneasy about it, because I wanted to establish permanent residence in Hollywood, and that's what Ella wanted too. She wasn't in love with Hollywood but at least she wanted the illusion of permanence.

We were down in Houston in the spring of 1927, looking into Toolco. We had two tax returns prepared – one for California and one for Texas. At the last minute, I told Noah, 'No, damn it, file the California return.' With a lot of muttering and mumbling, he dropped it off that night at the Internal Revenue office in Houston. There was a midnight deadline and he made it by less than ten minutes.

Early the next morning he called me and said, 'Howard, you've made a big mistake. I've been up all night figuring it out, and it's going to cost you more than just $10,000' – and he started giving me one of those complicated analyses of blocked income and joint interest in property. I didn't understand a word. I was only twenty-two years old.

'All right,' I said, 'get the California tax return back and file the Texas return, but please, for the love of God, don't bother me anymore with it.'

Noah rushed straight to the tax commissioner's office and gave them some cock-and-bull story that he'd filed the wrong return for me, and please could he have the California return back and submit the Texas one, which he had in his pocket, together with my check for the right amount.

They said to Noah finally, 'All right, mistakes can happen, and we don't want you to lose your job, so we'll take your money.'

When he came back to Houston we met for dinner. I asked him to please explain the whole thing to me in simple layman's terms. I listened, and I think I must have gone white. It turned out that what he'd saved me, in hard cash, was about a couple of thousand dollars a year for the next three or four years, and I had to go back to Hollywood and still be a resident of Texas.

I wanted to beat my fists against the wall, but I said quietly, 'Go back to Austin and switch the returns again. I was right the first time. I want to file in California.'

Now that was absurd of me, I know. You can't go switching your tax returns from state to state three or four times. It's not just that they'll think you're crazy, it's that the tax people won't bend over backwards until their spines snap. They won't do it for John Doe and they won't do it for Howard Hughes either.

Noah pointed this out and I left the dinner table without another word and went upstairs to my room in the Rice Hotel. I was in such a turmoil that I thought, I'm going mad. This man can rattle my brains like popcorn. There was only one thing to do. I dived into a cold bath and lay there until it was time to sleep, and then the next morning l left a note saying, 'Noah, it may cost me a small fortune, but you manage the finances the way you think best, in my life and at Toolco. You make the business decisions. I'll make movies.'

And I went back to Hollywood.

The real point of that story is this: that's how and why I asked Noah to take over Toolco – all over this silly tax matter – and how I was freed to do the things I really wanted to do. Destiny works in strange ways.

3

Howard wins an Oscar, makes Hell's Angels, *has his first air crash,
and is seduced by Jean Harlow.*

THE FIRST MOVIE I made in Hollywood was called *Swell Hogan*,
about a Bowery bum with a heart of gold. I knew an actor named
Ralph Graves who had been a friend of my father's. He took me to the
Metro lot, and that time I got in.

Graves talked me into making *Swell Hogan*. In my office at the
Ambassador he played out all the scenes for me, acted it out before it
had been written, and convinced me it was a million-dollar picture. I
was impressed with his performance, and he said it would cost only
fifty or sixty thousand dollars to make.

'I'll go fifty,' I said. 'Let's get to work.'

So I was in the movie business, and I made *Swell Hogan*. Or rather,
Ralph Graves made it, and I watched and wept and paid the bills.
When it was done, it had cost me $85,000, and it was a terrible movie.
We couldn't even get distribution. For a while I was a bitter and
disillusioned young man.

But nothing could stop me, not even failure. After *Swell Hogan* I met
Mickey Nielan again, my father's old pal, and we made a picture
together, my first movie that was released. It was called *Everybody's
Acting*. I guess by standards today it was a pretty flimsy picture, but it
made money.

Then I hired Lewis Milestone, who had just quit Warner Brothers in
a huff. He was a man whom I respected very much, and I hired him to
direct a picture called *Two Arabian Knights*, a comedy set in the
trenches of France during the First World War, and it won an Academy

Award. That was the first year they had the Oscars and we won the award for best direction in comedy. It cost $500,000 to make – that was a lot of money, almost unprecedented, and people thought I was crazy, but it was a smash hit. If you take big risks there are big rewards. I knew that even then.

These films were made by and released through my own company, Caddo Productions, which was named after the Caddo Rock Drill Bit Company in Louisiana, one of my father's subsidiary interests that I'd inherited. Through Caddo Productions, Lew Milestone and I then made a gangster film called *The Racket*. All the time I was learning from my mistakes. I used to write everything down in a little ten-cent notebook I'd bought in Woolworth's.

One day I lost the notebook. I was beside myself, because it seemed that everything I knew was in that notebook. I'm not superstitious, I didn't think that the loss of the notebook meant the loss of my luck as well, but it had very valuable information in it and unfortunately, once I write something down in black and white, I tend to forget it.

I called Noah Dietrich. I had him retrace my routes that I'd traveled that day from Muirfield Road back and forth to United Artists. I told him to drive down that road and get down on his hands and knees every ten yards to see if it had fallen out of the car. He also had to creep around the studios – he sent me the cleaning bill for his trousers – but he still couldn't find the notebook. I advertised in the newspapers. I offered a $500 reward and spent more than a thousand dollars in advertising to get that little ten-cent notebook back, and I never did. That still burns me up when I think about it.

By 1927, when I was twenty-one years old, I had decided that I wanted to make a big, realistic picture about flying in the First World War. I wanted to do something important. I wanted my life to be of significance. I had the energy and arrogance of youth. And I had money to back them up.

They'd made a few flying pictures before then, but none were realistic, and by then I'd started to fly regularly and I knew all the hot pilots around Southern California – Charlie LaJotte, Frank Clarke,

Frank Tomick, Roy Wilson, Jimmie Angel, Ross Cook, Al Johnson, Lyn Hayes, all of them. A lot of those guys had flown in the war and they'd seen some of these films that had been produced, including *Wings,* and they said, 'Howard, it just wasn't like that.'

I said, 'Well, tell me what it was like.'

We had a lot of bull sessions – they liked me, because they thought I was crazy, like them – and the more they told me, the more I could see there was a great picture to be made, if it was made the way it was. The first time I heard that phrase, 'the way it was,' was from Ernest Hemingway. But that was twenty years later, when Ernest and I were friends.

In 1927 I made the commitment. I began to shoot *Hell's Angels*.

We did things in that movie that had never been done before. I'm talking about the second version, because there were two. I shot it silent, and then talkies got started and I decided it was impossible to do this picture as a silent. The Vitaphone process had come in and I knew that it was to movies what the Sharp-Hughes drill bit had been to the oil business. I'd learned my lesson young: if you move with the times you can survive and do well, but if you want to come out on top of the heap you have to move just a little bit *ahead* of the times. You have to take the risks involved as well.

I decided to reshoot the picture in sound. It wasn't necessary to do the flying scenes a second time – and it would have cost a fortune – because there was very little talking during the battles, and that could be dubbed in the studio. It did take me a while to figure out how to get the sound of planes in combat, but I finally hit on the solution. We hung a pair of microphones from a helium balloon about a thousand feet over Caddo Field in the San Fernando Valley, and I got Pancho Barnes – a famous aviatrix and stunt pilot – to buzz the mike two hours a day for nearly a week. Pancho flew a Travel Air Mystery S racer, and that engine could sound like a squadron of Fokkers when she revved it up and did a steep climb. We mixed those sound tracks every which way and got all the effects we needed.

We did something in that picture that was revolutionary. First of all we shot some of the scenes in Technicolor, which was a new process. There's a scene in England, where the pilots, just before they're taking off on a mission, have a big dance – and that was shot in color and cut into the film, which was of course made in black-and-white. And we had a red glaze over the film in some of the other parts. That was all new.

I did another thing that was even more exciting. We used a wide-screen film like Cinemascope but then it was called Magnascope. There's a moment in the picture just before the night sequence when the boys, Ben Lyon and Jim Hall, go out over France on a mission.

A title flashed on the screen: 'SOMEBODY ALWAYS GETS IT ON THE NIGHT PATROL.' And then the German planes started to come over. We had a system of pulleys rigged up in the theaters, and the screen got wider and wider and you'd hear the German Fokkers coming. We had special amplifying equipment and the noise got louder and louder, until that whole screen opened up and you saw a skyful of planes. That was a revolutionary device and it was my idea. We never had a preview, but I sat in the back row in some of the first performances. People shrank back in their seats when the German planes roared on to the screen. The screen kept growing bigger, and those planes looked like they were coming right at you and you were going to get chopped up by the props. Men sucked in their breath. Women screamed. I loved it. I was like a kid with a new toy, I'd built the toy, and my toy *worked.*

I had three airfields, and several hundred planes to simulate the actual combat aircraft. Most of the planes were real, like the Sopwith Camels, Avros, and a captured Gotha bomber, and I had some of the Fokkers shipped from Germany. I got Fokker himself, the man who built them, to round them up for me. I spared no expense. My whole idea was, and still is: once you commit, don't hesitate or skimp. Do it *right.*

The guys who flew these ships were the real thing. Frank Clarke was a hell of a pilot, and a wild man. He was chief pilot on the picture, Tomick was in charge of the camera ships, and I was directing from the air in my Waco. Frank Clarke would fly anywhere in anything and take any risk – or, almost any risk. It turned out there was one he wouldn't take. There was a scene where a plane had to come in toward camera and make a sharp left bank at about 200 feet.

Frank said, 'I can't do it, Howard.' This was a Waco, with a Le Rhone engine, which has a hell of a torque. 'At that altitude,' he said, 'this goddamn plane's going to crash right into the ground.'

I didn't believe him. 'I'll do it,' I said.

'Howard, don't.'

'I can do it, Frank.'

He couldn't talk me out of it and I couldn't shame him into doing it. I took the ship up, went into the turn, and the next thing I knew I was in the hospital, half my face in bandages. I had a crushed cheekbone and needed some surgery to repair it; you can still see the indentation. That was my second crash. Frank ran up to the plane afterwards, they told me, to see if I was still alive, and I was, and he said, 'Thank God! I thought we'd lost our meal ticket.'

I laughed when I heard that. I loved those guys, those pilots. They could say anything, even the truth, and it didn't matter.

One time, when we were still getting ready to shoot *Hell's Angels*, we'd got the German Gotha bomber fixed up in pretty good shape. Frank Clarke and I, with a couple of girls Frank had lined up for us, flew up the coast – except the Gotha wasn't fixed up as well as all that, and we had some engine problem and Frank brought us down to a nice landing on a strip of beach near Monterrey, where we spent the night in a little Portuguese fishermen's settlement where hardly anyone spoke English.

Frank was a good pilot, but he wasn't much of a mechanic. And I was a pretty good mechanic but I couldn't fix what was wrong with the Gotha. We had to send back for parts and spend the night there with these two girls in a little shack. Kind of crowded, just one room with the four of us. An odd experience for me. I'd never gone in for orgies. It made me feel kind of funny, the four of us in one room. And we each had our own girl, and then we switched the girls.

I really don't want to talk about this incident anymore. I'm sorry I brought it up. The details of sex are either vulgar, boring or repetitious.

*Let's talk about the air crashes that took place during the making of
Hell's Angels.*

Three men were killed. Al Johnson was first, and then Clem Phillips.
The third man wasn't a pilot, he was a mechanic named Phil Jones. He
was in that Gotha that Frank and I flew. Frank didn't want to fly it that
day – he probably had a hangover. So there was another pilot, Al
Wilson, who went up with Jones, and they were running smoke pots
to simulate a burning plane. They were supposed to go into a spin, bail
out, and let the plane crash. Wilson bailed out at a thousand feet, but
for some reason the mechanic didn't. I was flying above them in a
scout plane. I landed in the field next to the crash and tried to pull
Jones out of the wreck. But there wasn't much left of him. And he
could never tell us why he didn't bail out.

Those were the only deaths, but not the only crashes. The pilots
themselves were calling it 'The Suicide Club.' I suppose the funniest
crash, if you can call it funny when you're facing death that way, was
when Al Wilson bailed out over Hollywood. He was in a Fokker
coming back to the San Fernando Valley. Los Angeles was socked in
with fog and he decided he was over the mountains to the north but
he had no idea which way to go. He was scared to ease her down, so he
bailed out. He didn't know it, but he was right over Hollywood
Boulevard, and the Fokker cracked up the backyard of a producer
named Joe Schenk. Schenk and his wife, Norma Talmadge, the famous
actress, were there, and some other people, and they had a hell of a
scare because a plane doesn't hit the ground like a creampuff.

The propeller hit Hollywood Boulevard and nearly took some
woman's head off. That was good publicity in one way and not so good
in another. We had a fair amount of complaints. Al Wilson himself
landed on some guy's roof. He was a lucky son of a bitch, more than once.

A few years later, around 1931, I made another picture about flying.
That was *Sky Devil*, with Spencer Tracy and William Boyd. We started
looking for the guys who had flown in *Hell's Angels*, and it turned out
that eight or nine of them were dead. That's not including the ones
who were killed when we were shooting the picture. They'd all cracked

up in just those few years. Lyn Hayes was dead, piled into a mountain somewhere. Ross Cook was dead, and Mory Johnson, Burt Lane, five or six others. All killed flying. It was a dangerous profession in those days – still is, only now you have to watch out for Arabs and hand grenades. But when I heard about this, I was very shaken up.

But it didn't make you stop flying?

Nothing could have done that.

Did you think you had a charmed life?

I didn't even think about it. I just kept flying. You read in the newspapers every day that thousands of people are killed in car accidents, but you don't say to yourself, 'I've got a charmed life, I'll keep driving.' You just keep driving because you need to get somewhere in your car. I needed to get somewhere in my plane. And I loved to fly. It was simple. Also, remember – I was young. A kid. I had many millions of dollars, but I was still a kid. If I was going to stop risking my life I would have stopped after I'd cracked up three or four times myself, but I didn't. That never occurred to me.

I had one scene in *Hell's Angels* where the Germans are forced by their commander to jump from their Zeppelin. The Zeppelin is being overtaken by the Allied planes, and in order to lighten the load the men have to jump. Being Krauts, and being ordered to jump by the captain, they jump. I shot that on the sound-stage, one of the few action scenes in that film that was shot indoors. We had a beautiful montage with a dark cloudy background. The men had to jump from the Zeppelin, down through the clouds. Of course we had a stack of mattresses on the bottom of the studio to catch them. That was one of the most dangerous scenes we shot. A lot of people thought the air stuff was the most dangerous, but this was worse, because the men had to land right on the mattresses, jumping from about forty feet, and those stunt pilots – guys who would do an Immelman or an outside loop without blinking an eye – were crapping in their pants. I shot that scene fifty or sixty times, because I wanted a certain effect.

Fifty or sixty times? Are you sure?

I'm not exaggerating. It took days. I drove people crazy. I finally got what I wanted in one sequence when the hat came off one of these Krauts' heads as he jumped. You saw that hat spinning through the air, and it gave a special feeling to the scene.

Noah was standing around the lot, and he had seen some of the rushes. He was pissing and moaning because he was thinking, that's our money going down the drain. Already he was thinking about it as *our* money. He told people that any one of these rushes was just as good as any other. 'I can't see what Howard is after.' But I knew what I was after and when I saw that one sequence, with the hat spinning slowly through the air, I thought, that's it.

After all this time, I consider *Hell's Angels* to be the best picture I ever made. It took me three years and over two million feet of film, not to mention over four million prewar dollars, but it still holds up. I looked at it not so very long ago and the dogfights were still the most exciting thing I've ever seen on the screen in the way of aerial battles. We had good technical men in Hollywood even then, and they're always the key people.

The acting, in retrospect, doesn't measure up. I'd cast a Swedish actress called Greta Nissen in the female lead. She was one of the most beautiful women in Hollywood, but she couldn't speak English. When I decided to reshoot more than half the movie in sound, it was obvious that Greta had to go. Years later, by the way, they made a movie based on this situation –*Singing in the Rain*, with Gene Kelly. Nobody paid me a dime.

Arthur Landau, Greta Nissen's agent, gave me a real sob story about her. I said, 'What do you suggest I do?'

Arthur sighed. 'If you're going to dump Greta,' he said, 'the least you can do is take another girl from my stable.'

'Who did you have in mind?'

'You'll love her. Her name is Jean Harlow.'

She'd been Harlean Carpenter until a few years before that, and in a few weeks she was the star of *Hell's Angels* – her first leading role. It made her famous. She never wore a bra – that was the Harlow trademark.

Were you involved with her personally?

'Involved' is too strong a word. If you want to know whether or not I had an affair with her, the answer is yes. I went to bed with her because she was the star and I was the director and in those days it was one of those obligatory things to do. She came to my office one evening after the shoot and asked me to read some lines with her. I did that, of course, and the next thing I knew she was down on her knees, unbuttoning my fly to give me a blow job. I said, 'Jean, this isn't necessary. You've got the part.' She answered something, but since she had her mouth full I couldn't make out what she said. I just decided to relax and enjoy it.

Later, on a few occasions, we made love on the couch there, and at her house. I soon grew tired of her. She had an appeal to me, in a kind of overblown, sexy way, but after a while we had nothing to say to each other. And as an actress she was awful. I tried as hard as I could to get her to speak with just the semblance of an English accent. The others weren't much good in that respect either, but at least occasionally they could do it. With Harlow it was totally impossible; I worked with her from midnight to dawn to get her to say 'glass' with an English *a* – to rhyme with 'wash' – because there's a scene where she has to ask for a glass of champagne. And she finally got it right the sixteenth time, but when we got before the camera it came out 'glaaas,' like toity-toid street and toid avenoo.

I've seen Hell's Angels *and there's a speech in it that Monty makes against war. I don't know what the climate of opinion was back in 1928, but it struck me as a daring statement. I wondered if you had a hand in that speech, or if you approved of it.*

I had more than a hand in that speech. I wrote it. That reflected my opinions exactly, and they haven't changed since. I was twenty-two years old, but I wasn't a complete fool. There was a period, I admit, when I fell under the hysteria of the Second World War – that's probably the only patriotic and just war that I've lived through as a man. But before, and since, and right now, I'm as antiwar as anyone you'll ever meet. I want to point out to you that during the period in the Fifties when I was so active against the Communists in Hollywood, it wasn't that I wanted to go to war with Russia. There may have been a cold war but I wasn't for a shooting war in any way, shape or form.

To me, the antiwar speech in *Hell's Angels* – that war is caused by politicians – was the key statement in the movie. Of course I wanted to do an action picture, but often you start out on a project for mundane reasons, not especially high-minded, and at some point along the line you see that you're able to make a statement of importance, and then that becomes the key to the whole thing. That speech meant a great deal to me. I had arguments with the scriptwriters about it.

They said, 'You're making this into a dogmatic picture.'

'I don't care,' I said. 'I have the money and the money gives me the power. I want that speech made, and nothing's going to stop me.'

I haven't changed much since then. I say what I want to say and I do what I please – and if people don't like it, they can go piss up a tree.

4

*Howard battles the film censors, receives an offer from
Al Capone, nearly gets wiped out in the stock market, and fights to
retain control of Toolco.*

IT WAS AROUND this time that I bought into something called
Multicolor. I had used the Technicolor process for the ballroom scene
in *Hell's Angels*. I looked into the future and could see that one day
nearly all movies would be made in color.

I was dead right, but I was premature. It's a hard lesson to learn,
but it's often best to let some genius do the spadework and suffer
the heartbreaks, and then, if you've got the capital and the
knowhow, you move in at the right time and take advantage of the
other guy's pioneering.

But it went against my grain to do that, and still does, because in
that sense I'm more of a pioneer than a hardheaded businessman. I'm
willing to take the risks if I believe strongly enough in something.

So in 1930 I bought the Multicolor process from its inventors, a
couple of men named Fraser and Worthington, and we started a small
company. I found a vacant lot on Romaine Street in Hollywood, built a
laboratory, and wound up more than $400,000 in the red. Eventually I
got sued by the other stockholders, the inventors and their backers,
because I refused to throw good money after bad. They were the charter
members of 'The Sue Howard Hughes Club.' The only thing I got for
my investment was the building on Romaine Street, and that building
became my principal offices for the next forty years. I've always referred
to it as 'Operations,' but I never operated from there. I gave it to Noah
Dietrich and told him to set it up in whatever way he wanted.

However, the issue was far from dead with these people who had sued me over Multicolor, and I was positive that they tapped my telephones. There was some piece of business – I don't remember what it was, but there was no way it could have leaked out without someone overhearing a telephone conversation. Today, as you know, there's no telephone in the United States that's safe, except usually a public telephone.

And so over the years I developed a system. I do a great deal of my business at night and most of it on the telephone. I function best in the wee hours of the morning, and since I'm the one in charge, I often call my people at any hour of the night, and I expect them to call me back from a public telephone. They know this will happen; I don't spring it on them. They can catch up on their sleep when they take their vacations.

I've used this to my advantage many times. But in these early cases it was simply for security reasons. I would call Ray Holliday in Houston, for example, in the early morning and say, 'Ray, I've got something to tell you. Get out to a public phone and call me back.' I'd give him the number of the private phone I was calling from, if it happened to be a private phone.

Then a few minutes later Ray would call me back and give me the number of the phone booth he was calling from. Then I would go to the nearest public phone booth and call him at that number. In this way we were talking from two public telephone booths and the chances of anybody taping our conversation were sharply reduced.

You must have had to carry a sack full of dimes and quarters around with you wherever you went.

I'd charge the call to my office number. One day Perry Lieber, one of my publicity men at RKO, was visiting Hedda Hopper, the gossip columnist. I called Perry and told him to get out to a public phone and call me back. A few minutes later he called. I asked him his number and he gave it to me, and right away I knew something was wrong. I checked my little black book, and the number he'd given me was Hedda Hopper's unlisted number.

I said, 'What the hell are you trying to pull, Perry? When I want you to call from a public phone I mean a public phone, because that's *private*. Hedda Hopper's private phone is about as public as you can possibly get.'

Perry started stammering, and finally admitted he was too lazy to leave Hedda's bedroom and had taken the phone into a closet, which seemed to him private enough.

'Private enough for you,' I said, 'but not for me. Get your ass out to a public telephone and call me back.'

I still wanted to make important movies, and the next one I did was *Scarface*.

I wasn't yet twenty-five years old, and still a bit of a smart-aleck. I know now that you get a good writer, turn him loose on a project and let him do it. But at that time I took over Irving Thalberg's idea, which was to put a number of writers to work on a story without letting any of them know that the others are working on it. I had Ben Hecht and W.R. Burnett and three or four other top-flight writers working on it, and none of them knew the others were involved. Around that time there were rumors around that I was going broke. I'd spent so much money on *Hell's Angels* and the other films, and movie people didn't know anything about the oil drilling business and probably thought Toolco was a printing plant where I turned out thousand-dollar bills and one day the government was going to catch up with me. Most people thought I was nothing more than a wild kid from Texas. People already had begun to tell stories about me that were off the wall.

Didn't that annoy you?

If I got annoyed at every man who told a lie about me I'd have to be annoyed twenty-four hours a day, and I haven't got that kind of time. You know, even $3 billion doesn't buy you more than twenty-four hours between sundown and sundown. I value time, I value it very deeply. That's one of the reasons I sleep so little. I trained myself to get along on four hours sleep a night, or an average of four hours out of every twenty four. It was a struggle for a while, because when I was young I liked to sleep. But I wouldn't give in to that natural urge. In my early twenties I set the clock and got up and did something. And I've done that ever since, except after a year or so I no longer needed a clock.

To get back to *Scarface*: I had the four or five screenwriters at work, and when they had all finished a version of the script, I took all four or five versions of it, picked out the best parts, strung them together myself and wrote in my own interim connecting scenes. We brought in this fine actor from the Jewish theater in New York – Paul Muni. That was his first starring role, and we had Boris Karloff in there too, playing a gangster.

It was a hell of a good film and I was delighted with the results. That is, until I showed it to Will Hays, the Hollywood censorship mogul, and our troubles started. Today people say there should be more censorship because of the violence in movies, but there sure should have been less at the time I made *Scarface*. Will Hays, with his holier-than-thou attitudes, made speeches about how my film was un-American and how we should present a better image to the world.

Why un-American? It was the story of a gangster.

But in America, according to Will Hays, we didn't have any gangsters – or if we did, we swept them under the carpet. I went along with them part way, because I knew otherwise I would have a tough time getting distribution. I changed one scene after another, even put in a totally phony ending showing Scarface hanged – the trial, the sanctimonious speech by the judge. They changed the title. They called it *The Shame of the Nation*. Joe Schenck of United Artists – UA was supposed to release the picture – was giving me a hard time too. He wanted to make a statement to the press just before the premiere in New Orleans that the picture was a social document which would help the police in their fight against crime – and some more bullshit to the effect that the changes were all good ones, and how grateful we were to the various police departments for suggesting them to us. He was afraid I'd open up my mouth about what a lot of crap this was and how the original version was so much better. He wanted the world to forget there'd ever been an original version, and he knew I'd never let them forget.

Then they showed the changed version to the New York censors, and the New York censors rejected it as unacceptable. 'Hell,' I said, 'if I'm going to have an unacceptable film, I might as well have an unacceptable *good* film' – and I threw out all the changes and went back to the original version. And that's the one that finally got distributed.

One other thing was notable about *Scarface*. In the Hays Office version, the New York Police Commissioner, Mulrooney, wrote the prologue to it, telling how noble everyone on the police force was, and how organized crime didn't exist in the United States, it was all a myth. I saw a copy of the text before it was used, and I said, 'This is pap for babies.' I figured that I had to give it some juice, some fire. So I changed it, saying that the best way to stop crime in the United States was to prohibit the sale of firearms and their distribution interstate. That was included in the commissioner's speech.

Did you really believe that, or were you making a statement to drum up publicity?

I believed it and I still believe it. I know it's odd, coming from a man born in Texas where everybody is supposed to walk around with a Colt .45 strapped to his hip, and where, to their shame, there are more murders committed every year than there are in all of England, Scotland and Wales put together.

I believe that if a man can't get his hand on a gun, he may give you a punch on the nose, but he's not going to shoot you. I believed this as early as 1931. You know the NRA line: 'Guns don't kill people – people kill people'? That makes me sick, because obviously it's people *with* guns who kill people. There was a big fuss about gun control when Jack Kennedy was shot, and then Martin Luther King, and then Bobby Kennedy, but nobody was saying it back in 1931 except a few oddballs, and I was one of them. I got this Irish police commissioner to include that statement in his introduction.

But we had other problems. Two of Al Capone's men dropped in to see Ben Hecht in Hollywood. Somehow they'd got hold of the screenplay and they wanted to know if it was about their boss.

Ben gulped and said no, it wasn't about Capone. They said, 'Then why do you call it *Scarface?* That makes it sound like it's about Al.' Capone had a big scar on his face. And of course it *was* about Capone.

Ben said, 'Because then people will think it's about Capone, and we'll make money.'

Money was something these hoods understood. 'Okay, we give you permission.'

They asked Hecht who I was, and he said, 'The sucker who's putting up the money.' He told me that story. He thought it was funny. So did I.

The sequel to this came a few years later, around 1933, when I was in Florida. I don't know if it was the same two guys, but two men came to see me. Capone was in Alcatraz for income tax evasion. He had been to see Cornelius Vanderbilt before then – not the old man, but the son – and made him some sort of proposition about how they could divide up the territory of the whole United States. When these two hoodlums came to see me in Palm Beach that's essentially what it was all about. They said that big Al was going to get out of Alcatraz one of these days, and he'd followed my career – I guess he got the newspapers in prison, and the picture *Scarface* naturally had interested him – and he would like to meet me when he got out.

Did they make a specific proposition to you?

They told me, 'Big Al likes your style.' I had the impression that what he wanted was some legitimate front, and he thought of me as a young kid with a lot of money who didn't know his ass from second base, and he could use me.

I said, 'That's very interesting, and when Big Al gets out of prison, have him contact me.' I gave them my telephone number on Romaine Street in Hollywood, which is about as much of a dead end as there is for reaching me. If he'd ever called I wouldn't have known, because no messages came through for me for anyone who wasn't on my 'approved' list.

In fact, much later on, I told the people at Romaine Street, 'Anything new that comes up, I don't want to hear about it. We'll just discuss subjects that *I* raise. I have enough ideas for two lifetimes.'

I had a lot of money, more and more all the time, no matter what I spent, and I thought I should be doing things with it, not just letting it earn interest. At one point I seriously considered buying a couple of studios to get myself some real weight out there in Hollywood. The cost made even me hesitate, but I would have gone into it if I had the chance. I did buy about a hundred theaters, the Franklin chain, and I went so far as to make an offer for Paramount and MGM, but those studios turned me down.

There was an idiotic rumor went around at one time there that I had offered to buy not just Paramount and MGM but United Artists, Warner Brothers, Universal, First National, and RKO, which would have made me sole owner of Hollywood. But that was a lot more than I cared to chew, even if I could have bitten it off. I couldn't have afforded it then. Toolco in 1932 was doing very nicely, but I was in no position to buy out Hollywood. Now, yes. But luckily for them I'm no longer interested in the movie business.

The other films I made in those years were *The Front Page*, *Cock of the Air*, and *Sky Devils*, which was Spencer Tracy's first big film. Ann Dvorak came out in that one too, and became a new star. They wanted to change her name to something more American – you know, Ann Roberts, Ann Dodds. I said, 'What could be more American than a Polish name? Stick with Dvorak.'

I don't want to give the impression that my early business life was an unbroken series of coups and money-making ventures. Aside from all the rest of it, I was busy losing a small fortune in the stock market. I took my bath in 1929 just like many others. Of course I had Toolco behind me, so there was no real danger of my losing everything, but nevertheless I dropped in the neighborhood of three or four million dollars. I was pretty heavily invested. I had Westinghouse and RCA, and some U.S. Steel too – all the losers, you might say.

In one day alone, I lost three-quarters of a million on RCA. This gave Noah Dietrich a few gray hairs. It didn't bother me much. I always figured, that's the bottom, now the market will bounce back and I'll make a fortune. That's how the losers always think.

At first, when I got involved in the market, in 1927, at twenty-one, I had visions of myself as the boy wonder of Wall Street. I thought I had the golden touch. I wanted my own ticker-tape machine set up in my suite at the Ambassador Hotel, where I was living at the time. Western Union didn't have a line running out to the Ambassador or anywhere near it. So I rented an office on Figueroa, near Seventh, where there was a line. I hooked it up myself. I drove down there in the middle of the night – because the whole procedure was illegal – and with my own two hands I laid this whole thing from downtown Los Angeles along the trolley power-line to my room at the Ambassador Hotel.

But somehow I got the terminals reversed, and this immediately showed up on the Western Union Board as a red light flashing. They sent a couple of workmen to the Figueroa Street office that I'd rented. I wasn't there at the time, but they found Noah Dietrich in the office, standing there like an idiot with the glass dome of the ticker-tape machine in his hand but no ticker-tape. He called me, and I rushed up there, and paid these guys some money to keep them quiet. When they left Noah told me I had the terminals reversed, and so I hooked the terminals up again properly, and the machine ran perfectly, and my ingenuity only cost me about $4 million when the market crashed.

Did you stay in the market after that after the crash in 1929?

I got out for a while. I've been back in since. I owned a little TWA stock at one time. Half a billion dollars' worth, to be exact. And I had some Northeast airlines stock, Atlas, RKO, and a few others. But I rarely speculated again. Nineteen-twenty-nine took the wind out of my sails, and I decided there were better ways to lose money than in the market.

But even before the market debacle, I put my money in some strange ventures. My father had a Stanley Steamer, one of the first cars in Houston, and I was always taken with the steam car. In fact I still am – it's never been developed, never showed its true potential. And so in 1928 I decided I was going to build one.

I already owned two – a Stanley and a Doble. The Doble was a great machine, but from my point of view it had two big flaws. For one thing it took anywhere up to five minutes to get up a head of steam, and the garage could burn down in that time. Also you couldn't get more than seventy or eighty miles to a tankful of water. The motor would burn anything – kerosene, wood, buffalo chips, anything you wanted to throw in – but the water boiled away.

I went out one day to the California Institute of Technology and had a talk with Dr. Richard Millikan – he was president of the university and a Nobel Prize winner – and told him I had work for some of his engineers. I wanted two real bright boys to come and work for me and develop the Hughes Steamer.

He found two young kids named Lewis and Burns – I don't remember their first names – and I told them I wanted a steamer that would get up a head of steam instantly, or as close as possible, and that would give me four to five hundred miles without having to refill the boiler. I put them in a garage near Caddo's headquarters on Romaine Street and I turned them loose.

People are always saying that I won't let people alone, won't let them do their work. They complain that I interfered in the operation of Hughes Aircraft and TWA and RKO. Damn right I did, and for good reason.

Lewis and Burns came up with the machine. But in the first place, it would cost $50,000 to make each automobile. I'm sure you'll agree that in 1928 there wasn't much of a market for an automobile at that price. But we might still have gone ahead with it on a trial basis. I figured I could sell fifty to a hundred of them a year, and I would have had a new car for myself whenever I wanted one.

They showed me the prototype for a jazzy-looking five-passenger convertible. It was stripped down to the metal, because I hadn't told them yet what color I wanted it painted. They told me they had a flash-firing system worked out where they could get up steam in less than thirty seconds. I was certainly impressed. I asked them how they solved the water problem and Burns said to me, 'We just made the whole body one big radiator, full of tubes.'

I looked at them – these bright, eager Cal Tech kids – and I said, 'You mean the whole body is a radiator, including the doors?' Burns said, 'That's right, Mr. Hughes. You can go 400 miles on a tank of water.'

'So tell me what happens,' I said, 'if a car runs into me. Into my door, for example. Won't I got cooked? Boiled? Burned to a crisp?'

They scuffed their toes like a couple of country boys caught in the pasture humping daddy's favorite sheep. I walked away, called Noah, and said to him, 'Turn that goddamnn thing into scrap metal. Project's finished.'

It cost me $550,000 to have that car developed, made, and scrapped. That's what happens when you turn technicians loose on a project without close supervision. I realized that right there and then, and I was only twenty-three years old, the same age as Lewis and Burns. But realizing and learning are two different things. It took me twenty years and about $200 million before I really learned.

The experience with the steam car did help me, however, when a crisis arose with the Tool Company in 1932. We were number One, like Hertz, and another company, like Avis, was creeping up from the position of Number Two.

I'll have to give you some background. Toolco, after my father had invented the cone bit, was way ahead of everybody else in the drilling industry. There was virtually no competition the way we had the patents sewed up. And then a guy named Clarence Reed, who worked for my father, quit Toolco and swiped a set of the blueprints for our bit. He started a company called Reed Roller Bit.

That gave me a lesson very early on in life about keeping things locked up. People have accused me of being oversecretive and being a maniac about security. There was no security then at all – that was the age of innocence – and this was an early example of industrial espionage.

But it backfired on Clarence Reed. When we found out, back in 1922, Reed tried to tell everyone that he'd only taken the blueprints to be sure that when he made his own cone bit he wouldn't infringe on our patents. He could tell that to a ten-year-old child, but my father knew it was cowplop. He'd come home and say, 'That fucking Reed,' which upset my mother because she didn't like my father cursing in front of her like some wildcatter just turned loose from Spindletop on a Saturday night.

He sued Reed and won the case. There was a $50,000 cash settlement of the lawsuits and, as part of the penalty for the patent infringement, one of my father's companies – the Caddo Rock Drill Bit Company – was awarded a percentage of Reed Roller Bit's sales. Since Reed Roller Bit had to send us a check every month, we knew precisely how much they sold and where the competition stood.

But later, by 1932, because I was away in Hollywood, Reed Roller Bit came creeping up on us. I could see clearly that if their sales continued to increase at the same rate as in '30 and '31 they'd soon be the Hertz and we'd be the Avis of the drill-bit business.

I sent Noah Dietrich down there to find out what the trouble was, because Toolco was the backbone of my little empire. I told him that if Reed Roller Bit was selling nearly as many bits as we were, there had to be a reason for it, and that reason had to lie in the bit itself.

Noah disagreed with me. Noah thought it was bad morale and my being involved with making movies in Hollywood. But I said, 'It's in the bit, and you get down there and find out if it's better than the Hughes bit, and if it's better, *why* it's better.'

Noah did that, and he found out their bit was a better bit than ours because it used a ball bearing. We didn't have a ball bearing in the Hughes bit, because a ball bearing, my father had believed, wouldn't stand up under pressure and would break apart after a while. But the Reed bits in 1932 weren't breaking apart, and that's what nobody could figure out.

I said to Noah, 'Get my engineers to cut that Reed bit in half and find out what makes it tick.' Sure enough, that's all they had to do. They found out that the Reed ball bearings were soft, made of lead, and wouldn't shatter. All we had to do was redesign our works for ball bearings of a similar type to the Reed bit. We held every patent there was.

But at the same time an even bigger problem cropped up. There was a palace revolt among my people down in Houston. Ray Holliday and Monty Montrose wanted me out. They felt that the place was being run by an absentee manager, and they were hamstrung in making important business decisions. The Toolco executives said to Noah, 'We're putting our life's blood into this company here in Houston, and that kid up there in Hollywood is humping the starlets and making movies.'

Through Noah the Toolco executives made me an offer: $10 million in preferred stock if I'd get out and stay out. They'd pay me 5% on that preferred stock, which meant that I would have had an income of half a million dollars a year.

They didn't see how I could possibly turn down such an offer.

'For Christ's sake,' I said to Noah, 'they want to make a fucking remittance man out of me!'

You could still have made movies and done whatever you wanted. You're talking about 1932, and $500,000 a year then would be equivalent to ten million now.

I wasn't interested in half a million or ten million. I said to Noah, 'Holliday and Montrose can take their convertible stock and shove it up their ass. If they want to quit, that's fine with me, I'll find other people in Houston to run the company the way I want it run. I'm not giving away the Toolco, no, sir, and that's final.'

Nobody quit. They were doing too well.

You may think I'm power-mad because I always want control. I'm not power-mad, but I do believe in power. Power can uplift, not just corrupt. If you have the power over a company or over a situation, and you know what you're doing, then you can achieve amazing results which otherwise would be impossible. That's proved by the fact that I've become, over the years, a billionaire. I can't be modest about that. I had some breaks, like with the sale of my TWA stock, but the breaks mean nothing unless you're there to seize them. Not physically there – that means nothing. I mean mentally there. And the billions didn't fall from the sky. I went out and got them. I didn't believe that crap that John D. Rockefeller handed out, that wealth was 'a gift from heaven, signifying "This is my beloved son, in whom I am well pleased."'

Wealth is an abstraction: a means to power and independence, nothing more. I got it through sweat, and daring, and foresight, and stubbornness, through knowing when to be patient but mostly knowing when to take risks.

As a result, I'm a billionaire three times over. But you can take my word for it – the first billion is the hardest.

5

Howard divorces, falls in love, is mistaken as gay, is blackmailed, and confesses to the death of three men.

IN THE LATE 1920s I was pretty well known, not only in Hollywood, but all throughout the United States, and a great many magazines and newspapers had nothing better to do than run stories about me. My personal habits and idiosyncrasies seemed to exert an amazing fascination on the American public, and I'll never quite understand why – like my public image of the unshaven man in a rumpled suit and dirty sneakers.

Was that how you dressed in those early days?

Not at all. I was a fashion plate. I got all my clothes from Savile Row.

You mean you went to London?

London came to me. Twice a year my tailors would send over men with swatches of samples and I would tell them what I wanted. They had my measurements – I didn't change much over the years and they'd go back and make a dozen suits at a time for me. My shoes were all bench-made on Jermyn Street in London.

Wearing sneakers came later, after it occurred to me that I really didn't have to impress anybody. I also developed the worst case of athlete's foot known to man, and sneakers are the only things I could wear with any comfort.

What about the stories they told about you not carrying cash?

Absolutely true. There are men out there that would knock you off for three dollars and fifty cents. I never carried money, not then or later, and I let it be known that I didn't.

In my early years in Hollywood I decided to build up a bit of a reputation as an eccentric. I thought maybe it would protect me from robbers. I once gave both Ray Holliday and Noah Dietrich instructions what to do if they got ransom notes from a gang who claimed to have kidnapped me. I said, 'Don't pay a cent without my approval. If I think I'm in real danger of getting my throat slit, I'll put down the amount to be paid on the ransom note, and I'll sign it, and right down with my signature will be the letters P.D.Q. In that case, and in that case only, pay the ransom.'

Was that a code?

It meant 'Pay Damn Quick.' You're laughing, but the United States is a violent country. I had a full-time bodyguard for a while, a former Texas Ranger. I figured they're the best. I put him up in an apartment over the garage on Muirfield Road. He had his pocket picked of his first month's salary. Then one day he was practicing quick draws in back of the house under the magnolia tree, and he shot himself in the foot.

Ella came to me and said, 'Howard, this man is incompetent. You don't need a bodyguard. You're a young man. You're tough, you're able.'

I knew she was wrong, but since this guy was such a jerk I fired him and pretended to Ella that I was doing it for her sake. I was a better shot than the Ranger was, although hunting wasn't in my catalog of interests.

My private life during the early Hollywood years was about on a par with my stock market experience and my steam car. In 1929, when I was still just twenty-three years old, Ella and I were divorced. She had actually left me during the filming of *Hell's Angels*, because I was never around. I knew it was coming. I gave her a settlement of close to $1.5 million, and she went back to Texas.

What were the reasons for the marriage not working?

Ella wanted to live as a lady, which meant I had to live like her idea of a gentleman, and I'd discovered that I wasn't interested in that kind of life. It paralleled my mother and father's marriage. I got married at the age of nineteen because I thought it would make a man of me in the eyes of the world, and then one day I woke up to the fact that not only wasn't it true, but that the world didn't give a damn one way or the other.

I could give you a dozen reasons for my marriage and another dozen reasons for my first divorce, and eleven of them might be true, but none of them would be precisely true. The real reason I got married is because I wanted to get married the way a child wants something that catches his eye. He says, 'I want it.' He doesn't know why. Human nature is to want and to not want. The reason I got divorced is because I didn't want to be married any longer. What we want one season, we don't want the next season, but usually we're stuck with it and we haven't got the courage or wherewithal to haul ourselves out of the hole or the rut. It's as simple as that, except people don't like simple reasons and simple answers. They want complicated answers. They're easier to deal with.

I just didn't want to be married anymore. Ella and I lived on different schedules. I've never been at ease socially. I was interested in pursuing my passions, and my passions were movie-making, flying, inventing –

And women?

Since I know you've done your homework, I'll tell you that there was one other woman during that period who meant a great deal to me. She was an actress named Billie Dove. In fact she starred in one of my films, *Age for Love.* I'd met Billie while I was still married to Ella. The marriage was breaking up and I was ripe for a serious affair. Not a fling, like with Harlow. A love affair, with all the drama and thrill and potential for disaster that those words imply.

I fell in love the way only a young man can fall in love: to the point of lunacy. Shakespeare called love a form of madness and he knew what he was talking about. I was surrounded by hundreds of girls in Hollywood, all of them beautiful and almost all of them willing, but for a while I was blind to everyone except Billie Dove.

It happened at first sight, corny as you can get. I saw her in the studio cafeteria. I walked right up to her, which was definitely not my habit. I said, 'Who *are* you?' I was twenty-three years old. She was a very beautiful girl.

Falling in love isn't something a man can help, and if he could explain it like you break down a chemical formula, then it wouldn't be love. Billie wasn't a sexy woman, the Yvonne de Carlo type. She was quiet, and underneath that quiet she was sexy as hell. Still waters run deep – sometimes too deep. I wasn't proud that Billie could twist me round her little finger because of my physical desires.

If you were really in love, why did it break up?

Sanity and day-to-day living restore the balance. I'm not sure whether that's for better or for worse.

In a way, the end of that affair was far more painful to me than my broken marriage. Billie was roaring along with her career, and at that time I was extricating myself from the movie business, and I knew I would be away from California a great deal. We drifted apart.

That still doesn't make sense.

I'll tell you the rest of it some other time. Anyway, the unfortunate aftermath of this was that I was hurt, and lonely for quite a while, despite the fact that I was surrounded by people. Some men can just shrug it off and go on to a second love affair, and a third and fourth, but I couldn't. I tried one with Carole Lombard, but it didn't work. I was always shy with girls and it took all my courage to speak to one of them for the first time. So you can see how bowled over I was by Billie when I saw her on the line at the studio cafeteria. I certainly didn't have the so-called social graces – you could never have called me a charmer.

Why were you so shy?

As a boy I was as tall as I am now. I reached my full height, six foot three, by the time I was seventeen. I didn't go in for sports except golf, and I felt awkward and gangling, conscious of my height, I wasn't at ease in my skin. I'd trip over my own feet. I mean it literally. I don't think I stood up straight until I was thirty years old. Until then I slouched and stooped because I didn't want to seem too tall. I didn't want people to have to look up at me, because I thought they resented that. I know that Noah Dietrich disliked me for being tall, and whenever he had the chance, when he felt his position was secure enough, he made fun of me a little bit – that I was gangling and thin and had a neck like a giraffe.

At one point I started going to a gym in Santa Monica. I went almost every day for a couple of weeks, worked out on the bicycle machine, tried to build my arms with weights, but eventually I began to suspect the place was full of homosexuals. They used to stand around flexing their muscles and admiring themselves in the mirrors.

One evening there was a power failure. I had just finished working out and was in the shower. The minute the lights flicked out there was so much shrieking and giggling coming from these guys around me that I fled, all lathered up with soap. I grabbed my clothes and got dressed and ran out into the street, dripping wet. I caught a cold. That was the end of my muscle-building period.

You never had any childhood homosexual experiences?

Are you kidding? When I was a boy in Texas, a fairy would have been run out of the state on a rail. When I went to Hollywood, I was just barely twenty. I wasn't Errol Flynn or Rock Hudson, but I believe it's fair to say I was considered handsome. Hollywood then, as now, was full of homosexuals. I don't know why they latched onto me particularly, maybe just because my interest in women may have seemed halfhearted. I certainly did stand up a lot of girls. I made dates and didn't keep them, and a lot of girls walked out on me because I didn't spend enough time with them. Then too, although I was married, I didn't see much of my wife, and maybe that looked funny to people.

Some years later, one time, Gina Lollabrigida walked out on me. This was typical. I'd brought her over from Italy to star in one of my pictures. Finally she came to my bungalow. I had a cramp and had to go to the john. I had magazines lying around in there. One of then was a technical journal about flying. I was sitting there, poking through it, and the next thing I knew it was an hour later and Gina was gone. She had walked out. I can't blame her. She was hot to trot, and who the hell wants to hang around an hour while some guy vanishes to take a crap?

Spyros Skouras, the movie magnate, once said to me, 'Howard, you really and truly like women? I'd heard you were a fag.'

It was a fact that I was being approached by men far more often than I should have been in normal circumstances. This was early in my career, when I was producing my first three or four pictures.

I went to a Hollywood party at Mary Pickford's house, and I had to take a leak. I went into the bathroom and Ramon Navarro – he was a famous actor, a latin-lover type – stood there right behind me, chatting away to me. I was thinking about something else. I must have said, 'Sure... yes... sure.' When I buttoned up, he tried to grab me by the pecker.

I lost it. I popped him one on the jaw. Poor guy, he backed off and apologized, and after that he left me alone. So did everyone else who was that way inclined. The word got around that I was liable to react violently.

What about the stories that you employed a man to look for beautiful, interesting young women and make dates for you?

Sad to say, they're true. I hadn't the time. It wasn't my nature to make quick contact. There was more than one man who did that for me. I had Pat DiCicco for a while, and then Walter Kane and Grady Reed, and then Johnny Meyer, and once there was a fellow called Bill Weston. But things didn't work out well with Weston. He tried to blackmail me.

He was the former husband of some movie star, and he got me a date. She was a very sweet girl but she was only fifteen. Weston knew this and I didn't, and you wouldn't either if you looked at this girl. We spent the night together and in the morning she casually told me how old she was.

I put on my clothes in a hurry, called for a car, and said, 'Nice to have met you. So long.'

Bill Weston came around soon after that, asking for a loan of $25,000. He said he had to make a down payment on a house and there would be other payments later, which made it clear to me that it wasn't a loan and it wasn't just $25,000.

I was taken aback and I said, 'Bill, I have to think about this.'

I thought it over and talked it over with Noah. I called Weston the next day and said, 'Meet me down at the railroad station at 7 P.M. sharp.' When he arrived I was standing there beside the Twentieth Century Limited, which was due to pull out in fifteen minutes. I'd called him in his office, you see, and told him to come straight from the office. Meanwhile Noah had arranged for several of my people to go to his apartment and pack his clothes, and all his personal belongings, and those items were in a compartment in the train.

I handed him an envelope and said, 'This is for you.'

In the envelope there was a ticket to Chicago. 'That train leaves in fifteen minutes,' I said. 'Please get on it. Your luggage is inside. Don't ever come back to California again, because if you do, something really bad, possibly even fatal, will happen to you.'

You didn't give him any money at all?

Besides the train ticket there was $10,000 in cash in the envelope. My speech, of course, was pure bluff, but he bought it. He got on the train. I figured ten grand was cheap to get rid of him.

By making movies I'd realized my first ambition. Flying came next. But there were a lot of hurdles to get over. Recklessness was one of them, and I suppose I never cured myself of it until it was too late. I was a quick learner and a damned good pilot in more ways than one, and I took chances. I was young. I was invulnerable. I had my share of crashes, and in the end they ruined my health. My second crash, as I've mentioned, was in the Waco 9 during the filming of *Hell's Angels*.

When was the first crash?

That took place in the same period, early in 1928, during the preparation for filming. Ruth Elder, a well known aviatrix, was flying with me. I met Ruth in one of the air meets, a Bendix Trophy Meet, and we developed a companionship rather than a love affair. In a sense, of all the women I've known, with one exception many years later, I was better friends with Ruth than anyone.

That time in 1928 I was flying a Sopwith Snipe, a World War I ex-combat plane, and Ruth was in an old Jenny. We were flying tandem from Caddo Field in the San Fernando Valley where we'd been getting things ready for aerial combat scenes. I detoured a bit to fly over Los Angeles.

But my motor gave up and I came down unexpectedly – and hard – near Inglewood. I crawled out with a couple of cracked ribs, twisted ankle, broken collarbone, black and blue all over. I was in the hospital for a couple of weeks.

As far as I know that crash has never been mentioned in anything that's been written about you.

The things that have been written about me aren't worth a fart in a windstorm. Nobody knows the facts. I've had four or five serious crack-ups in my life and maybe three or four others not so serious, and nobody paid the slightest attention to most of them. I'm not complaining. I didn't take a full-page ad in the *Los Angeles Times* and say, 'Howard Hughes wishes to announce he's cracked up another plane and is on his death bed.'

The worst accident, and the one I suffered most from physically, was the crash with the F-ll in Beverly Hills, which I'll get to later. But there was one I felt worse about.

This was in 1943 on Lake Mead in Nevada. I was flying an amphibian, a big twin-engine experimental job, a Sikorsky S-43. Glen Odekirk was with me, and a man named Cline who was a CAA inspector from Santa Monica, and Charlie Von Rosenberg, my co-pilot, and a mechanic named Dick Felt.

I was coming in to land on Lake Mead. The water was like a mirror, not a ripple. The sun was glaring off it, blinding me, but still I set the plane down for a perfect landing. We touched down on the water. Then we picked up some drag. Maybe I'd come down a little more quickly than was normal, but it was eighty miles an hour and I'd done it before and never had any trouble. We picked up drag and then, without any warning, that Sikorsky veered off, put its nose down, and began skipping across the lake. The whole plane came apart, piece by piece. Each time we bounced it was like a separate crash. That ship weighed ten tons. Finally we stopped, still afloat.

I had cut open my head badly, and I was in shock – in fact, Charlie Von Rosenberg had to practically shove me out the pilot's window. He saved my life. Some fishermen pulled us out, and everyone got clear except the CAA man, Cline. I hired navy divers and we hunted for him for a long time and couldn't find him. He's still down there at the bottom of Lake Mead.

When I recovered and found out what had happened I was very upset at this man dying that way. Von Rosenberg broke some bones in his back, but they patched him up in Boulder City. He had to wear a cast for a year. And the mechanic, Dick Felt, died from head injuries he'd suffered in the crash.

It was a bad crash. For a while I felt responsible, but they had federal investigation and ruled it an unavoidable accident; they said the plane had been incorrectly loaded by the ground crew and her center of gravity was out of whack. But that didn't bring Cline and Felt back to life, and it didn't make me feel any better about being at the controls.

The only other accident I had where someone got killed was an automobile accident in 1936. I'd been cited for speeding twice before that, once in the San Fernando Valley and once in Gilroy, California. That Rolls of mine was a beauty – it made you want to speed. But that night there weren't any cars on the road, and I wasn't endangering anybody even though I was driving fast. You feel safer in a Rolls or a Duesenberg doing ninety than you do in a Chevy doing fifty or sixty.

I was in the Hancock Park area, on my way back to the Ambassador. A car came at me from the side and forced me toward the curb. A department-store salesman, a sixty-year-old man named Gabe Meyer, didn't see me and started to cross the street. I couldn't possibly have stopped in time. I was speeding – how fast, I don't know – and to this day I remember the crunch of the man's body smashing into the front of the car.

I must have carried him on the hood of the car for twenty-five, thirty feet, and then he sailed through the air for another thirty or forty feet and smashed against the pavement. He was dead on first impact. It was a terrible mess. It was his fault. He darted out at the wrong time from a streetcar safety zone, gave me no chance whatever to stop – although that doesn't make it any the easier to bear the burden of guilt.

I was with a society girl, the daughter of some rich Pasadena people, and I told her to leave, not to get involved, and I got my lawyer, Neil McCarthy, down there pronto. He was a good man and he did what had to be done.

I make no bones about it: I paid off the LAPD. If I hadn't been Howard Hughes and a multimillionaire, I wouldn't have got off so easily. American justice works that way. There's never been a really rich man convicted of any serious crime except where embezzlement of big money is involved and other rich men are the victims. I don't feel guilty about using my money and influence, because it was not my fault. The man literally darted out in front of me. I had no choice. The coroner's jury acquitted me of negligence.

In 1933 I closed down Caddo Productions. I was a man of twenty-seven, and that's an age, I think, when you first start feeling you're a man.

I should qualify that. I felt a man in the sense that I had accomplished part of what I had set out to do. I had made movies – some good ones, some bad ones, but over-all I was not dissatisfied with what I had done. And of course I had made a lot of money. I was proud of the fact that I had stood up to a great many people much older than I was, much more experienced, who had looked at me with a certain disdain and didn't think I could accomplish my goals.

But in other ways I was not a man and I knew it. I had a long uphill way to go before I reached maturity. I already had one broken marriage behind me, which pained me and made me feel inadequate. A broken marriage is a failure even if it's a mistake from the word go, as mine was; it's evidence of an emotional failure somewhere within you. I had also had a broken love affair, and it contributed to that feeling of uncertainty and failure.

There I was in my late twenties, and I had made a splash. I look back now on the age of the late twenties. You may not be a man yet, but you have a tremendous energy and a tremendous manly strength. You're out of the first flush of youth but you still have all the power of your youth and a little of the experience that comes with age. Most men I know who ever accomplished anything were on the track of it by the time they were thirty or they never did a damn thing.

Toolco was growing steadily. I can't say it was doing very well, because it was the Depression, but it was holding its own, and even in the years that it lost money there was enough cash flow so that basically I could do whatever I wanted. If I wanted to I could put my hands on ten or fifteen million dollars without straining the resources of Toolco. I was worth, all told, about sixty or seventy million. Not too shabby. I already had my base of operations on Romaine Street, I had Noah Dietrich handling things for me in California, I had Ray Holliday and Monty Montrose handling Toolco's affairs in Houston, and I had a highly competent engineer and pilot ln Glen Odekirk, who was absolutely devoted to me, helping me in my flying ventures.

I had achieved a kind of superficial personal freedom. I had ordered my life so that I could do whatever I wanted to do without any strain.

I looked back eight years to the nineteen-year-old gawky kid standing in a Houston courtroom, listening to the judge say, 'Okay, Sonny, go out and be an adult,' and I realized I had done it. I had made mistakes in those eight years, but I had gained a great deal of self-assurance and I had a clearer idea of what I liked and didn't like.

I avoided one big mistake. That's the mistake of the young man who says, 'All right, I'm going to go out and I'm going to make ten million dollars,' and then suddenly at the age of thirty-five finds himself with his ambition realized and nothing else to do. He set his sights too low.

A lot of people said, 'You've made a hell of a lot of money, Howard. Why don't you spend some of it? Take a trip around the world. Play golf in Europe. Enjoy yourself.'

I couldn't do that. Sometimes I went on a vacation aboard my yacht, but after a week, or a week away anywhere, I was restless. I was an active man, always have been an active man, can't stand sitting on my tail for too long.

Even now, despite the physical condition I'm in, you have no idea how I fret at enforced inactivity. I know it's absurd – a sick man of sixty-five can't go out there and *do*. But I would love to.

But then I was in my late twenties. Okay, what next? I had maintained a continual interest in flying, right along through the movie-making period, and in 1934 I decided it was time to devote all my energies to it instead of working with my left hand.

I thought it out and made a decision.

I assembled a crew of friends, hired some other competent men, and we started building a plane of my own design with which I was going to make an attempt on the world speed record.

6

Howard builds the fastest plane in the world, crashes it, breaks all existing speed records, and meets with the U.S. Army Air Corps in his pajamas.

IN THE EARLY 1930s flying was a hit-or-miss proposition. The world's best pilots were the eccentric daredevil types who flew by the seat of their pants. Instrumentation was haphazard, standards were indifferent, and the Bendix Trophy winners, practically every one of them, built his own plane in his backyard. I was out to do quite a bit more than that – to set standards for the vision I had of air travel.

The first record I went for was the world land speed record held by the Frenchman, Raymond Delmotte. I wanted to break records, and that was why I started out to build the H-1. The H stood for Hughes.

But if you're going to build a plane that's the fastest plane in the world, naturally you have to make some innovations. And while breaking the record may have been my motive at the start, I quickly became so interested in the engineering problems that long before I was finished, and certainly long before I flew the ship, it was the engineering that had begun to fascinate me, to the point where I said to myself, 'This is it. This is what I want to do with my life.'

I became totally absorbed in the concept and problems of design, and that stayed with me for decades. The rest of it – speed records and even the commercial airlines that I pioneered – took second place. As for the technical stuff, I don't see how these details would interest anyone except me, and maybe a few airplane buffs. I don't want people picking up this book and thinking it's a manual on aircraft design. Let's just say I designed the H-1, then built it, then flew it on Friday the

13th. I tried a day or so before, but you had to do four runs to qualify for the record and it got dark and I didn't finish.

Glen Odekirk said, 'For God's sake, Howard, don't try again on Friday the 13th.'

But I did. I was never a superstitious man. I broke the record that day at Martin Field in Santa Ana, California. Amelia Earhart and Paul Mantz were there as witnesses, and a guy named Therkelsen was up in a Lockheed Vega as official observer.

After I broke the record I decided to see what the ship could really do. It was about the sixth or seventh passage and I was all in a lather and could have flown all day. I pushed the ship too hard. We gave out a story that some steel wool had worked its way into the fuel line, which unfortunately led to rumors that there was sabotage, but that wasn't true. I didn't want any aspersions cast on the H-1 so that was the simple thing to say, and I said it. The truth is that when I pushed the ship too hard, the engine froze. She conked out. The landing gear wouldn't come down either. It was still retracted and it stayed that way. I couldn't make the airfield. I made a dead stick landing on some farm just short of it.

With a small airplane – anything piston-driven, except for something as large as a Constellation or a big passenger jet – you come close to stalling when you land. At a certain point on the glide path you throttle down and put the nose up. A full stall landing, with your nose up high, gives you the slowest possible landing speed and a short ground roll, which you want if you've got no engine. Getting the wheels on the ground is only half the battle, especially if you have a tail wheel and there's no weight resting on it. You still have to bring her to a stop without going ass over tit, and without power that's not easy. You have, or you had, just as many accidents after a ship touched down as you had on the glide paths.

Anyway, it wasn't a bad crash and I wasn't hurt, just knocked out for ten minutes or so and bruised.

The transcontinental records that I set were in 1936 and 1937. I flew a Northrop Gamma for the first trip. I'd put in a new supercharged engine designed by the Army and it was in a sense an uneventful trip. I just flew like a bat out of hell and didn't have too much trouble. I didn't let on that I was out to break the record. I told people that I wanted to fly to New York, and then I took off. I was really testing the airplane and myself. I just tried to see how fast I could get there – nothing more to it than that.

This wasn't a breakthrough in aviation technology, although it led to many other things. I wasn't out for publicity and I don't think I would have got half as much as I did if I hadn't been Howard Hughes, a young buck with an enormous amount of money and the producer of *Hell's Angels*. If I had just been some barnstormer I'd have been treated as a thirty-year-old good pilot who broke a few records, which everyone knew would be broken time and time again, and that would have been that.

However, I was what they called 'good copy,' and from my point of view that was unfortunate. I would have accomplished a lot more in my early life if reporters hadn't been hanging around waiting to pump me and ring wedding bells for every girl I took to a night club or for a flight. That drove me crazy.

Were there any particular incidents on those trips that weren't reported at the time?

The incidents happened on the way back, the first time, when I flew from east to west. I usually prepare things pretty well, and in this case I'd certainly prepared the ship well, but I couldn't do anything about all the gauges that were supposed to be working, and weren't. I had realized en route that I didn't have any aerial maps to continue with from Chicago to California, and you won't believe this, but when I landed at Chicago they didn't have any maps at the airport, either.

I did, of course, have a general idea of which way to go, and I headed west, following the great circle route at twenty thousand feet.

But then everything went wrong. My oxygen blew out. I had no oil pressure whatever – I had to pump the oil by hand – and I had ice on the wings. I was lucky to make it over the Rockies.

What did you do when you had no oxygen?

Took deep breaths. What the hell else can you do?

And you could survive at 20,000 feet without oxygen?

I'm here to tell the tale. I wouldn't recommend it to anybody else, and I certainly didn't want to try it again, at least not with that kind of faulty equipment.

But I was a young man. It was marvelous, it was a battle, and I loved every minute of it. Of course that doesn't mean I wasn't terrified half the time. The newspapers at the time made a great deal out of the fact that I'd made a $50 bet with a friend that I'd have my lunch in Chicago and my dinner in Los Angeles. They didn't tell everything that happened, though. I won the bet, but I was in such a state of nerves when I ate the meal that I got the worst case of indigestion I've ever had in my life.

Those flights, in a sense, were false heroics. I look back on them now and I can see that I did such things out of ego. But I don't want to apologize for them. I've done many things I'm ashamed of, but flying isn't one of them. In fact that's one of the cleaner, brighter images of my past. Because when you're flying, people don't clutter up the works. It's just man and machine, and there's a purity and nobility to that experience that I haven't found in anything else. I've always been better with machines than I have with people. Machines are predictable; people are not. One thing about a machine – you can take it apart and put it back together and it's the same machine. You can't do that with a human being. I know. I've tried.

All my troubles – the reason I live as I do, the nearest thing to being a hermit – stemmed from personal relationships. I've always been able to deal with machinery with great pleasure. I invented a new kind of shock absorber when I was a fifteen-year old kid. I didn't patent it, but it worked, and my father had it installed in one of his cars. I've worked for hours and hours figuring out a new concept for some minor airplane part, or how to improve an existing design. But when I was called away from my work to deal with people, for either pleasure or business, my heart sank, because I knew it would almost always end badly.

I'm a recluse – that's obvious. I avoid meeting people. I didn't start this way, I can assure you. I had friends and acquaintances as a child and I desperately wanted people to like me. Maybe I never admitted it, but I wanted it very much. And, frankly, I don't think most people did like me. But I kept trying until finally I just stopped, because I had been hurt and disappointed in them and in myself, again and again, and I saw that I was incapable of dealing with people properly. I haven't had a real friend since I was a child. The closest I've come to it has been Bob Gross, president of Lockheed, and that was at least 60% business. My last real friend in the sense of a pal was Dudley Sharp, I suppose, and that ended as most such youthful friendships end. We drifted apart, lost contact.

That's one of the terrible sadnesses of life – this process of losing contact with people who mean a great deal to you. Sometimes it's physical circumstances – you're on the move, they're on the move – but more often it's because people don't keep pace with each other, they drift into different pursuits and develop different ideas, and one day they realize they've got nothing in common anymore. It's one of the most depressing things in the world to bump into an old friend you haven't seen for twenty years, and you realize you have nothing to say to him except, 'Hey, do you remember when... ?' It's usually better to live with memories than to try to update them.

For other people I'm sure it's easier. Their so-called friends probably aren't always out to get something from them. That's one of the problems about being very rich. Poor people don't usually do it to you, but anyone who's well off but not so rich as you are, invariably wants something from you – tries to use you. This happened to me time and time again.

There are times when I've thought I could only be friends with billionaires. And how many of those are around?

In 1936, after I broke the record with the Northrop Gamma, I set about remodeling my own plane, the H-1. I worked on that until early 1937. I redesigned the oxygen equipment and worked out a new type of experimental oxygen mask. I fiddled around with the retractable landing gear and the shape of the wings, and I put in a better engine, an 1100-horsepower twin-row Wasp, with fourteen cylinders. I rebuilt her to withstand stresses up to 550 miles an hour, although of course I couldn't keep up that speed for very long and didn't intend to. I gave her a name. I christened her the *Winged Bullet*.

Then in late January of '37 I was ready. I wanted to see what the ship could do at high altitudes – I wanted to make a long run at twenty thousand feet.

It turned out to be from Burbank to Newark. Coast-to-coast, about 2,500 miles. I took off in the H-1 at two o'clock in the morning, pitch-dark, and I said to myself, 'What the hell, I'll go all the way to Newark.' I thought at first I'd only fly to Chicago, but once I took off I just kept going, changed the route a bit and decided to keep flying.

I had a little trouble again – the oxygen valve jammed when I passed over Albuquerque and I had to throw the damn thing away and get down to 14,000 feet where I could breathe. I always had bad luck with oxygen equipment.

When I got to Newark I'd broken my own record, and I knew it, and the hell of it was I couldn't land. There was a United Airline Boeing 247 on the runway having engine trouble. I had to wait until they moved it out of the way. I had no radio, just buzzed the field a few times and waggled my wings so they'd know I wanted to land. That added about twenty minutes to my time, but I still broke the record by about forty minutes.

I put a guard on the *Winged Bullet* and took a taxi into New York and went to sleep for forty-eight hours. Of course the newspapers found out very quickly I'd broken another record and they were hammering at my door for days.

In many ways I've often regretted that I made that flight. The aftermath was disaster. It was one of those absurd events – or non-event, as it turned out – which nobody could predict or whip up out of their wildest dreams. Even after it happened nobody could realize its importance, but in many ways it was to change the course of my life and bring me more aggravation than if I'd opened the door to a cage of rattlesnakes.

I'd broken all the speed records with the H-1, and naturally the U.S. Army Air Corps was interested. They didn't have a plane that compared with mine. The speeds I had flown at were nearly double what any of their pursuit planes could fly, and that record stood for eight years, which I think is a record in itself. You can believe that the Army wanted to see that plane.

When I was in New York, a general named Oliver Echols called me and asked me to stop off at Wright Field in Ohio on my way back to California. The Air Corps wanted to look at the plane.

I said, 'Sure.' I was pleased.

But it was several days before I left, and I had a lot on my mind, and I was tired from all the preparations, the flight and the aftermath of publicity. I wanted to get back to California. I took off, and the first stop I made was Omaha, to refuel. Then I went right on to California.

What I didn't know was that Echols had invited all the top brass in Washington to Wright Field in Ohio to inspect the plane. They were standing around waiting while the *Winged Bullet* and I were up there above the clouds and headed for California. I forgot. I'm human, and I forgot. And they never forgave me.

Naturally the newspapers made as much of it as they could. The generals landed on Echols and blamed him, told him he'd screwed it up and must have got the date wrong. But he hadn't got it wrong and he could prove it.

The Hate Howard Hughes Club started that day, at Wright Field, and it had repercussions which were endless.

My ship, the H-1, was far better than anything the Air Corps had, but after that incident they wouldn't buy it, because they figured I'd snubbed them at Wright Field. Until the end of the Second World War they never built a plane to equal it. I was anxious to have that plane produced, but I didn't have the facilities. It might have made a tremendous difference to us in the Second World War, because that plane – the original, the one I flew, wound up in the Smithsonian – became the Japanese Zero.

Just before the war began, I told Noah to get together with Jesse

Jones to find out how I could contribute to the war effort. Jesse took Noah to see General Knudsen, who decided he wanted me to make some accessories for the B-25, struts and cannon barrels. But then, as a part of the chain of command, the red tape rigmarole, Knudsen sent Noah along to General Echols.

'If Howard Hughes gets any contracts from the Army,' Echols said to Noah, 'it'll be over my dead body.'

Noah told me that, and I got on the phone to Jesse Jones.

'Jesse, tell the Army to put old grudges aside. This General Echols is screwing up the war effort. I'm not going to make any money out of manufacturing struts and casting cannon barrels, but if it's necessary, you know I'll do it. You tell Echols to shove his grudges up his ass.'

Jesse bypassed Echols and we got the contracts. The Aircraft Division of Toolco made the struts and the cannon and six-inch shells during the war. But if Echols had his way, nothing would have happened. It's a wonder we won the war with people like that in positions of responsibility.

There was another reason why the Army had a grudge against me. This never came out at the Senate hearings in 1947, either, because it would have been too ridiculous to bring up a thing like this, but I happen to know that the Army brass always held this incident against me and it gave them a very poor opinion of me.

It seems that sometime during the war there was a question of whether or not the contract for the HK-1 would be renewed, whether the government would still pump money into the project, because things were going slowly at that point and I couldn't get the parts and the materials I needed. They wanted me to come to Washington, but eventually the top brass came to see me in California.

I was with Russell Birdwell the night before – he was my publicity man and we were working on *The Outlaw* – and I was exhausted, run-down, and Birdwell said, 'Howard, get some sleep. And in the morning you've got to shave and put on a suit and tie. You're going to be put on the spot by the United States Army and you have to make a good impression.' He was very considerate, anxious for my welfare.

Birdwell left, and I got a few hours sleep, but I overslept. The appointment with Echols and Admiral Towers and the rest of the brass was for an early breakfast at the Ambassador. I was in a terrible hurry – I shaved, as I'd promised, but I dressed very quickly and put my suit and tie on over my pajamas. To this day I don't know why I did that, but I did.

I gave my progress report at breakfast in the Ambassador to those generals and admirals, eight or nine of them, and it was warm in the room and at some point I loosened my tie and opened my suit jacket. I stood up, and there were my pajamas tops hanging out from under my shirt, and my pajama bottoms sticking out from under my pants cuffs.

I paid no attention. I was involved in trying to explain why there had been delays in the HK-1 and why the ship had to be completed, for the sake of both the Air Corps and the tremendous research we were doing in the field of large-plane design. But that's another story. The point of this is that all the Army could see was that Howard Hughes hadn't bothered to take off his pajamas before he put on his suit.

What an insult! What a thing to do! They thought I was making fun of them in their starched uniforms with scrambled eggs and chests full of fruit salad, their campaign ribbons. They also thought this was evidence that I was a little nuts.

That weighed heavily against me for the rest of the war. I was talking business and airplanes and I thought the military was doing the same thing. My sartorial splendor was totally beside the point in the long run, but not for them. For them it was worse than if I'd been Hitler's secret second cousin. They never forgave me for that. It was constantly brought up whenever they had their conferences about me and what I was building for them. I was told this by Jesse Jones, and at the time he had no reason to lie to me. Their attitude hampered the war effort, and the military has tried to make my life miserable ever since.

Think about it. If they'd bought the H-1 from me, the Japanese wouldn't have had the Zero. It was the fastest thing around, nearly twice as fast as anything the Air Corps had. After the Air Corps had bitten off its nose to spite its face, I got some little company in the midwest to agree to tool up for producing it. They went broke. But before they went broke, the Japanese sent a delegation of engineers to their plant, studied the modified H-1, went home, and within a year the H-1 had become the Zero, made by Mitsubishi.

Was the Zero an exact copy?

With modifications, naturally, but not so much that you couldn't recognize the H-1 with the rising sun on her wingtips. The Mitsubishi people had that ship in the air by early 1939. They rounded off the wings a bit, shoved in the armament, put in a 780-horsepower engine where I had a 1050-horsepower Wasp, and they got more than 350 miles per hour maximum speed out of her. That was better than anything this country had at the time. Naturally if any Air Force General admitted this when the war began and those Jap Zeros were buzzing all over the Pacific and kicking the crap out of the Navy, they would have had him personally cleaning out Oliver Echols mink-lined toilet. That was all hushed up. If we had had it in 1941 instead of them, the Japanese might never have attacked Pearl Harbor. Even if they had, we would have whipped their ass a hell of a lot quicker and probably wouldn't have had to use the atom bomb on Hiroshima and Nagasaki.

But none of that was to be, because I'd overflown Wright Field and worn my pajamas under my suit in a meeting with generals.

7

Howard flies around the world and breaks the speed record, and snubs the mayor of New York City to hide out with Katharine Hepburn.

IN 1938, WHEN I was thirty-two years old, I decided to fly around the world and break the round-the-world speed record while I was doing it.

That flight was far and away the most important I'd ever made, not in the sense that I cut Wiley Post's previous record time, but that I showed that with proper organization and care it was possible to make this kind of flight a routine, which it is today.

I don't mean to say that in 1938 it was a routine flight – no ice-breaking flight ever is. The preparations were extensive. I don't remember how many thousands of man-hours we put in to get the plane ready. She was called the *New York World's Fair 1939* and she was a Lockheed Lodestar, the model Fourteen.

At the outset I'd bought a D-1, made by Douglas; then I started fitting out a new model Sikorsky. But when Lockheed came out with their ship, which was the sturdiest and fastest transport around, I bought one of the first models, and I made the ship over from head to tail to fit my needs.

Actually I made Lockheed, too, with that flight. I'm not blowing my own horn, I'm just stating facts. Bob Gross admitted to me that it was always spoken about among the executives at Lockheed in later years: 'When Howard Hughes flew our plane around the world, everyone suddenly knew who Lockheed was.' And the stock went up five points that week.

The Model Fourteen later was modified and became the Hudson bomber that the British flew during the war. Lockheed sold them 3,000 planes before the war ended. The British also bought the *New York World's Fair 1939*. That's just an aside for the history books and the airplane buffs.

The planning and preparation for the flight were extensive. For one thing we had to put in oversized gas tanks, which caused problems. Going over the equipment lists took days. Every inch of space was used. We had a rifle, shotgun and revolver – protection against anything that might come along if we had a forced landing in Siberia, because I was told that the polar bears weren't too friendly. We had a solar still to convert sea water to drinking water in case we were forced down at sea.

Loading the plane was an incredibly difficult job. We were overweight, of course, but we used something called a Librascope, a relatively new invention which computed the weight of everything in the various cargo compartments and the hull and then told you the location of the center of gravity, the center of balance. If it wasn't at the optimum flight point you could shift cargo, which is what we did ten or twelve times before we got it right. The wingloading was enormous, the most I'd ever heard of, about fifty pounds per square foot. That scared me, and rightly so.

We also used an entirely new system of radio communications, and tested it effectively for the first time in aeronautical history. We could send and receive on twenty-five wavelengths and the aerial, which was adjustable, gave us a tremendously powerful beam. I arranged to beam from Siberia all the way to Hermosa Beach, California. I had Dave Evans and Charlie Perrine, radio director for the flight, set up in a house on the beach operating a short-wave radio station, and I hit them all the way from Yakutsk in Siberia, nearly 5,000 miles away. Nobody made much of a fuss about that at the time, because they preferred to concentrate on the circus aspects which were considered more newsworthy, but that radio transmission was a fantastic step forward in the communications world.

We ate nothing but sandwiches, mostly ham, during the flight itself. I wanted the men to get the most nourishment possible out of those sandwiches, so in New York I tested twenty different kinds of bread until I found the one I wanted. That was Pechter's Jewish rye bread.

But we had trouble the moment we took off. All that extra load we were carrying – mostly the gasoline in the wing tanks – made the takeoffs the most hazardous parts of the flight. We took off on Sunday evening, July 10, 1938, from Floyd Bennett Field, and I couldn't get the ship off the ground. I used up all the runway and still I couldn't get her off. I kept going, into the dirt, and one of the struts snapped – one of the wheel braces. I could feel it go, but there was nothing to do about it then, because the next second we were airborne.

Everything went well after that. We got to Paris in one piece, and on schedule. I had to go through the usual crap at the airport, shaking hands with the ambassador and a bunch of goddamn dignitaries. For a while it looked as though we weren't going to leave Paris because of the damaged wheel braces, but the Embassy turned up with an Army man named Cook, one of those handy types like myself that only seem to flourish in America, and he fixed the damn thing and we took off again with a minimum of delay. Then we went over Germany, flying at 16,000 feet for a while, which was the regulation altitude prescribed by the Nazi government. What happened then has never been told, because I was honor-bound not to discuss it, but I feel certain enough time has passed.

Shortly before leaving New York City I had a visit from General Hap Arnold, head of the Army Air Corps. He asked me to take aerial photographs of parts of Germany that were on my course, or could be on my course with a little adjustment. Specifically, he was looking for aircraft and arms plants in the western Ruhr and in Silesia, and large troop concentrations on the borders of Poland and Czechoslovakia. We didn't have anything like a U-2 then, and any aerial photo reconnaissance had to be done at very low altitudes and of course on a relatively clear day.

The Germans, when we went over, instantly got us on the radio and told us to get the hell out of their airspace. They were building up, and they thought we might be taking pictures. We denied it vigorously, and in the newspapers it was denied vigorously, by me and several other people connected with the project, that anything like that had been in mind. Of course that was exactly what we were trying to do. We came down as low as we could over the critical areas, but we couldn't break through the cloud cover. It was socked in right from the Black Forest to the Polish border. We were flying pretty low, hoping for a hole, and any minute I expected to see some of those Messerschmitt fighters coming right up at us.

Did any of the men with you on the plane know what you were doing?

If they'd used their heads they might have figured it out, because the camera was covered but mounted. One of them asked me about it, and I said it was to photograph polar bears in Siberia for the *National Geographic*. He believed me. Not all of those guys were terribly bright when it came to thinking about other things than their job.

We went on to Moscow. A lot of bigwigs were there at the airport, including the Russian Ambassador to the United States, Alexander Troyanovsky, on leave from Washington. I gave him the baseball scores and the American League standings – he was a Yankee fan, which was a safe bet in those days. The Model Fourteen had the red Lockheed star on the fuselage, and some of the Russian soldiers standing around the field thought this was a Communist plane making the trip. They got all excited – whoops, the Americans are Communists too!

One thing I appreciated about the Russians: we didn't have to pay any bills at their airports. It was all on the house. They asked me to keep that quiet – they didn't want an invasion of pilots figuring the government would pick up the tab. We refueled, and had to turn down some caviar which would have made us overweight.

And off we went to Omsk, in Siberia. They had lousy gasoline, very low octane, but we were prepared for that with a load of ethyl to boost it. That was only a minor inconvenience. But then the runway went uphill at Omsk and I didn't think we were going to get off. It's bad enough trying to take off on the level, on a good runway with the load we were carrying, but to take off uphill – well, it was like a landing strip in Ethiopia that I used many years later in a DC-3.

Leaving Omsk we were lucky again. I'd better qualify this by explaining that I don't believe in luck – it's a phrase that's applied after the fact. If a man prepares well, and is aware of all possibilities and mulls them over in his mind, and takes the necessary precautions to deal with emergencies – if a man does all that, and is ready to grasp opportunities, those opportunities come to him and people call that good luck. It's not good luck. It's the sum total of a man's preparations for any given situation. A poor workman finds fault with his tools, and only a hypocrite says, 'I had good luck.' A man stands up, thumps his chest and says, 'Me, I did it.'

The phrase 'bad luck' is really another way of saying that a man wasn't prepared, he didn't know how to deal with the inevitable difficulties that came his way.

But, as I found out flying around the world in 1938, there are certain exceptions, like when we ran into ten thousand-foot mountains that were marked as six thousand feet on the map. So it was fortunate that we reached them during daylight, because our schedule was messed up by the delays in Paris and Omsk. If we had reached these peaks at night, I wouldn't be here talking to you. The wolves would have picked my bones clean on some mountaintop in Siberia.

Then we went on to Fairbanks, Alaska. That was an awful hop, foul weather all the way so that the plane was mushing, but we made it. We headed on toward Winnipeg, where the weather was so lousy that we skipped it, stopped in Minneapolis, and then, from there, back to New York – three and a half days after we'd started out.

I was beat. I just couldn't face that mob. After the parade there was supposed to be a reception at City Hall, organized by Grover Whalen, the official greeter and hand-shaker for New York City.

You can imagine that I was in no mood for such shenanigans after a round-the-world flight – and besides, I had a date. At the time I was very friendly with Katharine Hepburn. Her family up in Connecticut thought I was an odd duck because I once landed a plane on their beach up in Old Saybrook, but nevertheless there were rumors that Katharine and I were going to get married. It wasn't true, we just saw a lot of each other. We had a fine friendship and I had seen Katharine before I left, and I wanted to see Katharine when I got back. Simple as that. I didn't want to see these guys in top hats and tails.

I drove down to the party with Whalen and Mayor LaGuardia and a big motorcycle escort. Fiorello LaGuardia was a funny little guy and I liked him. But our friendship was nipped in the bud. I hadn't shaved in three days and, what's more, I hadn't bathed in three days. I stank like a polecat. I could see people backing off from me every now and then when they got a whiff of what was coming out from under my armpits.

So I slipped the word to Whalen that before the festivities began, I wouldn't mind taking a bath. Whalen said, 'Okay, certainly, anything you want, Howard.'

They found an office at City Hall that had a bathtub, and I lowered myself into the bath and, by God, it felt marvelous. It was like the first fresh egg after you've been at sea for a week. Suddenly I said to myself, 'I don't want to go back in there. Kate's waiting for me. The hell with these ass-kissing politicians.'

So I got out of the bathtub and put on, unfortunately, the same dirty clothes I'd been wearing when I got off the plane, and slipped out the back door.

Maybe it was a bit rude of me to leave that way, but I guess I figured they would understand. I was wrong. What happened afterwards I got straight from the horse's mouth, because Grover Whalen told me.

Mayor LaGuardia said, 'Well, where is Mr. Hughes? Where is our hero?'

Grover went to look for me, and I wasn't there. They searched the building. No Howard Hughes.

Now LaGuardia was mayor of New York City when you were a boy, and you probably heard him reading the comics over the radio on Sunday morning. But LaGuardia's general language in private was unprintable. He had one of the foulest mouths I'd ever heard, and some of it I didn't even understand, because he spoke Italian a lot. His language was almost as bad as mine when I get riled up.

So LaGuardia started to rant and curse me in front of everybody, and then he pulled what I consider one of the dirtiest tricks that's ever been pulled on me – and there have been some lulus. First he called in the newspaper people and told them I had slipped out. Meanwhile some cop had phoned Whalen and told him that he'd tailed me from City Hall. He'd seen me slip out and thought it was his job to know where I was going, to protect me from the mob, and he'd followed me and knew where I was. I was at Katharine Hepburn's place on the East Side in the Forties. I took a taxi up there and the cab driver didn't know who I was, he thought I was a bum, and I could see he was worried I wouldn't be able to pay him.

This cop gave his report to Whalen, and Whalen gave it to LaGuardia, and then LaGuardia said to the press, 'Gentlemen, I'll tell you where that Texas son of a bitch has gone' – or words to that effect in English and Italian.

I was up there in the sack with Kate, in her apartment, and the next thing we knew there was a pounding on the door. I said, 'My God, they've found us!'

Neither of us wanted publicity, and that would have been the worst kind. Then I really might have had to marry her, which I think is what she wanted.

I piled all the furniture in the living room against the front door – the sofa, the chairs, the dining room table – because they would have gotten an axe, a battering ram, anything they could get their hands on, to get in there and find us. I whispered to Kate, 'Don't say a word. Even in bed. No groans or moans of passion, sweetheart.'

We had a great time, in total silence. It felt a little perverted, in its way.

And after an hour or so they gave up and went away.

What did this affair with Katharine Hepburn mean to you at the time?

Words like 'affair' don't always fit such relationships. Katharine and I were close friends. I saw her on and off in '36 and '37. We went sailing together, and flying, and I cared for her. I wanted to make a movie with her around that time, do the life of Amelia Earhart, whom I knew pretty well. It didn't work out. I was too busy and so was Katharine.

Once I did her what I think was a great favor. She was doing well, but she hadn't saved her nickels and dimes and she wanted to star in a film called *The Philadelphia Story*. She needed money to buy the property and I loaned it to her. She owned most of the rights when the movie was made, and she cleared a tidy sum.

I've been accused many times in my life of being a tight-fisted man, a man who can lose a million dollars and not care but won't give his best friend a hundred-dollar loan or even a cookie, according to Noah Dietrich. There's no truth to that. Katharine could have asked me for anything and I would have given it to her without any questions.

But I'll give you an example of real cheapness. I was supposed to get a special Congressional medal for that flight around the world. Some miserable senatorial son of a bitch said this was a good chance to practice economy, and they wouldn't vote the funds, all five or six hundred dollars of it, for that medal. Meanwhile they were pissing away millions on WPA projects, helping guys who in many cases should have gone out and helped themselves. It's not that I gave a damn about the medal – hell, I never kept a single one that I got.

You skipped over Katharine Hepburn a bit too quickly. Why did she appeal to you?

She appealed to me because she was very bright and a lot of fun, and, I thought, extremely attractive. Now someone can say that about almost every woman. That's what you think about any woman you care for, isn't it? These things are chemistry. She was very independent, very strong-minded. She didn't drink. Very clean woman – bathed two or three times a day when she could, and always said I was divine.

'Howard, you're *dee*-vine.' I kind of liked that. And I can tell you one other thing: I loved her voice. A lot of people didn't, but I did. I could *hear* her. I didn't always have to say, 'What? What?'

She was what I call a thoroughbred. And she was very strong-minded about her privacy. All these were admirable qualities, and then there was the chemistry, which I can't define.

When did you start seeing her?

I suppose it was in 1936. She was in a play on tour, not on Broadway, and I hopped around quite a bit to see her. I saw that play five times, by the way, and it was terrible – it was *Jane Eyre*. I told Kate the critics would boil the play in oil and even though she was great, she'd get scalded too. And she took my advice, and bowed out. But the newsboys were after us everywhere we went on this tour, and that took the bloom off it a little bit.

This, of course, was before Spencer Tracy. Leland Hayward was the man in her life before I came along, but he and I got along pretty well. We once carried Katharine from room to room lying on a sofa. She was lying on the sofa, and we were carrying her. It was a joke, just for fun, and I can't quite remember why we did that, except Katharine said it was '*dee*-vine.'

When did it break up between you and Katharine?

Just gradually. We stayed friends. She met Tracy when the war began, and then there wasn't much contact between us after she got herself mixed up with that guy Henry Wallace, the one who'd been Vice-President under Roosevelt and then ran for President on the Progressive Party ticket. She made a campaign speech for him in the Hollywood Bowl, and I thought that was an error of taste. All right, are you satisfied? You know, there are times when I think you're Hedda Hopper in disguise.

I'll change the subject. When you got back from the flight around the world, didn't you go to visit Herbert Bayard Swope, the publisher of the New York World?

Yes, because I had a hundred-dollar bet with him. He said I'd never make it around the globe in less than a hundred hours, and I was positive I would. Swope was a pain in the ass, a very lordly man, but I sort of liked him. He was living out on Long Island and I borrowed an Aeronca K. This was a few days after I arrived in New York. I wanted to try out some Edo floats and I flew out, landed right in front of his house in the Hamptons and said, 'Pay up.' He had a big party going. He always had big parties going, and I was dressed, I vaguely remember, in the usual way – dirty old pants and greasy shirt. I didn't want to embarrass his guests, so we just went into the kitchen and he paid me the hundred dollars, and I had a glass of milk and then I took off again.

Did you know Charles Lindbergh?

Lindy and I flew the Stratoliner together in Seattle. I didn't like him much, and I'll tell you why. I'm not taking anything away from his achievements – I'm talking about him as a man. Lindbergh was out for publicity. He was vain and egotistical, and he was greedy. When he flew to Paris one of the first things he did before he made the trip was to arrange stories and articles to be written about it. He made something close to a hundred thousand dollars out of that. Now I feel, and I felt then, that it was not my privilege to capitalize, to make profit out of a trip like this. That was not its purpose.

But you had the money.

Yes, I had the money, but you can always use a little extra pocket money, can't you? On the other hand, to give credit where it's due, after Lindbergh made that flight in *The Spirit of St. Louis,* he pulled some of the same stunts that I pulled. When he got back to New York City, Whalen and all those guys gave him the treatment. They took him to the Ziegfeld Follies one night. During the intermission Lindy said he had to go to the toilet, and he vanished right out of the theater. When he told me that story, I had a sympathy for the man which I hadn't had before. Because he couldn't take it, either. He wanted the notoriety, but when the chips were down he was a flier. The way to do things was to get up there and fly, do what you had to do, and take your satisfaction in private – which unfortunately, he didn't do all the time, and I did.

One more thing happened after I got back from the flight around the world, and I consider it important. There was a round of parties and celebrations in various cities. I flew the Model Fourteen down to Houston and there was a big flap for me there. All my father's people – his people, my people – were out at the airport. I mean Toolco employees, rank-and-file workers, and they had signs that said WELCOME HOWARD, CONGRATULATIONS HOWARD, YOU DID IT HOWARD.

All that fuss in New York didn't mean too much to me, but it meant something to me that Toolco people were out there, and that they liked me. Because it never occurred to me before that they liked me. That reception in Houston touched me very deeply. It's one of my fondest memories.

8

Howard becomes the principal shareholder of TWA, designs the Constellation, flies Cary Grant to Arizona to be married, and holds hands with an interesting woman.

IT WAS THAT same year, 1938, that I became involved in one of the major episodes of my life, which was scheduled to last for twenty-eight years. That was Trans World Airlines.

TWA had started long before that, in the Twenties. It was the first company that ever had a transcontinental flight across the United States, advertising 'coast to coast in forty-eight hours!' You started off in New York, took trains to some point in the midwest and then a series of hops by air, slept at night – you only flew during the day – and got to Los Angeles in forty-eight hours.

It wasn't TWA then. It was TAT, and they'd been formed from several airlines: Western Airlines, Standard Airlines, and an outfit called Maddux Airlines. They all got together under Paul Richter and Jack Frye. I knew Jack Frye from way back, and he was the man I really worked with. He became a good friend. He was one of the original Thirteen Black Cats, the first stunt pilots out in Hollywood.

TWA was the first airline to fly coast to coast without rail transport as part of the itinerary. It was just a few weeks after they started operations that they abandoned the railways. Jack Frye said, 'We're an airline and we're going to fly all the way.' And I don't think it took them more than twenty-four hours then, still flying Fokkers.

The American aircraft industry in those days wasn't what it is today. We had to go to Europe for a lot of our planes, which I felt right from the beginning was a mistake. I felt we had to lead. And we wound up leading until recently, when we found ourselves fast falling behind because of those politicians in Washington dragging their asses about the SST.

I had already flown once as a copilot, back in the early Thirties, for American Airways, the forerunner of American Airlines. They flew Curtis Condors, which were the first sleeper planes, and we also had the first stewardesses. I flew Los Angeles to Atlanta, Kansas City, and Cleveland.

Why did you take a relatively low-level job like that?

I wanted the experience. I had it in my mind even then that one day I was going to start an airline – I didn't know I was going to buy one. I was dreaming then of Hughes Transoceanic Airlines. And I wanted to learn from the ground up. The one thing I had never done was fly a commercial airliner, so I took the job with American Airways, using the pseudonym Charles Howard. That's because I didn't want people gawking at me all the time and saying, 'There goes Howard Hughes. Go up to the cockpit and have a look at the boy wonder.'

But I didn't make a secret of it to my people. I told them I was taking a job as a copilot on an airline. This wasn't like my trips to Ethiopia, or the time I went down to Lambarene to see Dr. Schweitzer, or my Cuban trips with Ernest Hemingway, or my trip to India. This was something that was known to the people who were close to me.

I flew only a very short time for American Airways, because I was a quick learner. I watched passengers' reactions and I wrote it all down in my notebook. I had a new notebook by then and I made sure not to lose that one.

It hadn't been my plan to buy into TWA, but I knew Jack Frye, who was president of the airline, and one day he called me and said, 'Howard, I need twelve million dollars.' A lot of stories have circulated since then about why Jack Frye needed this money, but none of them have ever told the truth. The truth is that the Board of Directors of TWA wanted to kick Jack out.

What had he done?

There's always a guy ready to take over and reverse the pecking order. That's all some people live for. I've been through that and I'm sure Jack was going through the same thing. I don't know what he'd done or not done. But I knew Jack, and he was a good man.

He came to me and he said he could keep control if he could get hold of a block of stock that was being peddled around by Lehman Brothers, the banking house in New York City. TWA didn't have much stock outstanding – less than a million shares – and Lehman Brothers had about 120,000 shares that were for sale. Jack figured if he picked up that block he'd have the controlling interest and they couldn't boot his ass out of there. And so he came to me for twelve million.

I said, 'Okay, Jack. It's a small fortune, but the money is yours. The only thing I want is to run the show with you.'

He thought it over for about ten seconds, and then he agreed. I guess he figured for $12 million cash it was worth letting me in on my terms.

Then a funny thing happened. I had a lot on my mind: the war was looming on the horizon and I was developing the H-1, which was supposed to be the big Army pursuit plane, and then it went to the Japs. And we had troubles down at Houston with Toolco, and Henry Kaiser wanted me to go into the car business. What with one thing and another, after I made my arrangements with Jack, they slipped my mind.

Jack called Noah Dietrich one day and said, 'I'm Jack Frye, and where's my money? Where's that check? Lehman Brothers hasn't gotten the check!'

Noah said, 'What's this all about?'

Jack became annoyed, understandably. Noah said he'd have to talk to me about it, which he did. I remembered. I was mortified. 'Shit, Noah,' I said, 'I'd forgotten the whole thing.'

Noah asked me how much I'd agreed to pay, and I said, 'Ten dollars a share.'

'The stock isn't worth ten dollars a share,' Noah said.

'Noah, you have no vision. It's worth more than ten dollars a share. That stock is going to be worth a hundred dollars a share in three years, if I run that airline.'

'That's not the point, Howard. I had a feeling from talking to this man Frye on the telephone that he's in a tough spot, and he needs that money from you badly. If you hold out for a week or so, if we can spin him some story that Toolco has to approve the transaction' – because the funds had to come from Toolco, since I didn't have a dime of my own – 'and you've gone off the deep end a bit, and the board of directors of Toolco says, 'Okay, but we'll only pay seven or eight dollars a share for it,' you can get it for that price.'

'Noah,' I said, 'that's not the way to do business with friends.'

But he talked me into it. Maybe I wasn't focused at the time. I said, 'Noah, you handle it in your own inimitable way.'

I don't buy that. You were the boss. It was your money, and you were the one who said yes or no.

Okay, I'm not trying to slough off all the responsibility for that tricky maneuvering. I knew what we were doing. Noah got back to Jack Frye and spun this yarn about the board of directors of Toolco having to approve the deal. I don't know whether Jack fell for it, because if Jack had an ounce of brains in his head, he'd know that when I said, 'Shit,' the board would squat and strain.

Be that as it may, Noah was right, and very soon thereafter I got the stock for eight and a quarter a share.

Jack Frye was a little sore at me. He felt that I'd gone back on my word, and it bothered me because in a sense he was right, and I've always regretted that I let Noah talk me into that. It made bad feeling between me and Jack Frye to the point where I had to appoint Noah to the board of directors of TWA after I'd taken over. Not that Noah really had any say up there, but he was a spy for me. He never got along well with Jack, because Jack always blamed him for the change in the original buying price from ten to eight and a quarter.

Eventually, because Jack disliked Noah so much, I made Noah step down from his position. But I asked him to keep in touch with a few executives up at TWA who were friendly to me and were willing to give out inside information about what Jack was doing. We set up a system where they funneled information to Noah and he funneled it to me. I had my pipeline to the head office. You understand that at the time, even though I was principal stockholder in TWA, I didn't have a position. I never had a title.

How was it possible for you to be principal stockholder if you only had $8 million worth of holdings?

I bought more. And of course by the end of the war I wasn't just the principal stockholder – I was running the airline. When I had free time I devoted a great deal of it to studying their problems and making suggestions. Not to be immodest, in the 1940s I was the principal factor in the growth of TWA as the only competitor that could stand up to Pan American, the python of the American air carriers. Unquestionably, TWA was the most progressive airline in the United States. I don't think you'll find anyone who'll disagree with me on that. Among other things, I got Eero Saarinen to design our terminal at Kennedy Airport in New York. I told him roughly what I wanted, what I thought a terminal of the future should look like, and I said, 'Go do it. It's your baby.' It's probably the most beautiful and functional airline terminal that's ever been constructed.

Concerning this pipeline to the head office, why were you so suspicious of people?

I had reason to be. I was suspicious of Noah too. One of Noah's secretaries was on my payroll at the time. I had to know what Noah was doing, because Noah had completely free rein, except on the decisions. He could have stolen me blind. There's an old biblical saying: 'Who will watch the watchers?'

It was also around this time, shortly after I bought into TWA, that I designed the plane that came to be known as the Constellation. It was the plane that, more than any other, changed the history of commercial aviation.

It made long-distance flights possible, in relative comfort, for large groups of people. Today that's commonplace, but then it was a breakthrough.

Jack Frye helped me with the design, and Bob Gross was in on it too. That's why Lockheed finally built it. Consolidated had turned us down, and then we went to Bob Gross at Lockheed. I got the idea for the plane when I was breaking the crosscountry record, Chicago to California, in the Northrop Gamma. I was so goddamn uncomfortable up there – the oxygen equipment wasn't working, I was gasping for air, the hard pieces of the seat were jabbing into my spine – that I said to myself, 'By God, when I finish this I'm going to design a plane that can carry people in comfort, nonstop from coast to coast.'

I really said that – it's not a line from a movie script. I said it. I always talk to myself out loud. It's not the habit of a lunatic, it's the habit of a man who wants to remember what he thinks.

And that ship was the Connie. The most successful commercial piston-driven aircraft that ever flew. A radical departure from everything that went before.

In what way?

If you want to get technical, the fuselage had a curvilinear design that cut down the drag factor in an entirely new way. And it also worked as an airfoil. That had never been done before in an aircraft of that size. The Constellation carried a payload of 6,000 pounds and cruised at 250 knots. She was a very stable ship with a very soft ride. It went through a hell of a lot of changes after it was operational, got stretched and stretched until I thought, Jesus, soon you'll be able to board the ship on the flight deck and walk aft and you'll have walked from New York to Philadelphia. Bob Buck, who became TWA's chief pilot, flew the first flight on regular passenger services. He said it was the finest aircraft he'd ever flown. And you know who else flew a Connie, one of the very early Connies, even before Bob Buck? Orville Wright. He took it up with me one day out of Miami. It was meant as a kind of tribute to him. I wanted to do something for him. He was a very old man then, on the way out, and I thought it would be nice for him. He flew it himself for over an hour.

While we're on the subject, did you prefer piloting propeller planes like the Connie, or did you prefer jets?

A piston-driven aircraft is a delight to fly. A jet is a headache – far more complicated, a very mechanical operation, a power plant. A prop plane, especially the smaller ones, like the F-11 or the Sikorsky, the

Lockheed Vegas or even a Northrop Gamma – that's something you can feel. With a plane like that, you can dance. You can hardly love a jet but you certainly could – at least *I* could – love a prop plane, and I'm sure that most pilots who have flown both would agree with me.

Actually I loved all the planes I designed and flew, but never for very long. I was fickle. You could say I had a harem of planes if you want to talk about it that way. I didn't actually get tired of them, but I always had at least three or four that were operational, and I used them all. Of course when I was building something from scratch, like the H-1 or the F-11, I put my heart and soul into it to the exclusion of everything else and to the exclusion of any other aircraft I was using at the time – so you could say those were very intense love affairs.

Anyway, on the first flight of the Connic, I broke the transcontinental record again, although it's really a matter of absolutely no significance. The record has been broken a hundred times since then and it will be broken a hundred times more. I wasn't setting out to break any record. I was just setting out to prove that the Constellation was a plane that could carry people in comfort from coast to coast, nonstop. And it did. But in the light of what we have today, in the light of what we're going to have in future planes, in the history of aircraft, my record-breaking flights in the Constellation will be a footnote on page twenty-nine. My contributions to the industry were more basic than that.

You know, I almost didn't make that first flight in the Connie. We were ready for takeoff from Burbank when two young women came running out in the lights of the field. It was late at night, about three o'clock in the morning. One of them was a girlfriend of mine named Fran Gallagher, a gorgeous dark-haired woman, really talented and passionate in bed. She'd brought a girlfriend along – I seem to remember that her name was Valerie, and she was another knockout. So I had a ladder lowered and went out, and got involved in conversation with Fran and her friend Valerie. Fran wanted to come along – she said, 'If you let Valerie and me come on this flight and the three of us are alone in the cockpit, Howard, this will be the most memorable flight of your life.'

I was tempted, needless to say, but it was a proving flight and I didn't want any noncontributing passengers aboard, even if they promised memorable fun and games. Still, I hesitated.

When I looked round, the ladder was up in the cockpit and the plane was taxiing down the field. I said, 'What the hell's going on here?' Jack Frye was my copilot and he was at the controls. It was just a joke, he wanted me to get moving. And so I kissed Fran goodbye and waved to Valerie and ran after the plane. They stopped and put down the ladder and I climbed up, and we were off.

Didn't you break the record again, in 1946, on a second flight with the Connie?

Yes, we broke the speed record that time too, but again it was the kind of record that would last until the next favorable tail wind. That was a publicity flight for the plane, more than anything. You could call it a VIP flight, in a way. Some senators were aboard, and Danny Kaye and his wife, and Linda Darnell. Poor Linda, I was fond of her, and we had some wild times together, but she came to a bad end. Burned to death, set herself on fire smoking in bed in a drunken stupor.

At one point I stepped out of the flight deck and went up to Linda and said, 'Dig out that bottle of hooch you've got in your handbag.'

She gave it to me, and everybody watched me walk back carrying a bottle of bourbon. I heard afterwards they thought I'd finally gone off the deep end and was going to go up there and get plastered. But I needed it. One thing we'd forgotten on board was the methylated spirits to clean the windshield. I needed alcohol, and I knew Linda had it.

In 1946 I developed a radar system for the Connie, and that was a significant step forward in airline safety. It was the only radar for commercial aircraft that was worth a damn at the time, and I demonstrated it in 1947. It was the only device that gave the pilot a warning if he was too close to mountains or any other obstacle. It flashed a red light, and a warning horn sounded in the brainbox, the flight deck.

I demonstrated it near Mount Wilson, in California, because, as usual, there were skeptics who didn't think it would work. I took a group of newspaper people up in a Connie, and I scared the holy hell out of them. They thought with a 500-foot warning, that only allowed a few seconds for the pilot to avoid whatever obstacle there was. But that wasn't the case, since this was a radarscope that picked up the obstacle at ground level.

I flew them all around Mount Wilson and into those canyons around there. Naturally, the moment we got close to the mountains the red light went on and the horn started to sound. It was loud as hell – I'd had it amplified because I was too deaf to hear it at its normal pitch. I knew that part of the country pretty well, and I went up in the evening, just when it was getting dark, and each time the horn would sound and the light would flash on, I'd start a conversation with one of these guys and pretend I hadn't heard the signal, which drove them out of their minds. I knew I still had thirty or forty seconds to get the ship out of danger, and I used pretty near every second of it. I proved my point. The newsboys weren't skeptical anymore.

Of course I could handle that ship, the Connie, like no other pilot in the world except maybe Bob Buck. I offered to take the same gang through the Grand Canyon if they wanted more proof. But they didn't take me up on it. They had to file their stories and change their pants first – they wet them on that flight.

You may have read that I was supposed to have lived in one of my Constellations, but that's not quite true. It's a fact that one of them was equipped for living, and I did spend an occasional night on board, but that's all. Apart from that I had a lot of fun with my planes, and my friends did too. Cary Grant and I used to go to Mexico every once in a while, and there was one flight where our radio went on the blink and we were reported lost.

Cary and I were good friends then. I arranged his marriage to Betsy Drake. I don't mean I was a matchmaker – I mean I arranged the wedding. I picked them up at the airfield in Culver City, in my Connie, very early in the morning. They had to hop over a wire fence and run out to the plane, and I took off and flew them to Arizona. We went there because Cary and Betsy wanted to avoid publicity. They were being hounded almost as much as I was.

This was Christmas day, 1949 – the day after my birthday. I landed in the desert at an abandoned Army airfield. It was an old strip, and it wasn't built for something as big as a Connie. We came down right to the end of the runway and I almost overshot. I had to jam on the brakes hard to avoid running into a mess of cactus. I had arranged to have a car waiting to pick us up and we drove to the house of the local justice of the peace. I was Cary's best man and I was so nervous I did everything ass backwards. First I stood next to Betsy, and then when the J.P. told me to move over to Cary's side I did, but I stumbled and dropped the wedding ring and had to get down on my hands and knees to look for it under a sofa.

Anyway, despite my efforts, finally they got married. We drove back to the landing strip and by then it was pitch dark. I hadn't realized we would have to take off at night – I had to hustle back into town and hire a couple of taxis to come out to the airport and shine their lights on the runway so I could see where I was going. We took off, and toward the end of the flight Betsy came up and sat with me in the cockpit for a while. I thought I'd give her a little charge, so I buzzed Wilshire Boulevard.

She turned white. She said, 'My God, Howard, I'm not going to die on my wedding day, am I?'

I put the ship down at Culver City, they hopped back over the fence, and that was that.

Cary and I also went on a wild trip one time to Mexico – this was a couple of years before I arranged the gala wedding with Betsy. It was 1947, a few months after I'd cracked up the F-11. I was in a big hurry because I had a date down there with a woman.

Lana Turner?

No, sorry to disappoint you. This is someone you never heard of and I won't mention her real name because... well, I'll tell you this much. This incident happened in 1946. Not my flying to Mexico with Cary Grant to see her, but meeting her for the first time. It was one of the most extraordinary things that ever happened to me.

I was flying to San Francisco from New York on a United Airlines plane. (I sometimes flew with the opposition, just to see how well or how poorly they did things.) Anyhow, there I was in my seat, dog-tired from whatever I'd been working on, and there was this woman sitting in the seat next to me. Not a girl, you understand – a woman in her early thirties, well-dressed and beautiful. I've never been much on small talk so we didn't say more than a few words to each other, just stuff like 'Pardon me' and so forth. But I did notice that she was exceptionally attractive, with unusual features, and lovely blue-green eyes. Startling eyes, very clear. After dark I fell into a kind of doze, and I swear I don't know how this happened, but when I woke up we were holding hands.

Isn't that incredible?

We talked, and one thing led to another. Nothing happened right away – not in San Francisco, because she was being met by her husband. We lost touch for a time, but then we made contact, and she agreed to meet me in Mexico that time. That's why I was in such a rush – I hadn't seen her since that crazy time on the flight to San Francisco.

You can't give me her name?

No, she's still married to the same man. He was in the consular service. He's a very highpowered diplomat now, he has a very exalted rank, so I won't tell you his name. Her first name was Helga.

Did she know who you were?

Not during the flight, but later I wanted to keep contact with her, so I had to tell her. What I liked about her was that it didn't impress her one way or the other. She just said, 'Oh, you're the man who flew around the world.' I gave her some flying lessons, as a matter of fact, once in Santa Fe.

Do you still see her?

The last time was years ago – well, some time after she met me in Acapulco. Later I'll tell you more about her.

9

Howard becomes a rich multimillionaire, has problems with a colonel
in his brewery, and develops the first great growth company.

IN THE PERIOD when I was first making movies in Hollywood I made the leap from a millionaire to a multimillionaire. And then in the period from 1937 through 1943 I made the leap from a multimillionaire to a rich multimillionaire. There are plenty of rich multimillionaires now, in 1971, but there weren't many then.

How do you define a rich multimillionaire? How many millions does it take?

It's not a matter of numbers. A man with five million may still be just a simple multimillionaire if he focuses on keeping what he's got and worries about where to invest it. A rich multimillionaire doesn't concern himself with those things – they seem to take care of themselves. Moreover, in my time there weren't many men or women who had more millions than they knew what to do with. That was my status.

I became a rich multimillionaire through a peculiar chain of circumstances.

There were more cars on the roads in the United States than ever before, and whether times were good or bad they needed to run on gasoline. In order to make gasoline you had to refine crude oil, and in order to pump crude oil out of the ground you had to use the Hughes tool bit. It was around that time that I made a remark so some reporter which was very widely quoted. It was a smartass thing to say, and I regretted that I said it. But it was still true.

I was asked if Toolco didn't have an illegal lock on the drill bit industry, and I got a little huffy and said, 'No one's forced to use our bit. They can always go out and buy a pick and shovel.'

We had just begun to move back on to the profit side around 1938. But I went over the books, and things didn't look right to me. We were making money in Houston but not as much as we should have been making. The company didn't seem to be growing fast enough, and I smelled that something was wrong.

At the time I was pretty much involved in setting up Jack Frye in TWA so I called in Noah Dietrich once again. 'Get down to Houston, Noah, ingratiate yourself with the good ole boys, and straighten things out for me.'

Noah took the train down and put his finger on the trouble, and it came right out of the brewery.

In 1935 I had bought a brewery called the Gulf Brewing Company. In later years it became sort of a nickel-and-dime affair, but during the Thirties and Forties it was the biggest brewery in Texas. Actually, whenever I'd had enough of an executive in any of my companies in Houston or somewhere else, I would offer him a promotion. I'd send him down there to be brewmaster. The executive found the brewmaster's tasks nonexistent and he was eased out by Noah, and that was the end of it. So I was spared any face-to-face confrontation with these people.

If you want one of the various faults I have – and which I'll admit to – that's one. I couldn't fire a man. I almost always had to have someone else do it for me. I don't have the hardness, I suppose, deep down. Any sad story will make me change my mind when an individual's concerned. Once, early on in Hollywood, I wanted to fire one of the first people who ever worked for me. That was the cameraman on that picture, *Swell Hogan*, which never got released. When I told him he was through, he said, 'Gee whiz, Mr. Hughes, I've got a wife and three children to support... ' and I couldn't fire him, He messed up his part of the picture, as he'd been doing all along. After that, in other similar situations, I always told somebody else to fire a man if he had to be fired.

Down in Houston in 1939 Noah learned that the brewery operation had a by-product. That was cereal mash, which they sold as cattle feed. When Noah went over the books of Gulf Brewing it didn't show any money coming in from the mash.

Noah quickly found out that Gulf Brewing's trucks were being used to carry this mash out to a man who had a large cattle ranch. That man was Colonel Rudolph Kuldell. He'd been with the company since around 1920, he'd been a friend of my father's, and now he was president and general manager of Toolco. He was more a figurehead, because Holliday and Montrose ran the show, but he was a figurehead with his finger in the pie.

Noah called me and explained what he'd discovered. I said, 'Noah, when you find a few ants running across your lawn, you know there's a colony of them buried deep. Dig deeper. This guy's doing more.'

Sure enough, it turned out that not only was he stealing my money to feed the cattle, but his cattle were also supplying the milk for our cafeteria at five cents more than the normal price per quart.

And it went even deeper. They had a very poor accounting system in those days. Checks would come to Toolco for what are called non-recurring items, a rebate for insurance, and the checks were all being stopped by Colonel Kuldell and going into his bank account. They didn't use Swiss banks in those days to hide money – nobody was that sophisticated. He just put it into the Bank of Texas under his wife's maiden name. He was also an art collector. We found out he went to New York once or twice a year and used Toolco money to buy expensive French Impressionist paintings that were supposed to go in Toolco offices. Toolco offices had about the same amount of wall decoration as the average men's room in a railway station. The paintings wound up in this guy's parlor and attic.

It took a little while to get all this information together. Then I brought Noah back and he was fire-in-the-eye, ready to call out the Texas Rangers. He said, 'What are we going to do about this?'

Thieves are not necessarily unpleasant people, they can be very personable men, and if we had thrown Kuldell out he would have gone right over to Reed Roller Bit and taken all his accounts with him and all his knowledge. I made a simple calculation. Toolco had just made $7 million profit that past year. This guy had bilked the company to the tune of about two hundred and fifty thousand dollars. If I wanted to save two hundred and fifty, I might be losing my seven million – I might be throwing the baby out with the bathwater.

'Noah,' I said, 'here is your assignment. I want you to make sure that Kuldell is not in a position to steal more then $250,000 a year from me.'

That was my limit. I didn't like what the man was doing and I wouldn't encourage others to emulate him, but I was stuck with the situation and I had to make the best of it.

My plan didn't work. By then all the other good people down at Houston had gotten wind of it and knew that the man was a thief, and they didn't understand why I didn't get rid of him. They threatened to quit unless I did.

That shows you, in a sense, that they had very little imagination. You'd think, once they realized that I didn't mind a guy stealing from me, they would have done a little pilfering themselves.

I finally decided I had to handle this myself. I flew down to Houston in my plane and I took Colonel Kuldell to dinner.

Was he really a colonel or was that just one of those honorary Texas titles?

He was a United States Army colonel, retired, second in his class at West Point. He was assistant to the Chief of Engineers in Washington when my father hired him.

'Rudy,' I said, 'we know what you've been doing. I'm sure you're going to see the error of your ways and, for the sake of Toolco morale, you're going to resign.'

He dawdled around for a while – I didn't exactly give him a time limit. Finally Noah called him in and said, 'Get the hell out, you're fired.' Kuldell popped off a little to people, said it was a palace revolution and Big Howard would turn over in his grave.

I told Noah he'd moved too fast. And just to show you that I was right, the year this man left, Toolco business profits dropped considerably more than two hundred and fifty thousand dollars.

There weren't many good men available, so I put Noah in charge of

Toolco for a while, and then I hired Fred Ayres, who had worked for the Cadillac company. Between Noah and Ayres, with me supervising, they modernized the company and the profits went up and up and up. They got up to $60 million a year by 1947.

Which meant $60 million a year in your pocket?

Which meant $60 million a year that I plowed back into the company and my other companies. If there's any one reason that I can give for the fact that I've become a multibillionaire, that's it. I never had more than $50,000 a year income myself. I submitted an account of my expenses each year to Toolco, and the Board of Directors automatically voted me a dividend equal to the expenses. That ranged from $50,000 to about double that. Anyway, that's what I paid taxes on. Not having any stockholders to have to satisfy with dividends and reports and those damn fool meetings, I just plowed the rest of the money back in. Toolco was the parent company that owned Hughes Aircraft and the brewery, RKO, TWA; whatever I bought I bought through Toolco, one way or the other, and I didn't have to pay income tax.

All you hear from investors these days is talk of growth companies, but some very smart guy said a while ago that a growth company is any company your broker wants you to buy stock in. That's more truth than poetry. Toolco was probably the first truly great growth company in the United States.

There's another reason too, for my becoming a billionaire, which I admit didn't hold true all the time, but most of the time. I spent a lot of money freely until after the war. I always owned about one or two dozen cars, which I kept parked in various parking lots and side streets all over the United States. But I didn't buy new cars, except during the period when I first went to Hollywood. I bought old cars. I didn't see any sense in buying a new Cadillac when a second-hand Chevrolet would do just as well. If you drive a second-hand Chevrolet, nobody looks twice at you. I had a fleet of them, mechanically perfect, very well maintained. I could have had my own taxi company.

One Christmas I made Noah Dietrich a present of a Mercedes-Benz 300 SL gullwing, with those doors that open straight up. I drove it, and it was a joy, and I was tempted to buy one for myself. Then I thought, no, this is exactly what I've been trying to avoid. I didn't want people watching that flashy car go down the street and yelling, 'There goes Howard Hughes! *Get him!*'

The point I'm trying to make is that after my Hollywood years, and after my boats and various personal airplanes, like my Boeing, which was pretty lush, and which I sold to some drunken son of a bitch from Texas who abandoned it at the Houston airport, I stopped spending money on myself. I didn't have any quirks and fancies, no Taj Mahal in Palm Beach or Palm Springs, and I didn't maintain two or three mistresses in the fashionable capitals of the world. I had no hobbies except golf, and I had to give that up after my last air crash.

But didn't you rent a number of houses in California at this time, where you kept women?

I rented several small bungalows. One or two were decent-sized houses. I didn't have a home of my own. I had to rent. If women stayed there it was because they had no place else to stay and because they were connected with me businesswise in one manner or another. I put up various executives there too. And I had to have some place to stay when I got somewhere. Because by then I had begun to realize that most hotel rooms were filthy, were very poorly cleaned, and I required a special sort of accommodation. It was cheaper in the long run to have a bungalow somewhere than it was to walk in and take the honeymoon suite at the Bel Air Hotel.

What sort of rents did you pay?

Whatever was fair. I didn't pay them. Toolco paid them. They were charged off as business expenses. I ran the company, so if I stayed in them it was a business expense. And if friends of mine stayed in then, they might have been doing business for TWA too. I can't remember every single person who stayed in my houses. But that's the secret – that's another reason for my getting rich and staying rich. I was a frugal man. I still am.

Frugal? I've gotten an estimate that your bill at the Britannia Beach averages $50,000 a month. And you're not even there most of the time.

Where the hell did you find that out? Wait, don't tell me. I don't want to know. I'm positive it wouldn't come to more than twenty thousand a month, which you'll admit, is very modest for a man of my means. Naturally if you add up what those guys eat, and various other things, it's going to run a lot higher. But that's a drop in the bucket. I know $50,000 sounds like a lot of money to you, but that's the interest on my capital for an hour or two.

I want to repeat what I said, because I don't think you've gotten the point correctly. And that is, despite what hotel bills I pay, and despite what secondhand cars I maintain around the world, I do not have any expensive fancies and quirks. I don't piss away my money. I don't personally own a luxurious jet – the company has several and I use them and others. But I still don't have a large income, and therefore I'm not a drain on my companies' resources. I pull my own weight.

10

Howard produces The Outlaw, *fixes its sound track, turns down
Jane Russell, and is slugged by Ava Gardner.*

AFTER THE CONSTELLATION, the next thing I tackled was *The
Outlaw*. It's not a major event in my life, but I want to give my version of
what happened, since there's been so much nonsense written about it.

I say it's not a major event in my life, but you may have noticed by
now that whenever I've tackled anything I've gone into it heart and soul,
and I haven't always kept a sense of proportion. I've devoted as much
time to unimportant projects as I have to things of more substance.

It's only in retrospect, however, that I consider *The Outlaw* to be an
unimportant project. At the time I thought I was breaking new
ground, as I did with *Hell's Angels*. I had that in mind from the very
beginning, and that's why I searched as hard as I did for someone like
Jane Russell and chose her to be my star. And once I found her I meant
to see that her assets stayed in the public eye.

I hadn't made a motion picture in many years, but I had a yen to
break down some of the puritan barriers that I felt had been holding
back the American cinema. Today, of course, all the barriers have
been broken, and what I did seems quixotic, but if you place it in the
perspective of the history of the cinema, you'll see that it was a
major breakthrough.

The story I selected was a version of the old Billy the Kid saga. I got
a very fine director, Howard Hawks, but he didn't work out very well
– he got sore because he thought we were shooting in Arizona on
location, and one day he arrived at the set and everyone was gone. I'd
ordered them back to Hollywood to the sound stage, but Hawks hadn't

got the message. I still respect his work very much, and in fact he worked for me later at RKO.

So I took over *The Outlaw*. I directed it. You don't have to be a genius to direct a movie. You don't even have to be terribly artistic. You just need the common sense to listen to the technical people around you – they usually know what they're doing – and at the same time you have to let them know you're the boss.

I budgeted the picture very low, at a quarter of a million dollars. I had trouble immediately because Noah Dietrich got together with Hawks and said, 'It can't be done for a quarter of a million. It's going to cost half a million, and knowing Howard that figure will probably be closer to two million.'

He was wrong. It cost nearly four million. I have a tendency, when I plunge into something, to forget the costs. In my view, the costs are not important – it's the finished product that matters and, maybe even more important, what you learn in the course of getting to the finished product.

I started shooting, and what interested me, as always, was the opportunity to educate myself at the same time as I was making the movie. I always did that, and still do. You can never stop learning. There isn't a day passes in my life that I don't learn something. I try to learn one fact a day, or think about one new idea.

One of the things that particularly interested me in *The Outlaw* was the background music, which was done by Victor Young. I got terribly involved in it.

In those days we didn't have the kind of magnetic sound track that they have now. We had what was called an optical track. You could literally see the sound track, and you could fool around with it – by putting masking tape on certain positions of the track you could block it off, raise and lower the volume, do what else you pleased. The technicians on this picture were not everything that I'd wanted them to be, so I took over and did the sound track myself. It took me, I would say, three or four weeks, working ten or twelve hours a day on it, and, mind you, not only was I half-deaf but I was doing other things at the time. By then it was wartime and I was building the Hercules and the D-2.

As everyone knows, we had a great deal of trouble getting a release for *The Outlaw*, and it wasn't until 1946 that the picture was released. It premiered in San Francisco at the Geary Theatre. I went up there, stayed at the St. Francis Hotel, and I wasn't feeling well. I had a bout of pneumonia, and I decided I couldn't make the premiere. Besides, I didn't want to go out into the crowds and deal with all that horseshit.

I stayed in my room that night, and I could hear that sound track in my head the whole time, and I suddenly realized something was wrong. So I got on the pipe to my film editor, Walter Reynolds, who was also up there in San Francisco. I can't give you the exact hour and minute, but the point I'm trying to make is that the picture had already started, the audience was in their seats, Jane's tits were on the screen, and I said to Walter, 'Get the hell over here in a hurry and bring Reel Three to my hotel room.'

He arrived in a terrible state. He had the jitters, because the reels ran about twenty minutes. At the Geary they were halfway through the first reel, and without the third, the premiere couldn't go on.

But I said, 'Something's wrong, Walter, and I want to make a cut.'

'Howard, you can't make a cut up here. You have no equipment, and I've got to bring that reel back to the theatre within fifteen minutes.'

I've learned in my life not to let other people's panics panic me. I said calmly, 'Take it out of the can, Walter, and give it to me.'

'You don't have any film rods,' he said. 'You have no cutting equipment – and how are you going to hear the sound track?'

All my life I've improvised, right up to now, when I put my own leaded glass screen in front of the TV set to cut out the gamma rays.

So I ran the film over a fountain pen – you have to have something to run it over in order to count the frames – and while I was doing it I had the musical score in my head. I've told you that as a child I played the saxophone and the ukulele. I hummed the music, and I moved the film, and I found the exact spot where I wanted to make a cut and where I didn't want any music in the background. I wanted that silence to create a certain effect, a mood which you can get sometimes by silence. I've thought a great deal about the nature of silence. As I've grown older, silence has become much more precious to me – in fact, there are times when I am grateful for my deafness.

Walter had been sensible enough to bring a splicer. I cut twelve feet of film and he ran back to the Geary Theatre carrying Reel Three. Of course, it's an art in itself, to cut twelve feet out of a finished film. But what astonished Walter was that I'd been able to cut the twelve feet of film and there was no awkward jump in the sound track, because I had it in my head and I knew that we moved from a C sharp to another C sharp chord.

He came to me next day and said, 'Howard, that was an absolutely perfect cut.' He was impressed. Deep down I was a little impressed too, but I just said, 'Sure, Walter. What did you expect?'

Julie Furthman wrote the screenplay, but I wrote a good part of it too, and Joe Breen, the front man for the Hays Office, also made some contributions. This is hardly believable, but so help me, it's true. There's a scene in the movie where Jane Russell, Doc Holliday's girlfriend, climbs into bed with Jack Buetel, who played Billy the Kid. Billy's been wounded and has to be kept warm.

Walter Huston, who played Doc Holliday, comes back and finds them in the sack. Doc is pretty annoyed at this hanky-panky and threatens to gun Billy down. And Billy, who had loaned Doc his horse, reminds him of the fact, and says, 'A fair exchange is no robbery.' That was Julie Furthman's line and I didn't think it was clear, just a touch too highbrow, and I changed it to, 'You borrowed my horse, so I borrowed your girl.'

That made Joe Breen's hair stand on end. He'd already seen the rough-cut of the picture and he was yelling about the showing of Jane's tits and the fact that everybody was climbing into bed with everyone else. It all boiled down finally to covering Jane's cleavage here and there and eliminating that one line, 'You borrowed my horse, so I borrowed your girl.'

I said in disgust, 'Okay, Mr. Breen, you want to change it, go ahead. Just give me another line in its place.'

He said, 'Well, how about "tit for tat"?'

I couldn't believe my ears, but I very grudgingly said, 'Okay.' When this got back to Will Hays, Breen's boss, *his* hair stood on end. Finally he said, 'Look, Hughes, you cut that one line out, "tit for tat," and put in something else, and we'll give the film the production seal.'

I said, 'How about, "You borrowed my horse, I borrowed your girl"?' – which of course was my original line.

Will Hays said, 'Yes, anything, I'm sick of this argument, I'm getting ulcers.' And that's how it stood at the end.

That was the first time I used Russell Birdwell as publicity agent. I knew that this picture needed a tremendous publicity campaign and Bird, which is what we called him, had been the publicity man for *Gone with the Wind*. I didn't know him personally, but in those days when I wanted to meet a man I didn't necessarily call him on the telephone and say, 'I'd like to meet you. Please come over.' I liked to meet people in more subtle ways.

I arranged to be out one night with Norma Shearer and I knew that Russell Birdwell would be at a certain night club. So I sat down with Norma and Myron Selznick at a table and listened to Birdwell talk to them. I didn't say a word and he didn't know who I was. He must have thought I was just another hanger-on, because by then I wasn't paying attention to the way I dressed – I would wear a shirt until the collar frayed, socks till they'd stand up by themselves and walk out of the room. If people didn't like the smell of my feet, they could go somewhere else and smell some other millionaire's feet.

I hired Bird because Jane was unknown. Some agent had given me a photograph of her – she was nobody, not even an actress. She was a receptionist for some dentist out in the San Fernando Valley. She wanted to be an actress, but so did everybody in Hollywood. She had great cleavage, that was her principal asset.

I never gave screen tests – I didn't believe in them. I wanted one thing: a still photograph with no makeup, because if a woman has got It, and you know what I mean by It, that certain star quality will come through. A woman in the morning, after you've spent the night with her and all the makeup has worn off, if she's not beautiful then, you don't want to have anything to do with her. Take my advice – that's the acid test. And that was my method to find out whether or not these girls had It.

However, I did not spend the night with Jane Russell, I can assure you of that, even though she made it known to me that she was willing. I tend to favor a more slender woman. And at that time I was prettily heavily involved with Ava Gardner. You couldn't exactly call Ava slender, but her proportions were a great deal more pleasing to my eye than Jane Russell's. Ava was young then – she hadn't bloomed yet. At the time I was seeing her, she couldn't have been more than twenty years old. It was just at the beginning of her career. But kid or not, slender or not, Ava was tough and she packed a mean wallop. She slugged me once with a bronze statue. I'm lucky to be here talking about it, and Ava's lucky she isn't behind bars for manslaughter.

It was around 1942, when she was getting a divorce from Mickey Rooney. Ava and I had been seeing one another off and on when she was breaking up with Rooney. But when I went with a woman, she went with me only, and I wasn't about to share her with somebody else – I'd had my fill of that in the past and I knew the risks involved. Ava is a hell of a woman, probably one of the most attractive women I've ever known. Sexual as hell. And certainly sexual enough for Mickey, because he screwed her from time to time at her place when I wasn't there. He was a little guy but they say he was hung like a donkey. That's not true of me, not at all.

I have ways to learn things, and once I found out this was happening, I confronted Ava with it and gave her a piece of my mind. In fact, I lost my temper and threatened to slap her across the chops.

But I reckoned without that gypsy temperament. I was on my way out, and she picked up a bronze statuette and let me have it behind the ear. I hit the carpet and was out like a light. They told me later she was leaning over me with blood in her eye, ready to plant that bronze statuette six inches into my skull, when her maid heard the yelling and stopped her. That would have polished me off for good. The colored maid saved my life.

Wait a second... I'm not sure that stories like this have a place in my book.

I think they do. It's not all high finance and breaking airspeed records.

Well, all right. I was the injured party.

Was there any talk of marriage between you and Ava Gardner?

The usual talk. She shot her mouth off to the newsboys every now and then. I knew her for a long time, you know, but I usually made it a point to see her when she was between husbands. When she split up with Sinatra she sent me an SOS and I got her out of Las Vegas, because she thought the little bastard was going to kill her. She was hysterical. I sent a plane to Las Vegas and had her flown down to Cuba, and I arranged for a bodyguard for her, to protect her from Sinatra and his ratpack Mafia friends. It was the least I could do for her, to give her some peace of mind.

You were still friendly with her, even after she'd tried to brain you?

I didn't turn my back on her again, you can be damn sure of that. But she came back weeping and said she was sorry, she didn't know what had gotten into her.

To get back to Jane Russell – I made a contract with her years later, well after *The Outlaw* was done, and I still pay that girl a thousand dollars a week. I give her credit, she's learned to act, but when I hired her for *The Outlaw* she couldn't act worth a damn. But Jane had what I was looking for, so I signed her to a contract. She was bright, and I liked that. I hired this other unknown young actor, Jack Buetel, who was a jerk. Then I turned Russell Birdwell loose to build them up. I didn't have the time for that kind of thing. I was involved in the HK-1 by then, and the D-2.

Of course the best bit of publicity that Bird had was a fluke, and that was when a Japanese submarine fired at Jane Russell on the beach near Santa Barbara. This happened during that long period between the time we finished *The Outlaw* and the time it was released, because the goddamn Hays office wouldn't go for it at first. One day Jane went up the coast to take some publicity shots, and a Japanese submarine surfaced and fired a shot at some oil rigs, but fortunately Jane was in the way, or nearby.

Also fortunately, there was a man there taking publicity shots. He snapped photographs of Jane holding the shell fragments and looking very frightened. And that hit all the papers: front page. That made Jane Russell. (Now that's an example of what's called good luck, but if the photographer hadn't been quick enough to take the photographs there wouldn't have been any good luck.) We were off and away because Jane Russell was a target for the Japs. It would have been a bad break, of course, if one of these shells had nipped off a chunk of her natural endowments, but in that sense we were lucky, and so was she.

Then the Hays Office refused to give its seal of approval to the picture. We fought them on and off from 1941 to 1946. Jake Erlich, my lawyer, went into a courtroom with a bust of Venus de Milo, who as you know doesn't wear a brassiere. The whole time that Jake conducted the case he had that bust sitting there in the courtroom, just to impress the people with the fact that the Greeks weren't ashamed of the bare facts, and why the hell are we? And then the Motion Picture Producer's Association got into the act and banned the film. I wound up suing them in 1948 for $5 million on the grounds that they were breaking the antitrust laws – boycott in restraint of trade.

Despite the fact that it was wartime and I was involved in far more serious endeavors, I had a showdown with these creeps in New York in 1944. We plastered the office with blow-ups, photographs of great female film stars of past and present, all of whom showed considerable amount of cleavage in their bosom. I hired a professor of mathematics from Columbia University. He came up there with his slide rule and calipers and measured the various amounts of cleavage and the amount of flesh that was showing, and he proved to the satisfaction of these people from the Hays Office and the Producers' Association that, proportionately speaking, Miss Russell showed less of her natural endowments than the overwhelming majority of the great film stars of the past.

The point I was really making was that there should be no censorship at all, because it's in violation of the First Amendment to the Constitution of the United States. And time proved me right, for better or for worse. You look at movies that have been made years ago, and if you know the cuts that have been made you say to yourself, 'Now why in hell did they ever cut that?' Let's say I had a much longer view than these shortsighted idiots who are out there to protect the morals of America's children. Look what's happened to the morals of America's children. You think the Hays Office or the Breen Office could do anything to stop that? That's a runaway freight train.

Didn't you design a special bra for Jane Russell during the shooting of the pictures?

That was a simple problem in mechanical engineering – how to prop up two falling monuments. She was tied to a tree and I wanted those things sticking out like cannons.

I've tackled bigger problems than that in my life, although I guess I've rarely tackled bigger breasts. I told my engineers how it should be done, sketched it out, and the boys did it for me. That received a lot of publicity. I can't understand why people make such fuss over petty stories like that. I certainly considered it a trivial achievement. That wasn't the design of my life – lifting up Jane Russell's breasts. I had started work on the flying boat. *That* was important. That was something I believed in, even though it led to one of the biggest disasters of my life.

77

After a visit with President Roosevelt, Howard flies wartime combat missions out of England.

IT WAS WARTIME. We were fighting Germany and Japan. Many things were happening in my life at the same time besides *The Outlaw*. I wanted to do my part in winning the war – airplane design and manufacture was of course the area where I felt I could best contribute. I started in right away, two days after Pearl Harbor. Actually I started a year before that, when I realized that one of these days we'd have to help out Great Britain and fight Hitler and the Nazis.

The experience with the Army turning down the H-1, which became the Zero, was what made me decide: to hell with those armchair generals. I said, 'I'm going to make a new plane on my own. I don't need their money.' And in 1940, completely at my own expense, I built what was called the DX-2.

The DX-2 was meant to be a long-range medium bomber with a five-man crew and a speed of 300 miles per hour. Then in December of 1941 we changed it to a fighter plane with a two-man crew. But the plane was made of Duramold, and that was the whole trouble – the Army didn't believe in wooden airplanes. The wooden De Havilland Mosquito saved the British Empire, but the U.S. Army pretended the Mosquito was an accident. They wanted only metal aircraft.

I was perfectly willing to let the Army have a look at the DX-2 anytime they wanted to, and in the middle of 1942 Echols and General Carroll and his boys looked, and made their report. They said, 'It's just another hobby of that playboy Howard Hughes. And it's made of wood! We can't buy a wooden airplane! We've never done it before, and what would people think?'

So they kept turning it down and I kept working on it. I had it ready sometime in 1943, and I flew it at 450 miles per hour.

That was exceptionally fast, you realize. It was the fastest thing around. But it needed modifications. There are a lot of kinks in a ship at that stage. The military saw the certified results of those tests. They were finally impressed and they said, 'We don't need another fighter, but we do need a photo-reconnaissance plane. If you can make the D-5 into the F-11, we'll buy it.'

How did we get from DX-2 to D-5?

X means experimental. By then we'd worked up several new models and the last one happened to be the fifth, so it was the D-5. We dropped the X when the plane was finished. The F-11 – F stands for photo-reconnaissance – was the XF-11 at the beginning, because it was experimental. Got it?

The only difference was that they bullied me into making the F-11 out of metal. I was willing, since the plane wasn't going to carry armament and had to be pretty tough. I was also willing because for the first time the sons of bitches were going to make metal available to me, which they hadn't been willing to do before that – I suppose they thought I might wake up one day in a bad mood and use their aluminum to make experimental yo-yos. After all, how can you trust a man who wears pajamas under his suit?

I received a contract for a hundred planes. They were pretty specific about what they wanted in a reconnaissance plane. It had to fly a minimum of four thousand miles without adding any fuel tanks. They wanted external tanks so that it could go another thousand miles. They wanted a plane that could cruise at 30,000 feet, because as I later found out, the stuff they were flying then, those converted P-38s, had a lot of trouble above 18,000 feet. They wanted a ship that could fly 450 miles an hour. Naturally they had to have reasonable protection for the crew, which meant armor plating and positioning of two men so they were less vulnerable to machine gun fire and flak. And no armament on the ship.

This is a hell of an assignment, but I was willing to do it. I felt I had the basic plane in the D-5. However, it's one thing to have the specifications laid out on paper for you, and it's another thing to have the experience in the kind of flying that this plane was required to do. I had flown the hottest planes in the world of my own design. But I had never flown a recon plane, and I had certainly never flown one in combat.

The first thing that occurred to me was, I don't know what the hell it's like up there, I don't know what this ship has to do in actual combat conditions. So I decided to get a firsthand look at how things were in combat – to try the available planes and see what they were lacking and what my plane would need to have to justify its existence.

I went to General Benny Meyers, a friend of mine. Benny couldn't do anything. Even Elliot Roosevelt, while obviously well placed, couldn't open the right doors for me. But his father could. So I called Jesse Jones and told him I wanted to see the President, although I didn't tell him why.

You went straight up to FDR?

He was the Commander-in-Chief, the boss, just like me. What he said, went. I'm not a Democrat, but neither am I a Republican. In fact I have no use for party lines. But Roosevelt was a horse of another color. He was an intellectual, a brilliant man, and he pulled the country out of the worst hole it's ever been in, at any rate since I can remember.

He gave me a few minutes of his time after a White House dinner reception for a visiting Russian, between the rubber chicken and Eleanor's apple pie. He was amused at my request, but he tried to talk me out of it. He said, 'Howard, you're a lunatic. It's a mistake for a man in your position to expose himself. We need generals as much as front-line troops, and you're in the general class.'

I said, 'From what I've seen of your generals, Mr. President, you need them like a dog needs fleas in August.' And I talked him into it. I was pretty stubborn and I think Franklin always liked me. He had given me a medal years before – we had a private lunch following my round-the-world flight – and I guess he had a paternal attitude toward me, which certainly manifested itself when I showed up in Washington in 1944 and said I wanted to fly some missions.

He passed the word down. Several of the TWA stratoliners had been commandeered by the Army, and within a few days it was arranged for me to fly one of them to England. Oral orders were issued by Roosevelt himself, and I had a high priority pass. I was carrying OSS men, all destined for parachute missions in Europe.

The base I landed at was north of London somewhere, near Oxford – it was called Mount Farm – and it was the 7th Reconnaissance Group with the 8th Air Force. Never been so cold in my life. The sun shone about ten minutes a day, on a good day. It was even colder indoors. I don't drink, I don't even drink coffee or stimulants, but I must have put away a gallon of tea every day while I was there, just to keep my insides warm.

I was in uniform but I had no rank, just one of those olive-drab uniforms with some kind of insignia patch on the shoulder. But that was enough, with my presidential pass. I wasn't used to wearing a uniform and I hadn't worn a tie in years, except when I absolutely had to. I walked into the officers' mess the first day, and I was still wearing the same pants I'd worn flying across the Atlantic, and my shirt was rumpled, and I wore an old tattered sweater over it, and earmuffs.

A kid marched up to me and said, 'Who the hell are you?'

I said, 'I'm Major Henry Hughes.' That shook him up, and he just stammered something and left. But pretty soon the commanding officer, Colonel Paul Cullen, marched up to me and said, 'Listen, Major, this isn't a spit-and-polish outfit, but we do expect our officers to walk around in something other than a sweater with torn elbows, and you might have those pants pressed, and take off those red earmuffs.'

I said, 'My ears are cold.'

'Take them off. That's an order, Major.'

'Yes sir, I'll do that, sir,' I said, finally, because I didn't want to make any waves.

I went up to Oxford and got my things cleaned and pressed and bought a new beige cashmere sweater, and for the rest of the time I was just as beautifully turned out as any of the brass around there. But I wasn't there long. I didn't have any time to fool around – I got out on the first clear day, the first recon mission since I'd arrived.

I was flying a modified P-38, called an F-5B. Good plane, but no match for the Kraut pursuit planes, because they crapped out too low, about 22,000 feet, and weren't fast enough. Any higher than that and you were likely to throw a rod. At that, they were an improvement over the F-4s, the unmodified P-38s, which threw rods as low as 17,000 feet. Elliot Roosevelt told me they lost a lot of pilots that way, especially in Africa.

But the F-5B had one big advantage: two engines, so if one was shot out you could limp home on the other. I was familiar with the P-38. Frankly, I think, and I have often said, that I designed the P-38 myself. I proposed the basic design to the Army and they turned it down. And then by some strange coincidence, as often happens in industry, they gave the contract to build the plane to Lockheed. And sure enough, when it came out, the P-38 had all the earmarks of my design. I didn't squawk too loudly about this – it wouldn't have got me the contract by then – but anyhow, I was familiar with the plane.

After a few days we got a little break in the weather and the squadron went out on a dicing mission. That's a low altitude flight, using a nose oblique camera. We were flying along the channel coast of France, on the Cherbourg peninsula, photographing the Kraut defenses. The air was full of flying metal – no flight for a sane man to be on.

Were you scared?

Are you kidding? I'd never been in combat before. I thought maybe I knew what it would be like, from *Hell's Angels*, but it's not the same at all. You can't duplicate that on a movie set. I was petrified.

Did you get hit?

A couple of bits of shrapnel in the fuselage, but nothing compared to what some of the other planes took. One of them had one of the booms – the P-38s had twin booms – torn right in half. Went into a spin. Crashed. Killed. Anyhow, the flight gave me some idea of what was expected of a recon plane at low altitude. You understand, I'm not telling this story to make myself out a hero. Our American boys and those English and Polish pilots flew hundreds of thousands of missions. I only flew three, and I didn't do it to be a hero. I'm telling it because it was a part of my life and it had repercussions.

A few days later we went out again. This time we were mapping in Normandy near Ste.-Mère-Eglise. They were already building up for D-day and they wanted checks on the German defensive measures. This time we flew much higher. If one of those Focke-Wulfs came down at you, you were a sitting duck. We were too fast for an escort. The motto of the squadron was, 'Get 'em, got 'em, gone.' I gave the plane a real workout this time, took her up to damn near 30,000 feet. Now I had been briefed that the plane couldn't operate very effectively over 20,000 feet – it was supposed to, but it couldn't. I did it because I had the instincts of a test pilot. And that's why I was there, to find out how these aircraft behaved. And I got back all right.

When I landed at Mount Farm, I noticed a couple of pilots out there sandpapering the hulls of their ships. I spoke to one of them about it and he explained that if they got it smooth enough they could pick up as much as ten knots in speed. And I smiled, because that was my own thinking when I devised the flush riveting on my H-1. The Japanese went even further – they used an oriental method of lacquering their planes, and one very thin coat of paint on their Zeros, slick as ice.

And the entire time you were in England, the men never realized that you were Howard Hughes? They thought your first name was Henry?

The men didn't, but I suspect the C.O. knew. I had to show him my pass from President Roosevelt. Paul Cullen was a bright and much-loved man. No discipline in the old-fashioned sense that he kept aloof from his men. He was one of the guys sandpapering the plane. He'd go out with the boys in the squadron, pick up the English girls, and he was a hell of a man. He reminded me – well, he was my age – but he made me think my father would have been like that in a similar position. He was one of the boys, which I've never been. I don't think I spoke more than two words to men in the BOQ, the Bachelor Officer Quarters, where I stayed.

You always say you weren't one of the boys, not even then, in England. But that was an opportunity where you really could have been one of them. It was wartime, you were eating with these guys, flying with them...

No, I wasn't eating with them. I ate in town on a park bench. And I brought my own milk and things back to the BOQ. The English milk was delicious, very fresh. Their milk bottles looked far more scrubbed than our American bottles.

But that's not the point. You were comrades in arms. If you wanted to be one of the boys all you had to do was to make the effort.

I didn't know how. I told you I was shy. I don't tell dirty jokes. I didn't chase after women. If I wanted to be with the men, I would have had to lie to them about myself, make up some story, and in those circumstances I don't think it would have worked.

I was in England maybe just a week. I could never talk about it because it had been done in such a way, through my personal contact with Mr. Roosevelt, that I just didn't want to get him in any trouble. And certainly when it came time to be up there before the Senate investigation committee, I had to keep it quiet. I was scared to death it would come up, because they had tried to subpoena some of the President's private papers. He was dead by then, and the papers were up in Hyde Park. I remember thinking, hell, if they get hold of those, then they're really going to make a scandal out of this. Not that there was anything to make a scandal of, but it would have been said that Roosevelt and Hughes were bosom buddies, and that would have given them just that much more ammunition to shoot me down in 1947 – to try and shoot me down.

The Krauts couldn't shoot me down during the war. It took the United States Senate and the Republican Party to have a really good crack at it.

12

*Howard designs a wooden flying boat for the war effort, offends
the Air Corps again, and swears he'll leave the country if the Spruce
Goose doesn't fly.*

THE FLYING BOAT has been a running theme throughout my life. In
a sense it was Henry Kaiser who conceived it, but Henry dropped out
and never implemented the idea in any way. Let's call him the oyster
and me the pearl. He gave me the grain of sand around which I built
the Hercules, which is what I called it. That idea has been incorporated
at least in part in all the big jets that are flying today – the Boeing 747,
the C-5A, and so on.

Henry Kaiser first came to visit me around 1941, just before the war
began for the United States, and I think he had a very poor impression
of me. He came up to my hotel room in San Francisco, at the Mark
Hopkins. I was in bed recovering from pneumonia and I had blankets
piled on top of me. I hadn't told people I was sick and he thought it
was simply another eccentricity on my part, for which I was already
famous at the age of thirty-six.

But he didn't seem to care. He had already talked to Jesse Jones, who
was head of the RFC, the wartime Reconstruction Finance
Corporation. Jesse was a Texan and he had been a friend of my father's.

Henry Kaiser said to him: 'Tell me about Howard Hughes.'

'Mr. Kaiser,' Jesse said, 'I've known that boy all my life. He's a man
you can trust.' He called me a genius. He said, 'I wholeheartedly
recommend that you and young Howard work together. All I suggest is
that because of Howard's methods of work, his concentration, and his
attention to details, you leave him alone when he does the building.'

Kaiser sat by my bed at the Mark Hopkins. 'Well, Howard, how about some way to lick those goddamn German U-boats that are chewing up our shipping?'

I asked him what he had in mind.

'I have in mind,' Henry said, 'a flying cargo ship. Something big enough to carry a battalion of troops and all their gear right over the Atlantic.'

I was speechless. I don't want to detract from Henry's inspiration, but something of the sort had been buzzing around in the back of my head for some time, and Henry's words crystallized it for me. Right then and there I had the vision of what is commonly known as the Hercules, or HK-1, or the Spruce Goose, as it was later nicknamed.

I immediately got interested. The only thing, I told him, was that I didn't know if I could mass-produce a ship of such scope and size.

He said, 'That's my specialty, Howard. You just design and develop it.'

I said okay, and we shook hands.

Literally?

Oh, I was half dead with pneumonia, practically a one-man germ factory, and it couldn't have made any difference if I'd shaken hands with a crap-smeared ape in the zoo. It was Henry who took the risk that time, not me.

We set up a nonprofit paper corporation, and put up a few thousand dollars apiece. Henry was very useful to me, not only because of his knowhow, but because he got along much better with those guys in Washington. They already had me on their shitlist for that little incident at Wright Field. I let Henry handle all the socializing, and I set my mind to figuring out what we were going to build and how we were going to build it.

This was now in the beginning of 1942 and there was already a tremendous labor shortage. I had no idea where we were going to get skilled men to work on something of that scope. But I was going to go ahead with the project anyhow.

I worked up some preliminary designs and in September of 1942 Henry turned up with a Letter of Intent from the government, authorizing him to spend $18 million and build three planes. That's better than I could have done if I'd gone to Washington. They would have said, 'Why don't *you* cough it up, Mr. Hughes? You've got plenty of money.'

But Henry pulled one boner: he told the government that the planes would be ready within a year. I knew they'd barely be getting off the drawing boards by then, and we wouldn't be able to freeze the design for at least eighteen months.

I took over one of our sheds at the Culver City aircraft center and moved two of our other projects into an abandoned laundry. My first problem was that I couldn't get metal – it was in short supply, and the government wouldn't provide me with any because I was who I was. I could have been building the atom bomb and they would have given me spit and paper clips to do it with.

And so I worked out a way of bonding wood, a blend of plywood and plastic called Duramold, and we started work. It was chaotic, and I had to hire men from other companies involved in the war effort, otherwise the project would have died a-borning.

The U-boats were cutting us up in the shipping lanes and men were getting killed, soldiers who hadn't even seen battle. It was a pitiful situation. The advantages of a flying boat over a land-based plane were not so well publicized, but they were considerable. A flying boat could land anywhere where there was water, and this covers a lot of territory. It very much increased the safety factor of getting men secretly to their destination. This plane, understand, was eventually designed to carry more than 700 men plus their battle gear.

Did you really believe you'd get it finished before the war was over?

Who the hell could figure how long the war was going to last? You forget, before they knew the atomic bomb would work, the top brass were figuring the war might go on until 1947 or 1948. There was no way of knowing. Until early 1944 we didn't even know for sure that we would *win*. We believed we would – I believed it – but nobody had a crystal ball or a guarantee from God. That's something people tend to forget. Toward the end of the war there was a strong possibility that we'd have to keep on fighting against Stalin and the Russians. Roosevelt went to that conference at Yalta and cheated the

U.S Army out of a war that would have lasted another ten years, for which all those colonels who dreamed of being four-star generals never forgave him.

Anyway, at the time the Hercules was a highly practical concept. With both the Mars and the HK-1, and various other designs that were worked on after the war, the payload versus range comparisons showed the flying boat far and away superior to a conventional land plane of similar size. If you were trying to sell a project of any kind you had to make a comparison computation and on top of that a performance and utilization computation. But that's all technical stuff. I worked like a son of a bitch: that's what it boils down to.

I'd never tackled anything that big, and I don't mean just in size. They had another name for the Hercules besides the Flying Lumberyard and Hughes's Folly and the Spruce Goose. The guys who were working on it called it 'The Jesus Christ' – because every time they got a new workman in there, or some senator or one of the government engineers came to the hangar for the first time, he'd look up. The tail assembly was nine or ten stories high. And the first thing the guy would say was, 'Jesus Christ!'

Cost was another thorny issue. The government put up $18 million and I personally, out of my own pocket, chipped in an additional seven million. So the initial costs were around $25 million. Since then it's been even more. But I want to point out to you that in 1949 the British built what was supposed to be the largest land plane in the world, the Brabazon. Its wingspan was only 230 feet as compared with the HK-1's wingspan of 320 feet. It flew only briefly – the British didn't know what the hell they were doing. Labor troubles hurt them badly, just like now. I could have given them a few pointers, but it was the old story of every country wanting to be top dog. It cost them $48 million. Believe me, I could afford the money more than the British Empire could.

I also pointed out, then and later on, that a plane of this size and concept would be a magnificent research laboratory and well worth the government's investment. They built the B19, you know, a plane that never saw service, and it paved the way for the B-29 which helped win the war for us. So there was a precedent, and the Army knew it as well as I did.

But the Army didn't care about how much money I forked out or what this plane might lead to. It wasn't just that I'd flown over Wright Field without stopping, or that I'd worn pajamas under my suit – it went deeper than that. I was an independent. I didn't kiss their asses and play the games that other manufacturers played, and I didn't make the automatic assumption that because a man was a general in the U.S. Army Air Corps he knew everything there was to know about airplanes. A lot of them flew in World War One and were still thinking in terms of strafing and dogfights. They were the equivalent of the old-line army generals who thought the Second World War was going to be fought in trenches.

I wasn't supposed to be as smart as they were, but I was a hell of a lot more knowledgeable when it came to talking about aircraft design. And I was under forty and rich and had a sense of independence. So they said, 'There's a young punk multimillionaire who wants to build warplanes as a hobby.'

I never baited them. I never told them what I thought of them. But they probably could see it in my eyes. They hate anybody who's different, the same as these Eastern banking people. You know there was one guy involved with one of those banking houses trying to round up the money to help TWA who made a public statement which just about summed up the attitude of the Eastern Establishment, Wall Street, Washington, and the Army. He said that you can't do business with a lunatic who wants to meet you in parked cars and men's rooms to talk about hundred-million-dollar loans. He was saying, 'You're different from us, and we won't tolerate it.' That was the Army's attitude too.

By 1947 I was out of pocket $10 million. It was a nonprofit venture from the start, and it got more nonprofit as it went along. Henry Kaiser lost money too – his half of the $5,000 we started the corporation with. He turned tail within a year. I don't blame him – he had other things to do and he agreed to leave me on my own.

Bear in mind I never owned the plane. I don't even own it now. The United States government owns it. I just lease it from them. That's a sop they threw me for my first ten million and the forty or fifty million I've put into the ship since then. I'm leasing it, even now, for ten grand a year.

There were two men, Roper and Edwards, with the Defense Plant Corporation, whose contention was that you were never in the factory and there was terrible confusion there, and...

Stop right there. I've been through this before, with a battery of lights on me and the inquisitors throwing their questions. I don't need you to do it too. I don't want you to do it.

It was not true. Of course I didn't breathe down my people's necks. I told them what do, and I said, 'You're grown men, capable men. Get off your asses and do the job.' I knew every goddamn thing that went into the plane, every problem and everything that was going on at the plant. If I had my drawing board at home, what the hell possible difference did it make where I tackled the problem? You tackle problems in your head, and your head is on your shoulders and it doesn't matter whether your shoulders are at home, sitting on the john, or in an office. That's the mentality of small men, that you have to do a job in an office with secretaries and eighty-seven telephones buzzing and ringing, and conferences and all that bullshit. I don't do things that way.

Weren't you once accused of building the Hercules as a movie set?

That came up at the hearings in Washington, the Senate hearings, later on. Can you imagine?

I thought Cary Grant actually suggested it to you.

Cary wanted to do a movie about a guy who travels around the world on a spaceship of the future. That got into the newspapers and Cary may have made some unfortunate statement that I was going to produce this picture and we'd use the Hercules for the set. Obviously I wouldn't consider such a thing. I've never in my life capitalized on any of my aeronautical achievements. Two or three studio heads came to me in Hollywood during the war and said, 'Let's make a movie about your flight around the world,' and I wouldn't give those guys the time of day, if I knew it, which undoubtedly I didn't because I didn't wear a watch.

I certainly wasn't going to consider vulgarizing a project that was still in the building stage, and where the U.S. Army was involved. I was working eighteen to twenty hours a day on the HK-1 and the F-11 and other Army work during the war, plus my own private projects and companies. I think Cary suggested the idea of a movie and I said, 'Yeah, great, that's interesting, you work on it.' And that was all there was to it. They just brought that up because they needed something else to bellyache about.

They also didn't like the incident that happened with Hap Arnold, who was still head of the Air Corps. I'd given orders – normal orders in such circumstances – that no one was to be allowed into the hangar where work on the HK-1 and the F-11 was going on. So Hap Arnold showed up with some other brass, and the guys at the plant barred the door and said, 'Mr. Hughes says no one gets in.'

'I'm General Hap Arnold, you goddamn idiots, let me in.'

But the guys said, 'You may be Hirohito in disguise or you may even be General Hap Arnold, but it doesn't matter because Howard Hughes, the boss, says nobody. And nobody includes you, even if you're somebody.' And they wouldn't let him in.

It took Arnold a while to find me and get through to me, but a few days later he reached me and started yelling.

I said, 'Hap, I don't know where you're calling from, but if you're anywhere within 500 miles you don't need a telephone, just yell out the window. Deaf as I am, I'll hear you.'

He calmed down. All he wanted was an apology, which I gave him. I had nothing against Hap Arnold. I would have let him see the ship if I'd been around. And I don't have anything against apologizing to a man. I've apologized thousands of times in my life. I don't have any false pride. And I hate people yelling at me – I just wilt. Or I used to. Nobody's yelled at me in many years.

What about the statement you made when you were discussing the

Hercules with the press, that if it didn't fly you'd leave the country and never come back?

That was one of the dumbest things I ever said. They really got my goat, and that shows how foolish it is to make public statements, to let those reporters and those officials get you over a barrel and wring you out. You wind up gasping for air – a squashed mackerel. I don't think I've ever been correctly quoted in my life except once or twice when there was something I didn't want to get into print, and I said, 'Boys, that's strictly off the record, don't print that.' Then, of course, they got it word for word, and put it on page one.

But you repeated that statement several times, about leaving the States if the Spruce Goose wouldn't fly.

That's what they wanted to hear, and I kept getting sucked into their trap and saying it. I guess I liked the sound of it. My father would have loved to hear me say something like that. That's the Texan in me coming out. I must have said it once too often, because I remember, at one time, I said to myself, 'Jesus H. Christ, if it doesn't fly, I'll *really* have to go.'

Would you have gone?

I'd have had to. They all would have remembered, and if through some mishap the Hercules wouldn't get off the water and I didn't go, they would have said, 'There's a man no one can trust.'

So it had to fly. It just *had* to.

13

Howard goes to jail in Louisiana, has his worst air crash, is visited in the hospital by a willing Ava Gardner, and confesses where he keeps his petty cash.

I CAME BACK from England in wartime and got to work on the F-11. Of course I was still working on the HK-1, the Hercules, and both projects combined, going on simultaneously, were breaking my balls. Getting a release for *The Outlaw* also took up a lot of my time, and the plant in Culver City was turning out ammunition feeder chutes for the Air Corps all the while, so you could say I was busier than a one-armed paperhanger. Being in the movie business during the war was the straw that nearly broke my back.

I look back on myself at that time and I don't know why I did it. It may have been because, with all that I'd accomplished, I was still desperately afraid of failing. I may have involved myself in a dozen projects at once with the unconscious feeling that even if one or two of them flopped, the law of averages was with me and I'd be bound to succeed at the rest of them and come out smelling of roses.

That can happen. The most frightening thing to do is put all your eggs in one basket – very few people are capable of that. It's easier to dissipate your energies. It's a form of cowardice. It's often called a conservative approach, but I'm beginning to equate conservatism with inborn cowardice and fear of the dark. Very few conservatives make history. There isn't a single great artist or great statesman who was conservative, except that sometimes, after the fact, we label them conservatives because we've already absorbed what they knew or what they did, and it seems obvious to us, with the advantage of hindsight, that they did what had to be done.

But the great men of history, during their own times, were all radicals venturing into the unknown, taking enormous risks and dealing with new ideas, and throwing their energies and their reputations without reservation into the battle. They never hedged their bets. Look at Joseph Conrad, Picasso, Stravinsky – Thomas Edison, Alexander Hamilton, Karl Marx, Einstein, Henry Ford, Roosevelt, Churchill, David Ben-Gurion – radicals, every one of them, in the sense that they broke new ground and were single-minded men on the verge of being fanatics.

I tried to plunge headfirst into all the various things I was doing, but you can't do that unless you've got six heads, and I wasn't that kind of monster. So a couple of my ventures fell on their ass, like my moviemaking. I hooked up very briefly, in 1944, with Preston Sturges, the director-writer-producer. Preston and I formed a company and made a couple of films. The first one, *Mad Wednesday*, starred Harold Lloyd, who I had talked into coming back in the movies. Then Preston and I made a film with Faith Domergue, a young actress I was fooling around with.

She had beautiful calves and wrists.

I tried to put the Hughes touch on all these films, where I could, but it didn't work out with Preston. We each had our own way of doing things. And when two such men come head to head, as often happens in a business adventure, the man with the bigger bat, the bigger sack of dollars, is the one who comes out on top. And that's me.

Be that as it may, Preston and I had an argument and almost came to blows. He had a theater and a club that he owned in Hollywood, very near that crazy place where Hemingway and Scott Fitzgerald and a lot of other people stayed – the Garden of Allah. Preston's theater was called the Players Club, and it looked like an alpine chalet. In those days everything in Hollywood, as you know, had to look like something else.

There was a restaurant on the top floor of the Players Club, and I liked to eat there because nobody bothered you. Nobody bothered me anyway, since I'd very often book the whole place, go in the back door and up the back staircase. There were all sorts of people downstairs in the bar, the cream of Hollywood, and the less I had to do with them, the better.

I had a habit of writing on tablecloths when I was bored, and unfortunately I was bored most of the time with most of the girls I knew. And it wasn't only boredom, because sometimes I'd get an idea, some new design for a plane I was working on, and I had to scribble notes. I had to do it immediately while the idea was fresh in my mind. I needed a lot of space and the tablecloth had the most space to write on.

Then I took the tablecloths home with me, to transfer the designs and notes, and Preston got annoyed. I said, 'Buy extra tablecloths and send me the bill.'

For some reason he thought I was being high-handed, and he blew up and accused me of stealing his tablecloths. One thing led to another until finally he said our contract wasn't equitable, and I walked out on him, and that was more or less the end of our partnership – but it all blew up, as I said, because I was designing a new flap motor for the Constellation on his tablecloth.

All this activity, this jumping from one thing to another to the point where I was getting about twenty hours sleep a week, took its toll. That was a time when I came nearer to going off the deep end than I ever have in my life. In 1945 I was working on both the HK-1 and the F-11, and I was still editing *The Outlaw* and fighting the censors. There were a couple of women I was interested in and I was having a tough time seeing them without one finding out about the other. On top of that I began to have nightmares about those recon flights I'd made in Europe. Those kids over there had been doing them daily, but I wasn't a kid and I was having nightmares.

I began to think I was mentally ill, and I went to see my doctor, Verne Mason. I told him that I was repeating myself all the time. Noah Dietrich brought this to my attention. In one telephone conversation with him, Noah claimed I'd said to him, ten or twelve times, 'Any five-year-old child knows that.' He said I'd better see a doctor, and for once he was right. Verne explained that I was under too much strain and I was close to a nervous breakdown.

I didn't listen to him.

I come into a vague period here. I remember getting into one of my Chevrolets, and I remember driving down to San Diego. I had a Sikorsky amphibian moored there, and I took off.

The next thing I knew I was in a filling station in Shreveport, Louisiana. Now why in the world I went to Shreveport, I don't know. I must have been behaving strangely, because the attendant called the police. I had fourteen or fifteen hundred dollars in cash in my pocket – that was unusual for me. I suppose I had taken that much because I was going somewhere, had something on my mind. I may have started off for Mexico, planning to spend some time down there. But I went to Shreveport, and I think something went wrong with the plane there.

I hadn't shaved in a week and my clothes were rumpled and smelly and I was mumbling, or was vague, because the gas station attendant called the police and they roughed me up a bit. I told them who I was and they laughed in my face. I told them I had a plane and they laughed some more.

They took me down to the station and next thing I knew I was in the goddamn bullpen with drunks lying next to me in their own vomit. I spent the night there, passed out on a bunk. In the morning I started to yell and make sense, and they began to do things. They called the Toolco man in Shreveport, a man named John Long, and he came down. He'd never seen me, of course, but he asked me some questions about Toolco and he realized immediately I knew what I was talking about, and he said to the cops, 'This man is telling the truth. He's Howard Hughes.' They let me go.

That never got into the papers. I didn't pay off the cops, but somebody did. And that wasn't even the end of the trip. I was still in a bad way and I went down to Florida to Palm Beach, to the house of a friend. I'd just got to his place and had a square meal and gone to bed when suddenly in the middle of the night I realized I was still wearing those clothes I'd worn in that filthy jail cell. I literally saw maggots and worms and other frightful things crawling out of my garments. This was what you might call the teetotaler's equivalent of the Dts.

I couldn't wait to get out of my clothes. I started to burn them in the man's backyard, by the pool. He came rushing out, thinking his house was burning down, and I was prancing around there like a naked savage around this bonfire, full of glee, and laughing like a maniac.

He said, 'Howard, what in the world are you doing? Come in, let me call the doctor.' He was very kind. He realized, as I did, that I'd gone off the deep end.

It turned out to be temporary, thank God.

On the F-11 I had to build three experimental prototypes, which were considered part of the hundred-plane contract, and a static test model which wasn't. A static test model is an exact duplicate of your experimental prototype, only it's not meant to fly. It's meant to be broken up on the ground, part by part, to see what's wrong with it or right with it. Eventually the static test model was ready and two of the prototypes were operational, and I announced delivery.

But this took time. When they knew they had the atomic bomb and could finish the war quickly by simply wiping out two or three hundred thousand Japanese men, women and children, they started tightening up on priorities, and quietly tooling up for peacetime manufacture – which meant that the first airplane manufacturer who was going to find himself short of the metal he needed to fulfill his contracts was none other than, guess who, yours truly.

Around late 1944 and into 1945 every time I needed something that wasn't on hand, that I couldn't beg, borrow or steal from some garbage dump in the Greater Los Angeles area, I had to go to the Army with my cap in my hand. They'd give me the runaround. So the F-11 didn't get finished until early 1946, which wasn't bad at all, considering the obstacles.

Then I flew it, and crashed it in Beverly Hills. That's the one I think of as the bad crash. I've had other crashes, but none of them like that. And that was the last one, thank God.

It happened on July 7, 1946. I'd finished two prototypes of the F-11, incorporating everything I'd learned on the missions I'd flown. The war was over, but there's always another one coming along – in this case, it turned out to be the fiasco in Korea. I finished the plane and I took it up on a Sunday, in the early evening. They didn't want me to fly it myself, but I've always said, 'If a man is unwilling to trust his life to his own work, his work can't be worth a damn.' There were things wrong with the plane, but nothing you could put your finger on – gremlins. I felt the only way to find out what they were was by flying it.

Was that your only reason?

No, there was more to it than that. A pilot had once said to me, 'Howard, why don't you hire me or someone else to fly these experimental planes? You're a busy man with a lot of responsibilities, and being a test pilot is a risky business.'

'Hell,' I said, 'why should I pay someone else to have all that fun?'

Around that time I went to a party at Newport Beach and met a nineteen-year-old girl from Ohio – a farm girl, really – who had just won a beauty contest at Ohio State and had been given a Hollywood contract. Her name was Jean Peters. I thought she was delightful and we really hit it off. I asked her if she'd like to come up to Culver City and watch the test flight.

She was there. I waved goodbye to her when I taxied out onto the runway.

I took off in the XF-11 – it was about six-thirty, and still light – and climbed. She climbed beautifully at better than 400 miles per hour. I headed out over the Pacific for a little way, put her through her paces, and then started back to the Culver City field.

Suddenly, with no warning at all, it felt as though someone was pushing backwards on the starboard wing: like I was dragging a bull elephant along with me by the tusks. After half a minute I unfastened the seat belt, flew the ship with one hand and tried to raise myself up and peer through the canopy. But I couldn't locate the trouble visually. I figured it out later. What had happened was that the pitch on the rear starboard propeller – these engines each had two propeller dual-rotation propellers – suddenly altered, went into reverse pitch, and was braking the plane.

We never found out why. At least those people at United Aircraft would never tell me if they found out. It was their Hamilton-Standard Division that made the propellers. There was a hell of a big investigation and the general theory was an oil leak, because even before the crash we'd noticed the starboard propeller was gobbling up oil. Maybe a faulty gasket, which was certainly the Hamilton people's responsibility. They tried to say later that I should have spotted an oil leak, because the propeller would have started to hunt, and I could have locked the pitch or feathered it. My point was that I had no way of spotting it because the blade angle was cockeyed, that is to say, the two blades of the starboard propeller weren't aligned properly – there was nearly a forty-five-degree difference, which threw everything out of whack. This was proved when they inspected the plane after the crash.

But of course, because it was me at the controls, they eventually claimed it was pilot error. I wasn't supposed to take up my landing gear on that flight and they made as much of a fuss about that as they could.

But it had absolutely nothing to do with the crash and nothing to do with what went wrong. I thought the landing gear door might have jammed broadside – the red light was still on. You may not know anything about aircraft, but you probably know enough to realize it makes no difference whatever whether the landing gear is up or down as to whether that plane is going to crash. The proof of the pudding is that the landing gear retracted perfectly. I could have bailed out, but at a greater sacrifice than I was willing to make. Eight million dollars worth of airplane, my life's work, was right there on the firing line. And it went deeper than that – I had a feeling by then that if I didn't bail out I still was going to lose that plane, and I had put enough of my guts into that plane so that I felt if I lose it, I'm going to go down with it, like a captain with his ship. That was my airplane, and whenever I fly one of my own planes, there's an identification there – it's my child. And I could no more abandon it than a mother could abandon her own child if it was in trouble.

I fought to get her down. Glen Odekirk was up there in an A-20, an attack bomber we were using as a radio plane, spotting me. I tried like hell to get in touch with him. Glen was the man I trusted most in the world. I couldn't get through. I managed to get Santa Monica air tower and told them, 'For Christ's sake, clear the airwaves! Get in touch with Odekirk and tell him to get a report to me on what the hell's happening with this plane!' I still wasn't sure the landing gear had retracted properly, and if I was breaking up outside I couldn't see it.

None of this made any difference. It was too late. I went down in a hell of a crash, right in Beverly Hills. I was trying for the golf course. I thought if I could make one of those long fairways, I could maybe have brought her down in one piece, kind of eased up to the lip of the green. But I couldn't do it. I chopped up a couple of houses and the plane caught fire. Naturally, I didn't know what was going on. All I remember was coming down hard, and they told me afterward that I was trying to crawl out and this marine sergeant saved my life, pulled me out of the wreckage.

I felt grateful to him, and later I gave him a job. He had to go off to China first, he was still in the Marine Corps. But after his tour of duty I sent him down to Culver City, got him appointed assistant head of security, in line for the top post. I sent him down with a note to Personnel that said: 'Don't fire this man, ever.'

When he pulled me out, I was in pretty bad shape. A number of broken ribs, a crushed lung, burned-up face, and my left hand has never been the same. The only time I ever played golf again, and it was a sad performance, was two years later in Ethiopia, when I came out of the bush. I couldn't even come close to my handicap.

After the crash, the doctors said I had less than a fifty-fifty chance. But I guess I just wasn't ready to die.

I knew I was going to make it when I suddenly got the inspiration for a special bed. It showed me my brain was still working the way it should. The bed was simply a gridwork with each square of the grid moved by a separate motor. This was so that I could shift my body without breaking into a cold sweat each time from the pain. They might even have done something with this hand, but I'd enough of the hospital – I had to get back to work. So I walked out of there before they got around to any surgery on it. Probably a mistake, but, well, life is made up of mistakes.

Didn't Linda Darnell and Lana Turner visit you in the hospital?

A lot of people tried to visit me, but most of them had to be kept out because I was in no shape to fool around, not with Linda Darnell or Lana Turner or all the beauty queens in the world rolled into one, or even with Jean Peters, if she'd been willing, which up to that point she wasn't. She did come to visit, though, which I appreciated. And Ava Gardner showed up with a bottle of bourbon, which she normally carried around with her in her handbag. This was some days after the crash. She got into the room somehow. I only vaguely remember what she said because I kept passing out, although at one time she was trying to shove me over to one side of the bed so she could crawl in with me. She said, 'How can I help you, Howard? Do you want a blow job?'

I said to her, 'For Christ's sake, Ava, wait till I'm on my feet again. Then, yes, I'd love a blow job. But not now, thank you. It might get me all worked up and kill me.' And eventually I found a nurse to get her the hell out of there.

An accident like that is like when a kid gets thrown off a horse: if he doesn't climb up on her right away, he's through riding. That's how I felt about flying. And so very soon thereafter, I climbed in my plane, my bomber, and flew to Kansas City. I couldn't have been more than a week or ten days out of the hospital. It was about two months after the crash. I've always had remarkable powers of recuperation, which probably means I just didn't give a damn. I had to keep going. I'm not the sort of man who stays down for the count. I'm up at six or seven. I flew to New York to tangle with those censors, the bastards who were giving me such a hard time with *The Outlaw*.

We had a second test model of the F-11, and I took her up the next spring, just before I had to go into the arena and be fed to the lions in Washington. I took her up for over an hour.

It's hard to believe what I had to go through before I could make that flight. The brass didn't want me to fly it again, not after the first crash. I had to apply for permission and this time Wright Field turned me down. I went to see Ira Eaker, an Air Force general. I hired him later to run Hughes Aircraft, which was a godawful mistake, and it shows you how sentimentality or the returning of favors has no place in practical business decisions.

But I went to Eaker and he told me he'd see what he could do, and he got me an appointment with Carl Spaatz, the commanding general of the Air Force and a hard-nosed son of a bitch. Spaatz said no dice, and fed me some crap about how I was too valuable a man to be lost in a crash.

I said, 'The plane won't crash and I won't be lost, and if you're worried about the money you've got tied up in it, don't be, because I'll guarantee the cost of the plane.'

Spaatz said okay, and I put it in writing that if the ship cracked up for any reason whatsoever, Hughes Tool Company would pay the Army $5 million. It wasn't me they were worried about, it was their money.

The ship performed beautifully. I got up to 9,000 feet and I had her well over 400 miles an hour. I checked the propellers very well, you can believe that. The second test model didn't have dual rotation. I was a little nervous, but I don't think I showed it.

Didn't you consider having another test pilot fly it that second time?

The F-11 was my ship. I had to fly it.

Wasn't it after that crash that you grew a mustache?

Yes, but not to hide any scar. That's what people have always assumed, but they're wrong. I wasn't vain that way at all. I grew the mustache because my mouth had been badly burned and it was very painful to shave. That's the only reason, and since then I've shaved it off many times. I like a mustache, but if you have a cold you sneeze into it and all the germs get trapped, and it's an uncomfortable feeling to have wet hair right under your nose. I certainly put my health before my appearance, so I always shave it off when I have even the beginnings of a cold, because you can sneeze in your sleep and not know that your mustache has become a culture medium for harmful bacteria.

You were wearing that brown fedora at the time of the crash, weren't you?

I always wore it. I got it back though. The cops took it, and I asked for it and got it back.

You've said to me several times that you're not superstitious. Did you really think of the hat as a good luck piece?

I'm not superstitious, believe me. I suppose it really doesn't matter anymore, and I can tell you the truth about it now.

I wanted my hat back because there was money in it.

I always carried money in the lining of the hat. And not only that hat, but *all* my hats. I didn't have just one hat. I had eight or nine like that, and they all looked alike. That's where I kept my money for emergencies. My house had been burglarized once, and I thought if anyone breaks in again or finds out where I'm staying he may blow up the safe but he'll never steal an old dirty hat. So I had all those hats and I kept my money in the lining. When I bought a new one it took me over an hour to scuff it up and trample on it, work the dust into it so that it looked disreputable enough, of no value, just like the others. I had those hats scattered all over, in each of the houses I had. I kept my money in the linings – about four or five thousand dollars in each one, in thousand-dollar bills. And a few singles in case I had trouble changing the larger ones. I never carried that much on me in my wallet or pocket. The hat I wore when the F-11 crashed had only $2,000 and change. But naturally, Jesus, I wanted it back. And the money was in it when they returned it.

And now where do you carry your money?

I can't wear a hat like that anymore. It got too much publicity, became my trademark. And of course people are always looking for me for various reasons, and that hat would be a dead giveaway. But I carry money. Never mind where.

74

Howard is accused of war profiteering, locks horns with Senator Owen Brewster and Pan Am, explains about lions and donkeys, and sings La Cucaracha.

YOU COULD WRITE a whole book about my battle with Senator Owen Brewster of the Republican Party during the 1947 Senate investigations. I've often been tempted to do just that. It was one of the most dramatic things that ever happened to me, because that was the time that I actually met some of those people who were out to get me, face to face, on their home field – and I whipped their ass.

I bumped into Bernard Baruch just before this happened, in Washington. We had a little talk about it and he said, 'Don't worry, the bastards tried to do the same thing to me.' He'd been hauled up before the Senate right after the First World War and accused of war profiteering. Naturally they couldn't prove anything, and that cheered me up a bit, to think that a man of Baruch's stature and reputation had to suffer the same mudslinging. He told me not to give an inch to them, admit nothing, not even the slightest mistake, because even if it was an innocent mistake, they'd pyramid it into the fact that I was the Dracula of the aircraft industry, sucking the blood out of innocent senators and generals. And Bernie said, 'Never get excited. Keep your dignity.'

He also advised me to hit back at them every chance I got, because they were more vulnerable than I was, since they were congressmen, and that meant thieves and hypocrites. That was a fruitful talk and it gave me good ideas on how to handle it, although I'd been hitting back already through the newspapers.

This whole experience – going up before that Senate committee those two times – taught me something I've never forgotten. I hadn't been totally aware of it before, but it stayed with me and was a tremendous revelation. I developed a theory.

You take any given situation in life – from the senate investigation to a business deal – where you have two parties or individuals who want something from each other. In other words, practically every situation in life, because that's what life is, one person putting the pressure on another person and that person trying to defend or attack or bargain or adjust. This excludes most situations where love is involved, but not all, because what passes for love – I've seen this time after time between people who are supposed to love each other – is often combat. Many times love degenerates into the most uncivilized form of combat precisely because the people won't admit it's combat.

In any situation such as I described – two parties or individuals who want something from each other – you have what I call a lion and a donkey. You can't have equality in bargaining, in arguing, or in combat. You may have an apparent equality but it's only an illusion, a false arrangement. You may get a tie score in a football game, or after thirty-six holes of a pro golf tournament, but if they play long enough someone's going to win. There are no ties in life except if they're arranged artificially. People are not equal; that's a pernicious lie.

This is my lion and donkey theory. It's not patented and it may not be original, but it's mine. You always have a *need* for one person to be the lion and one to be the donkey. Most people aren't aware of this, but it happens anyway.

Two men sit down to negotiate the price for some airplanes and the conditions of delivery. If one of them is accommodating and humble, and says, 'Oh, yes, I see your point, you're right, I understand your situation, your problems' – then the other one automatically is going to have to play the part of the lion and eat the donkey up alive. He may not be a lion by nature, but if there's a donkey sitting in front of him, all wobbly-kneed, his lion instincts are going to come out and he's going to chew up the donkey and spit out the bones. If a man goes into that meeting roaring like a lion and says, 'This is what I want! This is fair, and don't fool around with me!' – then it's the other man who's going to play the part of the donkey, like it or not. Has to. Because nature, as in the animal kingdom, demands that these two parts be played – that's nature's way.

My point is that if you know this – and I began to realize it when the investigations got under way – you know that it can be up to you whether you're going to be the lion or the donkey. And you can bet your last chip that if you don't choose your part first, then the other guy is going to choose his, and if he's got any brains or experience, or even peasant cunning, he'll choose to be the lion.

So you can't give him that opportunity. You can feel around a bit because maybe before you go roaring in you have a moment to see if he's a natural donkey, or if he thinks you're a natural lion, in which case he'll start out as the donkey without your having to do anything, and you can just be a kind of, well...

A friendly lion.

That's a nice idea.

Are you saying that you were the lion in the Senate investigations?

I'll tell the story and you be the judge.

This whole thing goes back a long way in time, and it's involved with politics and big money. The man who was out to pillory me was Owen Brewster, commonly known as the Senator from Pan American Airways. He was a Republican from Maine and he'd been lobbying for Pan American down in Washington for years. He was a close friend of Juan Trippe, president of Pan Am, and Sam Pryor, vice president of Pan Am. Trippe tried to keep his hands clean on this, as much as he could – Sam Pryor did his dirty work and was Brewster's contact.

The other chief honcho on the investigative committee was Senator Homer Ferguson from Michigan. Ferguson wasn't as bad as Brewster, but he was bad enough, and he was a longwinded son of a bitch. What he enjoyed most was strutting before the cameras. And there was Senator Joe McCarthy of later fame, although he kept his mouth shut most of the time during these hearings. He was learning his trade. Harry Truman had been the head of that committee and then they gave it to Brewster. There were a few Democrats on the committee, including Claude Pepper from Florida. Pepper was a gentleman. I don't remember the others' names, but their faces are etched into my mind in indelible ink.

It all started when Juan Trippe got the bright idea to wipe out the competition. Pan Am was going to be the only airline flying from the United States to Europe and other foreign points. This was going to be a great measure of economy and efficiency, and all it required was for TWA and the other airlines to step down and get merged. It was called then the Community Airline Bill, sponsored by Senator Brewster.

Juan Trippe and Brewster came to tell me this personally, in Palm Springs, California, just before the war. It had been in the wind for several years and was being discussed between the various owners of the major airlines, of which I was one. Trippe came out and put the proposition to me.

But of course my terms were that I'd be right up there on top with Mr. Trippe. That was not acceptable. Mr. Trippe and Senator Brewster didn't like the idea of playboy Howard Hughes horning in on their monopoly.

So the negotiations fell through.

The other part of the background was that this was 1947 and the committee, which was meant to be investigating the national defense program, had been jogging along, raising a little ruckus here and a little rumpus there, but fundamentally just shooting at clay pigeons. During the war the two major political parties buried the hatchet, decided to fight the Japs and the Germans instead of each other, but after the war they went back to the old business of cutting each other's throats. Elections were coming up. The best thing the Republican Party could think of to win that election was to discredit the late President of the United States, Mr. Franklin Delano Roosevelt, who had been my friend, by discrediting his son, Elliot Roosevelt, also my friend. Tar the father with the son's brush.

Senator Brewster had political ambitions as well. Harry Truman had previously been chairman of this committee. He jumped from there to Vice President of the United States, and from there to the presidency. I think Owen Brewster saw himself climbing the same ladder. In fact it came out later that he had been promised the vice-presidential nomination of the Republican Party by none other than Juan Trippe. Trippe was a shrewd man, with influence, and Senator Brewster would have profited very handsomely. He could have given the old one-two punch to Roosevelt Sr. and Roosevelt Jr., and if he could have decked me at the same time, that really would have put a feather in his cap.

We knew all this beforehand. The committee sent an investigator out to California, a man named Francis Flanagan, to look over our records.

Flanagan was indiscreet. He said to Noah, without batting an eyelash, 'Don't kid yourself, the purpose of this committee is to get Elliot Roosevelt.'

'Mr. Flanagan,' Noah said, 'I don't care whether you get Elliot Roosevelt or not' – Noah was a Republican – 'but if Howard Hughes is your whipping boy, then you're going to be doing an injustice to a man who doesn't deserve it.'

Flanagan paid no attention, because he had his orders from the top. And pretty soon came the famous incident at the Mayflower Hotel.

Brewster had been thumping the drums for days, weeks, about how he was going to drag me before the committee and prove that not only hadn't I delivered any planes during the war, but that I'd profited illegally. And also that I'd curried favor with Elliot Roosevelt, who was in the photo reconnaissance division, and that Johnny Meyer, a public-relations man for me, had bribed Colonel Roosevelt and various other important officials with sex and nylon stockings.

His intentions were public knowledge. I knew it, the newspapers knew it, the world knew it. The pressure was on me – because no matter how much I tried to keep in touch with what was going on in my company, I couldn't know whether the office boys were selling black-market stockings or what the hell was going on in every sphere. And if you dig deep enough in every man's life, you'll come up with dirt. Frankly, I felt a little uncomfortable about going before that committee.

That's when our friend Mr. Brewster came to me at the Mayflower Hotel in Washington. I was staying there with Noah Dietrich and my Washington lawyer, Tom Slack.

We had lunch in my suite, and Brewster said, 'Mr. Hughes, if you'll go along with Mr. Trippe and the Community Airline Bill' – in other words, if you'll bend down in public and kiss Pan Am's ass, and agree for TWA to suck hind tit – 'we'll call off the investigation.'

Don't think that deals and demands in Washington are subtle things. Maybe that's the way you'd write about them in a novel, but in real life there's no beating around the bush. The man comes up and says, 'I want you to do this, and this is what I'll give you in return, and you've got forty-eight hours to decide.'

It didn't take me forty-eight hours. I told Brewster to go to hell. Right then and there I made up my mind that I was going to face this committee, that I was going to clear myself, my company, Elliot Roosevelt, and everyone who was associated with me, and that I was going to wipe away the mud that man was flinging at us with both hands.

The first point of truth is that there had been no war profiteering on our part. I had lost a small fortune on my war contracts. I think I've mentioned that by 1947, out of my own pocket, I'd laid out $7 million for the construction of the Hercules. That was only the beginning. By 1951 I'd spent another ten million, and the fact is that the government had never put up the whole eighteen million they'd promised me. I had to sue the RFC for the difference. Not that I expected to get it, it was more a point of honor, and to set the record straight.

I had also taken a hell of a loss on the F-11. Both these contracts, which technically speaking I hadn't delivered on – that is to say, the planes were not finished by the end of the war, and therefore of no immediate combat use to the military – involved a total outlay on the government's part of about forty to fifty million dollars, which they considered money down the drain.

It wasn't down the drain, for all the reasons I've given you, but that's how they considered it, and even if they didn't really believe it that's what they were saying, loud and clear. Now that so-called forty- or fifty-million-dollar loss represented *less than one percent* of the entire amount the government lost during the war in unfulfilled military contracts. Less than one percent! And that total included manufacturers like Boeing and Republic and Lockheed, companies that had a Priority One for material. I had a Priority Five, which was the lowest you could get.

The total government loss came to over $6 billion. But there was more fuss made about my supposed fifty million than all the others put together, because they'd singled me out as the scapegoat and also, as I said, this investigation was political in origin, a way to crush Elliott Roosevelt and the Democratic administration.

Republic, for example, was supposed to make a recon ship called the XF-12. I brought this up at the hearings, but of course they didn't want to hear about it. They just brushed it off, because Pan American had worked with Republic on the XF-12 and Pan American was too delicate to touch. The XF-12 plane cost the government about $30 million and it was never delivered. There was never even a static model. The first test model nosed over and cracked up a minute after it got off the runway. But nobody cared about that because Howard Hughes hadn't built it. I can't remember the figures on how much money was put into aircraft that never flew, but you can bet that it came to well over $600 million.

As far as my employee Johnny Meyer was concerned, Johnny had been doing, on a small scale, what representatives of every single company in the United States had been doing throughout the course of the war, and on a much larger scale than Hughes Aircraft and Toolco – which is, specifically, lavishly entertain Army officers and government officials.

These men came out to meet you for an afternoon of business discussion. You couldn't just throw them out of your office at 5 P.M. and say, 'See you tomorrow morning, boys. Have a good evening.' You took them out, you provided for them. It was simple hospitality. The hypocrisy of these senators, who called each other 'gentlemen' – 'will the gentleman from Missouri yield for a minute to the gentleman from Montana?' – really, that's exactly how these pompous asses talked to each other when they were mouthing off in the senate chamber – the hypocrisy of these men who were living off lobbyists and accepting favors right and left, money, women, free travel, free vacations, gifts, every week of the year, was beyond belief.

What about Judy Cook?

Judy Cook was a girl who worked for Johnny Meyer. She swam around in a pool. I always think of her as the girl I saw a hundred times. This pool had reflectors, so that it looked like there were a hundred Judy Cooks swimming through the pool.

She was an Olympic swimmer and an actress, and the whole Judy Cook incident was completely innocent. Johnny found her and brought her down to Palm Springs for a couple of parties. What Judy did on her own time was her own business.

Let's get back to the senate committee. That was the important thing, not what happened or didn't happen with Judy Cook in Palm Springs.

Before I testified they had a parade of witnesses. By the time I got to the hearings they'd raked everyone over the coals, including Henry Kaiser and Johnny Meyer. They were digging into the entire story of the HK-1 and the F-11. A full transcript of the hearings runs close to 300,000 typed pages. Reading it is enough to make a man want to overthrow the United States government. The verbal inanity of those senators is beyond belief, and the American taxpayer has to foot the bill to have all that garbage put into print in the Congressional Record. The vanity of these boring little men almost passes human understanding.

This committee wanted to know everything – they had nothing better to do. They hauled people away from important jobs, and from their families and their children.

Then Johnny Meyer got on the stand. Johnny was a publicity man: flashy, accommodating, and not very bright. He had a hell of a way with girls, but that's about as far as his talents went.

I dreaded Johnny's testifying, because they'd asked to see all of Johnny's expense account records, and as Johnny admitted to me before he went to Washington, he had a habit of making them up quite a while after the actual event and skimming a few dollars on the side. I didn't mind that. He had to live.

But what mattered was that these records were not entirely accurate, and Johnny knew it, and I knew it. I've always had a kind of soft spot in my heart for Johnny. He was a congenial dope. I heard that at his birthday dinner a few years ago in Los Angeles his three ex-wives came to the party and toasted him. I don't mean over a slow fire, I mean with champagne. That's an eloquent tribute.

Before he went to Washington to face the committee I told Johnny, 'There's only one thing you can do that'll work. Go up before those senators and tell them the truth. Tell them that you made up the records long after the actual dinner at the Mocambo, or at '21.' You're human. They won't send you to prison for it.'

He tried, but they didn't let him get a word in edgewise. They flattened him. He was like a jackrabbit on the road, in front of the lights of a truck – he kept running and dodging, but he didn't have sense enough to get off the road, and they just ran him down like a goddamn dumb jackrabbit.

He testified for days. I wasn't there, but I heard about it, and I winced when I read reports of the testimony. Every word that came out of that man's mouth put me further behind the eight ball. He wasn't just Johnny Meyer sitting up there getting slaughtered, he was Howard Hughes' right-hand man, the man who was taking Howard Hughes' stooge, Elliott Roosevelt, out to dinner, and giving Elliot's wife black market-nylon stockings as a present from Howard Hughes.

The more he babbled, the blacker it looked. They got on to other people, but they told him to stay in town, they wanted him back on the witness stand at a later date.

Johnny called me and said, 'Howard, what am I going to do? I'm making a mess of this.'

'You sure are. You've got to get out of town, Johnny.'

'Where can I go?'

'I'll take care of that,' I said.

I got hold of a TWA plane and I put Johnny on it, sent him off to Europe and said, 'Go to the French Riviera and rent a diving helmet. Go to the bottom of the Mediterranean and stay there until I call you.'

That's not something I'm ashamed of. It would have been totally unfair for Johnny to have reappeared on the stand until I'd had my say. They were making hamburger out of him. They were chopping him up, without benefit of onion, and cooking him to a fare-thee-well. And it wasn't getting us any closer to the truth, because the truth lay back there in the Mayflower Hotel in the words of that viper, Senator Brewster.

When we got to Washington the second time, for the hearings, I stayed in the Carlton Hotel with Noah and my lawyers. Noah walked into my room the first day and started to talk to me about what was going on. I said, 'Noah, shut up. I haven't even searched the room yet. You can bet your sweet ass they've got it bugged.'

Noah said, 'Then let's go into the bathroom and talk.'

We went into the bathroom and I sat down on the toilet seat. I looked around and there was a ventilator in the bathroom. I jumped up and said, 'We can't talk here, Noah. They've probably put a mike in the ventilator shaft.'

Noah probably thought, Howard's going round the bend again. We took the elevator downstairs. He started to talk in the hotel lobby right by a potted palm. I said, 'For pete's sake, Noah, the easiest place in the world to put a microphone is in a potted palm!'

He thought that was all in the movies. I had to explain it happened in real life and every day. So we talked on the streets, which were safer.

Well, this was one of many occasions when Noah had to admit I was right. Because it came out later that the ventilator shaft in the bathroom had been bugged, and there was a microphone hidden in it. Years later some police officer in Washington admitted that he tapped my telephone and installed bugs all over the hotel suite, including the bathroom ventilator shaft, for a thousand bucks, at the instigation of none other than our upstanding senator from Maine, Owen Brewster.

All my life, ever since the telephones were tapped at Romaine street in 1931, I've been conscious of people eavesdropping, and since the advent of revolutionary sophisticated electronic devices there isn't a place in the world that's completely safe. There's a type of microphone called a shotgun mike – people can stand a hundred yards away from you and point that microphone at you and hear every word you're saying. Do you know that they have a microphone that can be fired from a gun? It's in the shape of a dart. A man can stand 500 yards away, aim his rifle at the side of your house, fire that dart into the wall of your house, and that microphone sits there and picks up everything that's being said inside. You think you're talking privately, but they're broadcasting it in the Hollywood Bowl. Do you know what people would give to listen in to some of my conversation? If they could invent a dart to shoot into my brain and find out what I was thinking, they'd do it, no matter what the damage.

After the incident at the Carlton Hotel in Washington, when I said a place was bugged, Noah believed it was bugged. I can smell a bug in any room, and I'm not talking about cockroaches. Not about *cucarachas.* You know that song? *La Cucaracha.* That's one of my favorite songs.

15

Howard has a secret meeting with a friendly senator, cross-examines a hostile one, and smites his enemies.

THE SENATE INVESTIGATION of me was the biggest post-war circus of its kind. All they wanted to do was make page one of every newspaper in the country, day after day, and they succeeded. Even before the circus started in Washington there were a lot of statements being made to the newspapers, mainly by me, because I figured once they got me in the witness chair, where I didn't have the right to question the cross-examiners, I'd be not just behind the eight ball, I'd be jammed right into the side pocket and they'd be ramming their senatorial cue sticks up my ass every chance they got. I'd be the donkey, not the lion.

What I was saying, principally, was what everyone who opened his eyes could see that Brewster and Trippe were in partnership and the whole thing was a smear campaign to ruin my reputation and take routes away from TWA, and put the pressure on me to merge with Pan American as the junior partner. And I got in my licks, because I let the world know that while Brewster was screaming about Johnny Meyer and my people entertaining Air Force people during the war, he, Brewster, was freeloading on my TWA planes. That took the wind out of his sails for a little while, but guys like Brewster, any politicians, have an answer for everything: a fountain of doubletalk.

I had to prepare this carefully, because I knew pretty well what was going to happen. I telephoned Homer Ferguson and told him I wasn't going to jump through the hoop like a trained seal and fly to Washington on twenty-four hours' notice. I also wrote an article for the papers in which I asked how come an earlier investigation of Pan American – they'd built some airports and socked the government hard for the costs – had been dropped by the committee, and why Brewster lied in public about the committee having no authority to investigate Pan Am because the airports were built outside the United States.

I still boil when I think about all this, and it was over twenty years ago. But my reputation, my personal and professional reputation, was on the line. This committee was like something out of the Spanish Inquisition. Every time you'd try to give them a straight answer, they'd interrupt you. Every time you were giving them answers they didn't like, they'd call a recess. And every time one of them lied, or got the facts balled up, and I tried to challenge them for playing dirty pool, they'd yell, 'You're demeaning the dignity of this committee, Mr. Hughes! You stay at the back of the bus where you belong.'

At first they wouldn't let me ask a single question. So the only thing to do was turn the tables on them. I decided to treat it like a military operation. Right away, before we got anywhere near the meat of the thing, I demanded the right to cross-examine the senators.

I kept hammering away at that until they were sick of hearing me say it. At the very beginning, before they could get their teeth into me the way they'd done to Johnny Meyer, I told them the story of Brewster propositioning me at the Mayflower. That hit the headlines. Then I said that, considering what had happened, Brewster should disqualify himself as chairman.

They didn't like all that, and we wound up with a compromise, something I hadn't foreseen. They agreed to let me submit a list of written questions to Brewster, which he would answer one by one, in the order they were submitted, and Ferguson would take the chair while this was going on.

Now, Claude Pepper, who I mentioned before, was a gentleman, and a Democrat, and he was on the committee. We had two private talks, once before the hearings began and once after the first day of my testimony. We met by the Lincoln Monument in a parked car. I remember some kids were playing softball on the grass there. One of the kids hit a foul ball and the ball rolled under my car. The kid came running over to get the ball, and Senator Pepper ducked his head and tried to hide under the dashboard. He was in such a hurry he hit his head and cut himself. He was afraid of being recognized.

I said, 'Claude, don't worry, these kids wouldn't know a United States senator from the Washington dogcatcher.'

He hadn't wanted to meet me there in the first place, but I said, 'A public place is the safest. Nobody thinks of looking for two people like us in front of the Lincoln Monument.'

He gave me all the information he had about Owen Brewster: where Brewster was vulnerable. And when it came time for me to submit my list of questions to Brewster, Pepper told me in advance what sort of questions might put Brewster on the spot, and I told him what I was planning to do, and he said, 'Yes, that's good,' or 'No, he can slide out of that for such and such a reason.' This senator, you understand, wasn't on my payroll, he wasn't someone I'd helped politically. This was being done out of his sense of fair play.

I was also filled in on some of the favors that Brewster had gotten from Bill McEvoy, who was a vice-president of Pan American and had taken Brewster to football games. I worked that into my questions too. I asked Brewster – Ferguson was asking the questions for me, but they were *my* questions – about McEvoy and the football games. He muttered around for a while, but he couldn't very well deny it since he knew that two of the senators on the committee knew, and he wound up saying, 'Yes, but I bought my own peanuts.' This was a United States senator telling the world: 'I bought my own peanuts.'

I personally didn't have the right to cross-examine, but the system worked – that is, with Ferguson asking questions for me. It worked not so much because of the advice I'd been given, but because of the method I adopted. Each night, as soon as the committee adjourned, I prepared a list of questions for the next session. I never flared up during those hearings. I kept absolutely in control of myself, but Brewster nearly went over the edge. He was yelling and pounding the table.

I went back to the hotel each night and I asked everybody to leave except Tom Slack, my lawyer, and he had to keep quiet unless I specifically asked him something. I worked all night preparing the questions. The point of it was that I didn't know what Brewster's answers were going to be. I couldn't really cross-examine as a courtroom lawyer would. But I could make a pretty educated guess what he might answer. So I geared the next question to what I figured he would answer to the last one, and the results were amazing.

I'll try to give you a small example. It was a little trap I set, and Brewster walked into it like a tame skunk on a string. In order to fathom the logic of the questioning, you need to know that Brewster was the one who pressed for the hearings to get started early, because he'd set up a timetable with Juan Trippe. There was even some doubt that the hearings would take place at all, but Brewster had his orders. He was pushing, and he bypassed Homer Ferguson when he announced it to the press. So first I asked Brewster a question: 'Isn't it true, Senator, that you yourself actually made the decision to start this hearing on July 28, the day it was begun?'

I knew that Brewster was going to deny it, pass the buck to Ferguson, and he was a long-winded son of a bitch and he was bound to get himself all tangled up in the denial. Which is exactly what he did. So then Ferguson read the next question. It was: 'Then, Senator, if you yourself didn't make the decision to hold this hearing, and if you left the decision up to Senator Ferguson, how do you explain the fact that Senator Ferguson was totally unaware that the decision to hold this hearing had actually been made until the day following the time when you announced the hearing to the press on July 24?'

Silence in the senate chamber. Brewster looks pale. Then he turns red. Then he looks down, then right, then left – then up – but God wasn't there to help him and neither was Juan Trippe.

All Brewster could think of to say was, 'I don't know.' He looked like a fool and he looked worse as it went on. A lot of the questions, since I couldn't cross-examine him, were stuff like, 'Do you still beat your wife?' But that's what they'd been trying to pull on me, and I figured two could play at that game.

The upshot of it was, when I finished with him he dragged his crippled ass out of Washington and whined to the newspapers that he'd been shot full of poison arrows, and Howard Hughes didn't play fair like a red-blooded American boy should. What he really meant was that he hadn't seen the color of my blood, which he wanted to spill into buckets and use to paint his campaign posters for the Republican vice presidential nomination, and this sort of irked him – he saw his political star sinking down the drain. He didn't know the half of it.

After that he made a speech telling what a great upstanding senator he was, and I made a speech and said he had the reputation for being one of the greatest trick-shot artists in Washington. And then I blew my own horn a little because it had pretty much come down to a question that one of us was telling the truth and one of us was lying about the lunch in the Mayflower. I said I was from Texas, where a man's word is his bond.

The upshot was that once Brewster got caught wetting his pants in this remote control cross-examination, he didn't have the whip hand anymore. The galleries cheered every time I told him off, told him how much money I'd lost on those contracts and how hard I'd worked.

There was a point where they wanted Johnny Meyer to take the stand again, but or course he couldn't be found. He was in St. Tropez. They asked me if I would make an effort to get him back to Washington.

I ducked it at first, and they kept badgering me, and when they asked me the last time I was fed up, and I said, 'No, I don't think I will.' I knew it would make them see red, but I didn't care. The United States Senate wasn't going to make me jump through the hoop and I wanted them to goddamn well know it.

When I finally got out of Washington, Brewster told the newspapers that he'd only just begun to fight.

I waited a long time before I got in my licks. I couldn't do anything about it right then, because Brewster had been reelected to the Senate in 1946, just a year before these hearings took place, and it was a six-year term. He didn't come up for reelection again until 1952. But I gave him warning that I'd get him before he got me. I sent him a letter offering him a job as an actor at double the regular starting salary. I said that was because he'd very clearly demonstrated his acting ability in the Senate. It was a private letter, but it got to the press. The important part of it was my suggestion that he'd be wise to take the offer seriously and not turn down the job, because one of these days, when the people of Maine got wise to him, he was going to be out of work. That was a pretty clear warning, I figured.

I waited. I didn't forget about him. I kept in touch. I sent him a telegram now and then to remind him that I existed, and I even sent him a birthday cake once from Texas, a fruit cake, to let him know that I hadn't forgotten him.

And when the time came in 1952, I did what I considered was a patriotic duty. I felt that the man was a disgrace to the state of Maine and to everything that the United States of America stood for, or was supposed to stand for.

I had an agency working for me, the Carl Byoir Agency. They handled my public relations. I got together with them and told them what I wanted. What I wanted, specifically, was the defeat of Senator Brewster in the Maine primary election.

There was a man up in Maine named Frederick Payne, a publisher, and he was one of the two other candidates running against Brewster in the Republican primary. I decided that Payne was the only man who stood a chance against Brewster. Brewster was the favorite, but a favorite can only win when he's got the right jockey riding him. I decided to ride Frederick Payne, and at the same time trample Owen Brewster into the ground. It was fairly simple. Noah Dietrich helped me a little, and the Byoir agency helped me, but what it took was just plain old cash.

I contributed sufficient sums to Mr. Payne's campaign, and certain men were hired in Maine to do what had to be done. Mr. Brewster's record in Congress was put before the general public, including his attempt to boil me in oil in 1947 and his offer to bribe me, and his association with Pan American. I don't remember how much it cost, but it was under two hundred and fifty thousand dollars. I would have spent a million if that's what was required. However, Maine is not a very populous state, and $250,000 goes a long way.

When you're dealing with a man like Owen Brewster you just tell the truth. Naturally it looks to the world like a smear campaign. We hired enough men and women to canvas door to door. We had the Girl Scouts out there campaigning against him – paid them off in cookies. No, that's a joke, we didn't pay off the Girl Scouts. They were happy to work for us. They knew Brewster for the cur he was.

And Brewster didn't have a clue until the brick fell on his head. I enjoyed it thoroughly – in silence. An Italian friend of mine once said to me, 'Revenge is a dish best eaten cold.'

Brewster lost the primary, but not by much, which should show you that if I hadn't pumped all that money in there, he would have won. He lost by under 2,000 votes.

That ended the career of Senator Owen Brewster. I'm proud to say, after all these years, that I was the man responsible for his exit from public life.

16

Howard attempts to fly the Spruce Goose, is asked to run for President of the United States, and sues the City of Long Beach.

IMMEDIATELY AFTER THE first round of the Senate investigations, I decided to test-fly the Hercules. It happened on a Sunday, I remember very clearly, because someone asked me if I'd gone to church to pray.

Nobody thought the flying boat would fly. I had said I'd leave the country if it didn't.

We trucked the Hercules down from its various hangars to San Pedro, part by part on the highway. I had a dozen trucks moving the fuselage, the wings and the tail assembly. Took a day or two to get it down there – they had to disconnect the overhead power lines all along the route so she could pass under them. That cost me a pretty penny, but most of the mayors of those Southern California cities were already on my payroll, so it didn't break me.

Huge crowds lined the highway: Barnum and Bailey had come to town. And when we got her down to Long Beach and tucked her away in the hangar; we still had a lot of work to do.

This was final assembly, and suddenly I realized the controls wouldn't work. They were manual controls, and they weren't powerful enough. This was an engineering oversight on my part. I'd considered the problem and I thought I'd licked it, but I was wrong. So I invented what was probably the first power-steering device, and installed it in the Hercules. That's what I mean, you see, when I say her value as a laboratory was incalculable. I made no secret about how I'd done it, and that information was snapped up by all the aircraft and automobile manufacturers, and the car you're driving today uses the same principle.

Eventually I was ready to test the ship on the water. She was winched from the graving dock, checked for leaks, and she was ready. Some newspaperman had the nerve to ask me if I was taking it down there to load it on a barge and dump it beyond the three-mile-limit. That's a guy I almost hit. There was a big crowd there when I finally decided to have that test run. There was a Navy cruiser, excursion boats, hundreds of other boats and even some aircraft which I told to get out of the way.

I hadn't planned to fly it. They wanted me to fly it. They wanted a show. 'FLY IT, HOWARD HUGHES, OR LEAVE THE COUNTRY,' one newspaper said in a headline.

I decided to take a few taxi runs on the water. I checked the engines. Dave Grant, one of my engineers, was with me, and a government observer, George Haldeman, and some reporter whose name I can't remember. Matter of fact he was the only newspaperman who stayed with me on the ship.

I took her across San Pedro Bay and opened up all eight throttles – we were probably doing close to a hundred knots by then. There's a certain feeling you have when you're at the controls of an airplane, and that was no ordinary airplane. That was like being at the controls of the *Queen Elizabeth*, except she was skimming across the bay at a hundred knots. There was a feeling of power and accomplishment, because all this was happening, you realize, after I'd gotten back from Washington and had been through the fires of hell. A lot of people said I was testing the Hercules in order to get good publicity for myself, make myself a national hero before the second congressional session took place. But I'd cracked eggs over Brewster's head the first time and I knew I could do it again. I knew he'd wind up smelling like a henhouse.

But you did get publicity, didn't you? Wasn't there a Hughes for President Club at that time?

A lot of them, all over the country. You don't think I paid any attention to that, do you? Imagine me as President of the United

States. The country would grow rich, we wouldn't have any more national debt, the Dow would jump to the moon, the government would actually make a profit. How would politicians thrive? Someone would have to assassinate me.

But there were more serious offers – serious and ridiculous. Both the state chairman of the Republican Party and the state chairman of the Democratic Party in California came to me and asked me to run on their ticket for governor. I'll bet I was the only man in history beside Eisenhower who was asked by both parties to run for the same office. I told them I had more serious things to do than be governor of California. That's for guys like that overcooked ham, Reagan.

All right, let me go on – I want to tell you how I felt when I was at the controls of the Hercules. I did a couple of taxi runs, and then a third. And then I hadn't planned it, but I said to myself, 'She's ready, she's aching to go, and they're all here for a show. I'll pander to the vulgar curiosity of the mob this one time, and that's the end.'

I eased back on the throttle. She never hesitated. She took off. We didn't gain very much altitude, because the ship wasn't ready for that yet. And I didn't fly her very far, maybe a mile at the most, before I set her down. I wasn't proving to myself that the ship could fly. I knew she would fly if I wanted her to. I was proving to myself that I didn't care one way or the other what people felt. They wanted a show – I gave them one. I felt great. I felt a moment of exhilaration that comes only a few times in a lifetime.

And it meant I didn't have to leave the country.

Of course I wanted to fly the plane again, in private, but not until we had ironed out a few kinks and I had run tests on her. Then the second round of the Senate investigations interfered and the whole goddamn thing was put off.

Then came the first of several incidents which I have never cleared up, in my mind, to my own satisfaction. I'm not accusing anyone specifically here, because I never could find a clue. I will tell you this. Sometime in 1948 or 1949 various executives of some of the top metal producing companies in this country – I mean Alcoa, Reynolds, and

Kaiser – approached me. They wanted to see the Hercules. It had flown and they were full of praise for what a wonderful job I'd done, and they said they'd like to look at it. I took them at their word. You understand, the boat's made of wood – of duramold – and I thought, they've seen the light.

They came, and I personally took them through the hangar, which by then I had leased from the City of Long Beach. They were impressed. And then they left.

We had excellent security on the HK-1 but nothing compared to the security that existed afterward or that exists now, because on the next inspection of that boat, we discovered broken ribs, smashed ribs, all throughout the after section and inside the tail assembly. A broken rib in a man is set by a doctor and that's all there is to it, but any airplane of that size – remember the tail assembly alone was ten stories high – is another story. But once we found the broken ribs and the tail assembly, naturally we checked her from stem to stern. We found bent propellers as well, and a bent propeller is not something you can see unless you have a practiced eye. If I hadn't spotted them and if I had flown the plane again, it would have been the end of Howard Hughes.

I don't want you to infer from this that I suspected a plot against me personally. In this instance, no. In my view this was a plan to destroy the Hercules, and whereas I say my suspicions have never been confirmed, I strongly suspect these metals people who came to look her over, because the success of your wooden flying boat would have wiped out the metal industries' role in airplane construction. But I couldn't prove it, then or now, though I hired half a dozen ex-OSS guys to go through the files of Reynolds and those other companies.

It took years to fix the Hercules. While the guys working on her were competent, they couldn't make an important move without consulting me. She was my baby, and in those years I was up to my neck in TWA, RKO, you name it.

Then it happened again.

I'd built this hangar, which is right on Long Beach Harbor, on land that I'd leased from the City of Long Beach. They wanted publicity at the time and I'd brought them a hell of a lot, with that 'flying lumberyard,' as they sometimes called it. So they met my demands. One of my principal demands was that nobody have access to that hangar, including city officials. That was written into the contract with the city. They swallowed that, but they didn't like it.

One day the fire inspector showed up on a routine check and the guys at the hangar wouldn't let him in. There was a big hullabaloo down at City Hall. They said the contract was illegal because the fire department didn't have the right to get in to make their routine checks, and that was against whatever laws the city had made back in 1850 or whenever it got started. But I made it stick – I had a good lawyer out there.

After the metals people tried to wreck it, my security was really tight. They tried to get guys in to see the boat on the pretext of writing articles for magazines, but I viewed everyone as a potential saboteur, and I killed every story on it. I didn't want any attention focused on it, because I knew the more it was played up in the newspapers, the more that Reynolds and Kaiser and Alcoa would panic, and the more efforts they might make to destroy the boat.

Some magazine, for example, was about to do a story on me and the Hercules. However, fortunately for me, the magazine was being sued for libel by a movie star I had under contract. We made a deal, sub rosa. The magazine agreed not to print the story, and my actress agreed to drop her libel suit. That kept things quiet for a while until, as I said, they tried it again.

This was in 1953, during the winter. Long Beach Harbor was protected – at least that part of Long Beach Harbor where my hangar was – by a dike, a cofferdam. And one day some barge came haring down, supposedly out of control, and broke through this cofferdam. Thousands of tons of crap, water, mud, garbage, poured right through, smashed the hangar, and smashed the Hercules. The tail, which we had managed to put into shape after the sabotage, was completely crushed. The wings were bent. The ailerons, the hull, the stabilizers – everything was crushed.

After an accident like that, did you think of abandoning the project?

Never. All I thought of at the time was: I'm not going to give in, they're not going to get me. I wept. I don't mean inside. I sat down in my car and I cried like a baby. Two business ventures have meant a great deal to me in my lifetime. One was the Hercules and the other was Trans World Airlines, which I always thought of privately as Hughes Transoceanic Airlines. Because I made it, I built it.

I dried my eyes with a Kleenex, left the car and went to see Noah. That's when he showed his true colors. That son of a bitch looked across the table from me, cool as ice, and he said, 'Howard, your problems are solved. You can junk that plane now and nobody will criticize you.'

'Noah,' I said, 'you're a small, mean, opportunistic worm, with no sensitivity and no understanding of what makes a man tick. If it's the last thing I do in this world, that plane will be fixed. And it will fly again.'

Now I want to tell you something that I may not even have admitted to myself at the time. Deep down inside, in the depths of my heart, when I saw how the Hercules had been crushed by this avalanche, I thought, well, that's fate – I wasn't meant to complete this project. It was a dream, and it's come to an end. No man can be successful in everything he tries. It passed through my mind that I would be wasting my money and my energies and my time, except that as a research project it could still have validity. But I saw jets coming and I doubted whether we'd ever put jet engines on the Hercules.

Noah Dietrich's remarks changed that. Maybe it was just to spite Noah Dietrich that I went on.

In dollars the damage would have cost a million to fix. But it was not a question of the money. It was a question of the time, and of the blood that I and my people had poured into that ship.

The first thing I did was sue the city for $12 million. The barge didn't belong to the city, but it was the city's responsibility to keep barges away from that cofferdam. The barge company didn't have a dime. Suing them would have made no sense at all.

I won the suit. Took me years, but I settled for half a million dollars.

Then you didn't come out too well.

That's the usual ratio. I didn't expect to get the $12 million. I just wanted to let them know that I wasn't going to take this lying down, and any future incidents would be dealt with severely. But then I almost got into trouble. The city was pissed off about the lawsuit. They sent a letter to me that said, 'Mr. Hughes: your lease, when it expires, will not be renewed.'

That's dirty pool. My suit was a legitimate one and they were threatening, illegitimately, to boot me out of there.

But I knew how to handle these kinds of situations. That's something I learned from my father. I can fight as dirty as the next man if I'm being unjustly persecuted. I know when to be the lion. I sharpened my claws.

I have to give you a little historical picture of Long Beach. It's the third largest city in California, and Long Beach Harbor has what's called an oil pool, tideland oil, under its harbor, worth at that time about several hundred million dollars. The City of Long Beach wanted it and the state of California wanted it. Just before the time that the cofferdam broke and my hangar got flooded, the city and the state had come to a tentative compromise agreement, which they were fixing up in the state capital, Sacramento.

I had friends in Sacramento on my payroll – well-placed people. I got them on the telephone and I said, 'Kick Long Beach in the ass.' In other words, put the pressure on, throw a monkey wrench into the negotiations so that the city thinks that the state is going to get all the tideland oil.

The city fathers figured they were going to get some hundred million dollars over the years out of this pool of oil under their harbor, but things suddenly ground to a halt in Sacramento. As soon as Long Beach found out who was the guiding brain behind the breakdown in negotiations, they came crawling to me on their hands and knees.

'Mr. Hughes, we didn't mean to offend you.'

I said, 'Well, you *did* offend me. And you better do something about it.'

They gave me a ten-year lease on the hangar. I called off my dogs in

Sacramento and, eventually, as I told you, I settled my suit for half a million dollars.

They also tried to harass me, while all this was going on, by citing me for low flying. The Civil Aeronautics Authority was going to do it on the basis of a complaint by the Long Beach Police.

I was flying a PBY with Glen Odekirk. We'd been using it over Long Beach to check out, among other things, the possibility of that cofferdam breaking again, and they tried to say we were less than fifty feet from the beach. We may have been, and it may have been careless in their eyes, but it didn't matter – I was able to prove that we were approaching a landing area, in this case the bay, and there was no minimum altitude specified in the city regulations for landings. So they couldn't get me that way.

You're probably wondering why, nearly twenty years later, I still keep the Hercules. I'll explain it to you. Once all this damage had been repaired, the ship became for me, among other things, a laboratory. You told me you flew across the Atlantic on the Jumbo Jet, the Boeing 747. You thought it was great. Do you think that 747 would be in the air if the HK-1 hadn't flown seventy feet off the ground in 1948? I doubt that very much. When that plane flew, it was of tremendous importance to the aviation industry.

The plane is the largest ever constructed, completed, and flown. It cannot be abandoned. It would be criminal to abandon it now, much less tear it apart. Would you tear down the Empire State Building? Let it go derelict? Some day, after my death, that ship is going to wind up on display either at a specially constructed housing, or at the Smithsonian Institute, because it's a landmark in the history of aviation. And these shortsighted bastards who delight in destroying these sorts of monuments won't get their hands on her. I'm keeping her in trust.

It's costing you several hundred thousand dollars a year, isn't it, to keep that plane in the hangar?

It's my money and I'll do what I want with it. Besides, it's tax-deductible.

17

Howard becomes a bush pilot in Ethiopia, refuses to eat a sheep's eye, visits Albert Schweitzer in the jungle, and has intimations of mortality.

AFTER THE WAR my whole life changed. I wanted it to change. After the Senate investigation, and my crash in the F-11, and after vindicating myself by flying the Hercules, I felt that the first part of my time on earth was over. I was in my early forties. I felt I had to get away. And so I went to Ethiopia.

The story of those trips is something I've told only to one person, and it's an oddly emotional subject with me.

After I finally took the Hercules up and made her fly, I was no longer content in any way with the things that I had been doing. Until then I'd been climbing my father's image, you might say. He had been up there in front of me, as a target – not just a target to attain, but a target to shoot down.

And I realized I had done it, I had shot him down. He wasn't there anymore, looming up in front of me larger than life. It came to me that this was a kind of a ridiculous thing for a man of forty-three to still be battling with his father's image. Then one day the image was no longer there for me. I had defeated him. I'd shot him down, as you put it.

But it left a hole in my life. What was I supposed to be doing? I owned TWA, one of the biggest airlines in the United States. Toolco was flourishing as never before, and I was a millionaire many times over. I'd known all the beautiful women in Hollywood and I could theoretically take my pick, so money and sex were no longer unattainable or even difficult objects. Money never really was, but it certainly wasn't then.

Family life – well, that's something else, and I'll get to it later. What matters is that I realized I was a dissatisfied man, and that dissatisfaction took me, of all places, to Ethiopia.

Flying was still connected with it. I went the first time in 1946. TWA had a management agreement with Ethiopian Airlines, like the one pending with BWA in the Bahamas. More or less the same, but much more complicated, because we were dealing with a vastly more difficult set of problems. The most complicated piece of machinery those Ethiopians had ever seen was a sewing machine, much less an airplane.

In Ethiopia, up in those mountainous gorges cut by the Nile, I had the feeling that I was plunging back 2,000 years into time. I saw places that I'm positive hadn't changed since the days of Christ. Almost the whole country is off the beaten track, and I remember standing on some mountaintop or even a few hundred yards off an airstrip, in the brush, and saying to myself, 'It's entirely possible that I'm the first human being who has ever stood on this particular spot of earth.' That gave me an eerie feeling, very beautiful in some ways. Did I ever tell you, by the way, that I once pissed in the Coliseum in Rome? I don't know why that occurs to me now, but I did.

I was in Rome on my way back from somewhere, probably Ethiopia – maybe that's why I think of it now – and I stopped off for a day to see the city, which I hardly knew. I was in the Coliseum at night, not another soul there, and there was the grandeur that was Rome surrounding me on a lovely moonlit night. I was impressed, so I walked out into the center of the arena and had a piss in the moonlight. I said, 'That's in honor of you, Julius Caesar. Howard Hughes salutes you.'

Then I saw a guard walking over to me, and I decided I'd better leave. He didn't stop me.

I wonder if any dollars grew there where you pissed.

Let's get back to Ethiopia. TWA was supposed to set up and run Ethiopian Airlines until the natives could take over and run it themselves. There was no Ethiopian air service at all in 1946. I've been out there several times – it's dramatic and savage and beautiful, and hell to travel. The standard mode of travel in Ethiopia was by mule, and the country was so cut by rifts that you could take a week to reach a village you could already *see*. Even when you landed at the airstrips, you could see the town a mile or so away, but it took an hour to hike up there. No roads, just dirt tracks. There's a railroad running down the coast to the port of Djibouti, but that's all. If ever a country needed air transport, it was Ethiopia.

We had one thing going for us, and that was a bunch of Italian airfields left over from the war. They were in terrible shape. But they were there. And so we – that is, TWA – signed a management agreement with the Emperor Haile Selassi and we went out there and started managing things.

I saw Selassi go by in his green Rolls-Royce one time. Everybody bobbed up and down like they do in Japan. But I never met him. When I went out there in 1948 I didn't go as Howard Hughes. I didn't want the treatment. I wanted anonymity as much as I ever wanted it, so I didn't use my own name.

Strangely enough, I felt very uncertain of myself. I felt as if I hadn't really done anything with my life. I had a kind of empty feeling, and I asked myself: where was Howard Hughes? I mean I knew where Howard Hughes was, but I didn't know where *I* was. I didn't know the man underneath the labels. Who had accomplished all those things I'd done? And who was the I? And how would it get me through the rest of my life? How would I justify what remained of my existence on earth? What good would all my money do me, or anyone else? What had I accomplished that was more than an effort to honor my ego? What was the meaning of an individual life?

These may seem like cliches to you, out of some psychiatric handbook or some hippie's ravings, but I was in my early forties, and maybe you understand that it's a crucial time in a man's life, a time when certain powers may be beginning to fail. I don't mean just the crude sexual powers; I mean the powers of sustained energy, the confidence and the recklessness and the supreme ego of youth. Those are the powers that catapult you into manhood. They say that the first forty years supply the text, the next forty years is the commentary. Schopenhauer said that, not me.

Well, I couldn't read my own text anymore. It was unfamiliar, almost in a foreign language. So how could I supply the commentary?

I felt I had a chance to become a new person, or to find the old person, the person who had been there all along, which I could never find back there in the USA, surrounded by people who were constantly wanting things from me, and from whom I wanted things constantly. I wanted to live in a world where I didn't have to want and other people didn't have to want with such a desperate quality. I would just have a challenge and a job to do, and in the quiet moments I could figure things out.

That's why I went to Ethiopia the second time. The TWA operation out there was in charge of a man named Swede Golien, and I didn't want to see Swede. He's an old-time pilot – been flying since not long after the First World War. He was in the capital, Addis Ababa, so I ducked in and out of there as quickly as I could. I went out as an airport engineer from the home office. I just called a few of the guys on top in Kansas City, and said a man I was interested in, an engineer named Charles Maddox, was going out to Ethiopia for me personally. I would take care of his salary, don't put him on the books, and no special treatment by the guys in Ethiopia.

And in early 1948 Charles Maddox, yours truly, went out to Ethiopia.

I spent a couple of days in Addis Ababa – filthy hole – and the first thing that hit me was the altitude. I'd been in Mexico and so I knew you had to take it easy for a while when you first go to a place that's more than 6,000 feet high. But it was much higher in Ethiopia. One of the TWA engineers had a heart attack the second night he arrived when he picked up some fancy whore in Addis. He conked out right in the middle of humping her. You don't do much humping at 9,000 feet, not even in the best of circumstances, unless you've been doing it all your life and know how to pace yourself. You need a heart of oak, lungs like leather, and a pecker of steel.

Did you...?

For God's sake, no. They had every venereal disease known to man. It was out of the question in Ethiopia.

I headed inland. That was some of the hairiest flying I've ever done in my life. The downdrafts knocked you down a thousand feet before you could get control of the ship again. Murderous. They lost at least one or two planes that way.

Sometimes I was the pilot, sometimes a passenger. I don't know which was worse. I got there just before the rains. The rainy season lasts from the middle of June to September, and it pours rain like a cow pissing on a flat rock. I was there a little before the rains hit, and the flying looked possible.

The first time I flew it was up to a strip near a place called Dobi. I landed, and had a terrible scare. I saw several hundred people gathered on the edge of the strip, like a crowd at a drag race. 'Christ,' I said to myself, 'they're not giving me much room, but I suppose they'll head for the hills when I drop my landing gear and put the nose up.'

But they didn't. They just stayed there and watched. Orderly; they didn't mill around or anything, but they didn't give an inch of ground. They had more dumb faith than I've ever seen in my life. They were in awe of the planes, like those people in New Guinea who have the cargo cult, only not quite so maniac about it. They didn't think the planes were gods who would one day drop down to provide bounty everlasting, but still they were in awe. You could see it in their faces. And it never occurred to them that if a crosswind hit you, you could veer and sheer off a few fuzzy heads with a wingtip.

The whole time the plane was there on the strip, which was a matter of some six or seven hours, from early morning until the middle of the afternoon, they just sat there, formed a big circle around the plane, a DC-3, got down on their haunches the way peasants do, and watched it. Men, women and children, just squatting there and watching that ship sitting in the dust. They had brought their lunches along too; it was a family affair. I thought this was wonderful. How simple people's needs are, when their minds aren't cluttered with all the garbage of modern-day life. I'm sure those people enjoyed staring at that DC-3, were moved by it – and it just sat there, completely inert – were more touched and thrilled than the average American is who sits like a chuckling moron in front of the boob tube and watches his favorite sitcom. They were certainly more at peace. And the Ethiopians didn't have to watch any commercials.

I didn't spend all the time out there working as an engineer. I did my share of that work, but for the first time in my life I took a good look at how other people, I mean people besides Americans, live – and you can go a long way before you find people as *other* as Ethiopians. They're a warrior people, old Christians, and they had an innate dignity which you don't find many places.

I don't mean I got friendly with them. I tried, but they're touchy, arrogant people – hard to talk to. And there was the problem of their hospitality. I'm a bit finicky about my food. I'm not talking about Ethiopia, I mean in the United States. I had a little silver rake, which I carried into restaurants and banquets   especially banquets, with their limp salad and fat green peas. If there's anything I hate in the food world, it's a fat green pea. So I'd take out my little rake and rake through the green peas, and the ones that slipped through the tines were edible. The rest was just trash to throw out with the salad, for the hogs. These days it's different. Now you can get tiny peas. But I don't like peas anymore.

What do you eat now?

I eat figs and fresh raspberries and other fruit – all organically grown. No artificial fertilizers for me. I'm under a doctor's care and he prescribes rare beef for me, but I can't take it. He'd like me to take it bloody, but I can't get it down, so I have it well done. Boiled, cut into small pieces.

This was one of the troubles I had out in Ethiopia, in 1948, when I met this tribal chieftain. It was in the southern part of the country, and the tribal chieftain invited a few of us to have a meal with him. The first dish was all right, except that the spice they put over it, called *wot*, could burn the roof of your mouth off. But I got through that part. Then four men came out carrying a skinned cow. I wouldn't call it a steer – it was a cow, raw – and they stopped in front of me, and I saw that I was supposed to choose a piece. I had the idea they were going to cook it. I pointed to a nice filet mignon. They whacked it off and dropped it down in front of me, *plop*, on the plate in front of me. I was supposed to eat it.

That was the end of any social contact, you might say. I said, as politely as I could, 'Thanks, but no thanks.'

I was concerned that this might offend the chieftain, but I didn't think it would offend him as much as if I'd eaten the raw meat and then vomited it all over his lap.

When I was out there I lived in the tin huts that were scattered all over the country, where our TWA men were living. They lived separately from the natives, and didn't have much contact with them. I managed some contact because I went out to find it. I had nobody to report to. I was a free agent, so I could take off whenever I wanted to, which suited my purpose. l would be a passenger going down to Desi or Kobbo or some even more remote place, and I would disembark and spend two or three days there, living in whatever accommodations were available. Once I slept in a place that was the equivalent of a flophouse for the poor people of the town. And poor in Ethiopia means poor in a sense that's hard to understand if you've never been out there. That's poor at the low end of the poverty scale – utterly destitute.

Of course I couldn't speak the language, but I could get by. It's amazing how, in situations like these, men understand one another. I made it known that I wanted a bed, but there was no hotel in this town. I had my own bottled water with me, and some dried fruit. That was enough for me. I didn't eat much, and I didn't need much sleep, but I'd been up for a day and a half before this trip, and I had to get some sleep.

I was taken to a little shack with maybe half a dozen men sleeping in it. It was cold, a few degrees above freezing, so I couldn't sleep outside. I came in late, just as it was getting dark. I was shown to a pallet on the floor.

One look at the men sleeping there and any sane man would have thought, 'I won't last the night, I'll get my throat cut.' The man in charge had a scar, looked like a knife wound, running down one side of his face. The scar was almost white, and in that black face it made him look positively evil. But the whole point of what I'm trying to tell you is: I wasn't really worried. If my throat had been cut during the night, I would have accepted it. I wouldn't have known, of course. What I mean is, for the first time in my life I was on my own, in strange circumstances, where the fact that I was Big Howard's son, the billionaire Howard Hughes, wasn't going to help me a bit. Nothing could help me. I had nobody I could turn to. If I had got in trouble and said to one of these TWA men, 'Get me out of this, I'm Howard Hughes,' he would have laughed in my face. And I couldn't very well say it to the natives, could I?

I bedded myself down on this pallet. You know I'm a fastidious man, and I'm often amazed that I was able to do that. I'm even more amazed that it didn't cure me of my fastidiousness. I lay there, and I thought, I'll never sleep. Not that I was afraid – it was just damned uncomfortable, and it stank of goat hides and men who hadn't washed in weeks. I thought, I'll never sleep, and I lay down there in all that filth, and the next thing I knew it was a beautiful early morning and I woke up and I felt very well indeed because I'd put my trust in myself.

There was an old Coptic church on a hill nearby, a broken-down white wooden building with a domed roof. I went up there to look at it. I'm not a believer. A priest – a black, black man with a big beard and long robe – was standing out in front, and something came over me, and I went in. I don't mean to suggest I had any mystical or religious experience, or anything like that. But I found a moment of peace such as I have rarely known in my life, in that quiet old church on the hill in Ethiopia. I didn't pray. I wouldn't have known who to pray to.

Just for a change of view, the first thing I did after leaving there was to get a flight back to Addis Ababa, where I moved into one of the best hotels. I showered, changed clothes, and played eighteen holes of golf at the Imperial Ethiopian Golf Club. I just had to get back to the flavor of western civilization after that sojourn with the fleas.

I went back to the States shortly after that. I didn't want to stay away for too long at one time. I was getting involved in RKO and I had plans for TWA, and the usual financial troubles. When I think about that period now, it strikes me as amazing that I was able to juggle all these things at the same time, but I've done that all my life. The following year, however, I went back to Ethiopia. I still used the name Charles Maddox. On my previous trip I had stumbled across a leper clinic, and it really shook me to the depths of my being to see those deformed, suffering souls. It made me stop to think about a man who was close enough to touch them. This was Dr. Albert Schweitzer, the great healer. He was in Africa then – he had a clinic down in Lambaréné, in French Equatorial Africa. I didn't stay long in Ethiopia that trip because I got some mild dysentery, not amoebic but damned uncomfortable – and I went back to California and had it looked after.

But on the flight back I started to think about Schweitzer. Here was a man who was universally respected. He was famous in any number of fields, and it seemed to me that we had something in common. He had reached the heights in his fields, and I had reached them in mine. I had gone right to the top of the heap, and so had he, and he had abandoned the whole show at an age not so much younger than mine. He became a doctor and he went down to Africa to serve humanity, but also, I'm convinced, to look for Albert Schweitzer.

Don't get the wrong idea that I was placing myself on his level. We operated on different spheres, and his, I believed, were far more exalted than mine, but we did have this one thing in common. We were both in the middle years, men who had accomplished something of note, and yet we were lost and we were looking for something more. I thought: I'd like to talk to that man.

When I make up my mind to do something, I do it. When I was feeling better I flew back to Africa, to Cairo, and then down to Lambaréné. I took a canoe from there to Schweitzer's clinic. The people who paddled the canoes were the most horrible collection of emaciated souls I'd ever seen. I'm sure some of them were lepers. I found out afterward there was a power boat I could have taken, but I didn't see it around at the time, or my French wasn't good enough to make myself understood and I had to get into this goddamn canoe.

I visited Schweitzer, and he reminded me of myself back in the States. Didn't want to see any visitors.

I didn't tell him who I was, because I doubt that it would have meant anything to him. The magic of the Hughes name didn't penetrate to Lambaréné. But in any event I found it impossible to talk to Dr. Schweitzer. I couldn't get a word in edgewise with the man. He was totally brusque, indifferent to me and to any problems I may have had. I realized after a short time that this wasn't personal – he acted this way toward everybody. He showed this Olympian detachment even toward the poor sick souls lying around in his clinic, which, incidently, was filthy. I don't know what kind of doctor he was, but he sure as hell didn't know much about ordinary hygiene. In that sense he might better have stayed in Germany and played the organ.

This place was a big establishment, not just a little clinic the way I imagined it would be. It was a compound, dozens of big buildings and lots of little barracks, like an army camp built in a swamp. The mosquitos nearly drove you crazy, and the heat, the humidity – well, it was hotter than Houston, and that's saying something.

I don't want to be too hard on Schweitzer. He looked awful, thin, and tired, and pale. I was there in the evening to see him. I was wandering about the compound, looking at the animals. There were a lot of African deer around, antelopes and other animals, and just before it got dark and I was supposed to go, I saw Dr. Schweitzer running around in a panic, shoving people into various huts and padlocking the doors. I asked myself, 'My God, what's happening?' I thought for a minute there was a mad elephant on the loose, or a new leper had come to the clinic and there was something especially contagious about him.

I ran around myself, trying to find out what was going on, and it turned out that this was just his nightly routine. Schweitzer locked everything and everybody up because he was afraid they'd steal his medicines and his books and whatever else wasn't nailed down. He wasn't a very elevated soul. He certainly had no detachment.

I came back the next day and managed to talk to him. He pretended not to speak more than a few words of English, although I knew damn well that he did. I asked him a few questions, because I also knew he had built the clinic, all those buildings and huts, with his own two hands. I complimented him on that, and he said, 'You can't trust these people to do anything. If you want it so it won't fall down, you have to do it yourself.'

That's the sort of answer I'd expect from some redneck planter in Mississippi. It wasn't what I expected from the great Dr. Schweitzer. You know, you can read all the Chinese philosophy in the world – he did, by the way, which is why I mention it – but if you come out of it with the feeling that you can't trust anybody else to build a hut, and, more to the point, if you don't choose to teach people how to do it, I don't think you've learned very much.

That was about the extent of our conversation. The last time I saw him he vanished back into the depths of his clinic, padlocked his doors, and I got into the canoe and left – waved goodbye to a hippopotamus.

It was a long trip for a meeting that came to nothing. And since then I've taken a different attitude toward the famous seers and philosophers of this world. I've decided the best thing is to read what they have to say, but don't meet them. They're too human, or they're not human enough. It's disillusioning.

I want to stop a minute to draw breath and give some perspective. I talked once about the time I was in my late twenties and I went into flying. I felt then that I was not a man in the full sense of the word.

When I got back from Ethiopia and French Equatorial Africa, I was forty-four years old. But I was a man in a lamentable state of bewilderment. I had made a great deal more of my life than if I had just stepped on my father's shoulders – I had made more money than he had, I had accomplished more, and he was no longer a challenge. Having done that, I had nothing to do. I was lost. I had contempt for my world and I felt that there had to be something else, and this is what I went to Ethiopia to find. I didn't find it. I certainly didn't find it when I went down to see the good doctor.

I was in search – drowning in a sea of impressions, all of them new and strange. And moreover I came back that last time with an even worse case of dysentery – it never quite leaves your system.

Verne Mason, my doctor, put me in a private clinic, but while he was checking me out he said, 'I'd better have a closer look,' and he did a proctoscopy.

They stick a pipe up your ass and shine a light through it, and look to see if anything is growing in there that shouldn't. He found polyps. They were benign, but it was better to take them out, Verne said, because they often turned malignant, if left to grow. Now this may strike you as fairly insignificant, and it was. But more even than my bad crash in the F-11, and more even than other close shaves I've had crashing in Lake Mead and during the war in England, this gave me a feeling of mortality. My body, which I'd always taken for granted, was betraying me.

One of the fools who wrote one of my so-called biographies quoted some other fool as saying, 'Howard Hughes isn't going to die in bed or as the result of a plane crash. He's going to die at the hands of a woman with a .38.' *Time* magazine printed that originally – it must have sounded colorful.

That's a lot of baloney. Howard Hughes is going to die, as most men die, because the machinery of his body is breaking down and betraying him.

The first realization of this was overwhelming. More than most men I had retained a feeling of immortality until quite late in my life, partly because I'd gone through so many crashes and come through them where others couldn't. But more than that it's something inexplicable, something innate. I had talked to some of these young fellows over in England who had lost this feeling very young. Every time it came time to go out on a mission, they'd get a haunted look in their eyes, and you knew they were aware they might die. They didn't have that feeling of immortality, of inviolability, that young men usually have – which is of course what makes wars possible, because you can't get an army made up of men who know they're probably going to die. You've got to get it made up of kids who can face the horrors feeling that it's going to happen to someone else, not to them.

This youthful belief in immortality is a wonderful thing, but you can cut your throat with it if you're careless. And it's a terrible thing when you lose it and first become aware of death, perched on your shoulder... waiting. I first became aware after that simple operation. From then on I was aware of my heart pumping, of the digestive process taking place, of the glands secreting their vital fluids. I became as death-haunted as any man could be. It's colored my every action, every thought, in ways I don't fully understand. It's not as if I'm planning to leave some noble monument for posterity. I'm a dying man – we're all dying men and women – but I'm more so than many others are.

Didn't you investigate the possibility of the deep-freezing of bodies, of going into suspended animation?

I'd heard about the cryogenic process, and I checked it out to see if there was anything in it, which there wasn't. The state of the medical art is a long way from being able to accomplish that. I wasn't looking for immortality, you understand. But I thought if I had another ten years of life coming to me, I'd prefer to live them in a later century than this one. I've had enough of this one.

Anyway, the dysentery cleared up, and I had this minor operation. But my physical condition in general was rotten. All the accidents, and all the illnesses – I've had pneumonia three or four times, and my lungs were weak – had taken their toll, and I felt fragile.

I went off to hide for awhile on the Pacific coast of Mexico, in a little fishing village called Zihuatanejo, still as Charles Maddox. I loafed around in a hammock under a *palapa,* careful of what I ate, read some books, thought about the past and the future, and at the end of that time – it was a couple of weeks – I knew what I had to do, which was very simple.

Be active. Bury myself in work.

I felt this was the only salvation, and so that's what I did. I not only plunged back into TWA and Toolco and Hughes Aircraft, but I bought RKO and went back to the film-making business. It was a way of avoiding a confrontation with the things in life that I didn't understand and thought I could never understand.

It turned out to be a terrible mistake.

18

*Howard buys RKO Pictures, joins the Communist witch-hunt,
has lunch with Senator Richard Nixon, and offends a
powerful woman.*

I DECIDED TO go back into the movie business. I had some new
ideas. I had learned that if you do something well and then stay away
from it for many years – provided that you work on something else
during those years of absence – you can go back to the original work
and find that the accumulated experience of the intervening time is a
tremendous plus. You don't pick up where you left off. You pick up far
ahead of where you left off. Your mental muscles are tougher and the
problems that might have given you headaches ten or twenty years
previously are problems that you can often solve, after all those years,
with a snap of the fingers.

This time I wanted to go into the movie business on a large scale. I
had the money, I felt I had the know-how. All I needed was the venue.
It wasn't a true creative urge and it wasn't a calculated business
decision. It was simpler than that. I liked making movies. It was a
business I already knew well, and it was a business that I thought, if I
got hold of the right people, could run itself.

I looked around. I had done some business previously with Floyd
Odlum, who was the head of the Atlas Corporation, which had the
controlling interest in RKO. Floyd had turned out a number of films
that made a lot of money, but he was ready to get rid of RKO by then,
partly because he had slow years in 1946 and '47. I thought the big
years were still to come.

I guess I hadn't learned as much as I thought, because that goddamn
company gave me nothing but headaches. RKO was a peanut-sized

business compared to Toolco, compared to Hughes Aircraft and TWA, but it wasn't as anonymous, at the time, as those other companies, and I wanted to put my own stamp on it, run it my own way. In 1948 I bought Odlum's controlling interest in RKO for about $10 million, and got into trouble right away with the people in there who were running the show. We didn't see eye to eye. The weight of the money counts, and out they went.

Peter Rathvon had been president of the company under Odlum, and I kept him on for a while. Dore Schary was head of production. Schary, of course, was an enormously talented and experienced man. He was a little too radical for my tastes, but I wasn't running a political party, I was running a movie business, so I explained to him he could pretty much make the kind of films he wanted to. He was a shrewd man, because one of the first things he told me was that a man in my position, as rich as I was, who had bought a film studio and had previous film experience, would certainly want to run it, and he didn't want to be in the position of being number two man. I assured him that he would be at least on a level with me.

This didn't hold up, though, because he got off on the wrong foot with me right away. He was making a film called *Battleground*, which he figured was going to set the pace in Hollywood for war films. He figured there was going to be a big run of them, and I disagreed.

I said, 'The timing is wrong. The public is fed up with war.' I was fed up with it, so I figured the public was – that was my mistake, to assume the mass thinks as I do – and I told him to stop production on it. What I didn't realize, and what I know now, is that the public loves blood and violence more than anything, even more than sex, and blood and violence is always a moneymaker, because the mass of people are sick.

That was one item of disagreement. The other one was that he was trying to make a star out of Barbara Bel Geddes. And that one I was right on. I didn't see star quality there, and it wasn't there. Schary and I came to loggerheads over these two things.

He said, 'Howard, you're trying to make a messenger boy out of me.' So I said, 'Quit.' And he did.

I was wrong about *Battleground*. He bought the property from me, took it with him to MGM and made a mint out of it. It was the biggest hit of 1949, as I recall.

Then I buckled down and lopped off some heads, cut off a lot of fat, fired about 700 people who were totally unnecessary. That's when Peter Rathvon quit. This was also the time I got into that terrible wrangle with Paul Jarrico. As usual it was only one incident of many – Jarrico was one screenwriter out of fifty or sixty who was blacklisted by the movie industry, and I was only one producer out of fifty who was wielding the axe and doing the blacklisting of left-wing people, but I was Howard Hughes and that meant headlines on page one.

This was during the McCarthy era, which in retrospect I view as one of the more shameful periods of American political life. But at that time it was a kind of mass purge and mass hysteria, and I got sucked up by it.

Everyone in Hollywood was bleating about Communist domination of the industry. I had no use for communism as a workable philosophy, and I thought for the most part that the Communists I knew were misguided idealists who were all messed up emotionally and got starry-eyed and wobbly-kneed and simply lost every ounce of their common sense when they talked about the glorious life in the Soviet Union.

I think I was right in the long run, and the simplemindedness of their thinking was proved to me when the same people who swore there couldn't possibly be such things as slave labor camps in Siberia – their argument, if you recall, was that it was theoretically incompatible with a Marxist workers' state, and if it was theoretically impossible it had to be impossible in practice as well, and it was just another lie coming out of Wall Street – it was these same people who quit the party and dived like lemmings back into the liberal and capitalist ranks when Khrushchev made his famous speech denouncing Stalin.

They knew, I think – because most of them were superficially intelligent men and women – that they were being intellectually dishonest. What they didn't know was that they were emotionally unstable, and they were just waiting for a chance to bail out with what they could call honor. Khrushchev's speech gave them their chance, and they took it. It's like a pilot who's flying an experimental plane he's claimed is the best in the world. The nuts and bolts start to fly off and the plane loses altitude, but he can't and won't give up. Then the engine drops out and he says, 'Thank God,' and bails out. It happens all the time in politics and marriage. And it's happening now in Vietnam.

Anyway, at that time, in the fifties, when I fired Paul Jarrico, I was head over heels in the fight against so-called Communist domination of the film industry. Jarrico, I'm convinced, was not a member of the Communist party, not a card-carrying member. He couldn't be; this guy was on a salary of $2,500 a week from the studio, which put him pretty clearly in the capitalist class. He was what they called a fellow traveler.

When he went up before that committee in Washington, he took the Fifth Amendment. The one thing that really got my goat, one thing that made me boil over, was a man who wouldn't stand up for his principles. Now if the man was a Communist or even if the man was only a sympathizer, he should have stood up there and said, 'Yes, this is what I am, I believe such-and-such, and I'll take the consequences for it.' For not saying that, I couldn't respect him, and I couldn't respect any of those guys who looked the other way and ducked out and avoided the responsibility. I didn't like those Reds who went to prison, they were hardly my friends and idols, but I had respect for them insofar as they said, 'Yes, that's who I am and that's what I stand for. You want to throw me behind bars for my beliefs, okay, my conscience is clear and I'm an honest man.'

Of course, far worse than someone like Jarrico, was a man like Elia Kazan, the film director, who went before the witch-hunting committee in Washington and snitched on all his friends. His excuse was that the committee already knew they were Communist; other snitches had named them. All the more reason not to give the names, since they weren't needed. The committee's purpose was to intimidate and humiliate, and Kazan bent over and spread his cheeks in order to insure his career. Arthur Miller, who wrote *Death of a Salesman*, refused to testify. He survived. Kazan was a great film director and a creepy human being.

After all these years, do you regret the role you played in the witch-hunt?

The answer to that isn't a simple one. If it has to be 'yes or no' I'd say, 'Yes, I do regret it.' But that would be a fundamental dishonesty on my part, because it would be too easy a way of skating out of something. I can't deny that I did what I did – I even went so far as to try and get the RKO Theaters Corporation to ban the showing of *Limelight*, because I considered Charlie Chaplin a pinko and a man who'd run away to Europe rather than stay at home and fight for what he believed in, whether it was right or wrong.

But I refuse to talk in terms of 'if I had it all to do over again,' because that's equivalent to saying, 'If my aunt had balls she'd be my uncle.' I did what I did because I was the man that I was. If I had done anything else I would have been a hypocrite and a coward and then I really would regret it now.

In other words, I don't regret what I did but I do wish that I had been a different kind of man, the kind of man who would not have done those things. That's also, I suppose, a kind of shadowy statement, but it's the best I can give, because I realize now that I was swept along with the mob and that's always demeaning to the soul and damaging to the man as a whole.

But it's even more damaging to go against your own nature. Sometimes you have to plunge in headfirst and wallow in the trough of your own stupidity just in order to climb out and take a bath and feel your own clean skin again.

As far as the anticommunist battle went, it was a battle, and in battle you fight with whatever weapons you've got and with whatever allies you can find. I was obsessed; I admit it. I'm not proud of it. I gave a talk before the American Legion at that time. Not that I was a great backer of the American Legion, I want to make clear. They're a bunch of warmongers, as I realized later on. It's simply, as I said, that you had strange bedfellows in those days. Must have been a good talk, though, because it was put in the Congressional Record by Richard Nixon.

He was then a senator from California. I had a letter from him, and we met around that time for lunch, rather quietly, because Nixon was sowing the seeds then for the future. And I was sowing mine. I didn't like him. A mealy-mouthed guy. But he was ambitious, and slick, and, I thought, just mediocre enough to make it. So I filed him away for future reference. I figured his time would come, and I would make use of him.

One other important thing happened when I owned RKO, although at the time I didn't see its huge significance, that it would cloud my entire future.

Henry Luce was the man who owned *Time, Life,* and *Fortune.* A publishing mogul, energetic, conservative, very powerful. His wife was Clare Boothe Luce. In her time she'd written a couple of decent plays but then she got herself elected to the House of Representatives as a Republican from Connecticut, so that will give you a good idea of her ideological bent. She spent part of each year in Hollywood throwing lavish parties for producers, because she wanted them to produce movies she wrote.

I never went to those parties, of course, but Liz Taylor brought her once to my bungalow in the Beverly Hills Hotel to meet me, and I bumped into her a couple of times on the beach in Santa Monica. I used to go for long walks on the beach and so did Clare Luce. So we were on cordial terms.

One day on the beach she collared me and bled my ear about a script called *Pilate's Wife.* I may have said we'd be interested in producing it if it was good, and she told me that René Clair wanted to direct it. She let it leak to the newspapers that the movie was going to be made by me and RKO. I paid no attention to that. Finally she turned up at the Beverly Hills Hotel with a draft of the screenplay. She left it there with a note that said, 'I'll be back in exactly a week, dear Howard, and we'll discuss who can play Jesus and who can play Mary Magdalene.'

I read it. It was pap, Sunday school stuff for children. It was absolutely non-producible in the form she'd written it, and when she showed up a week later she asked me if I had any ideas for improving the plot and the characterization. She thought of course the answer would be no, and she was right – it was impossible to improve the plot and characterization in the script, because they didn't exist.

But I couldn't say that to her. She showed up, and we discussed the script in the lobby at the Beverly Hills Hotel. I tried to be diplomatic, I tried to point out to her why I thought it wasn't right for RKO. Diplomacy, I guess, isn't my strong suit, but in any case it's not easy to be diplomatic with somebody who thinks she's a female apostle, the most brilliant thinker and writer of our time. When I finally said for about the third time that RKO was going to pass, she claimed I'd humiliated her because she'd told *Variety* and about three dozen top actors that I was going to make her biblical horror. I said, 'Well, you jumped the gun, Clare.'

Right there, in the lobby, she stamped her feet, spat like a cornered cat, and swore that she and all her husband's magazines, *Time, Life,* and *Fortune,* would hound me for the rest of my days. Clare Luce was a vengeful woman. That was not an idle threat.

79

*Howard hands cash to both presidential candidates, makes two movies
with Ingrid Bergman, and designs a special bra for Jane Russell.*

DURING THAT PERIOD I had to keep my eye on politics, and I made
a fair share of contributions over the years to both political parties. A
little here, a little there. I figured in the long run it would pay off. It
added up to two, three, four hundred thousand dollars a year. You have
no idea how many people you have to have on your payroll to get a fair
shake. I'm not just talking about sheriffs and tax assessors. I'm talking
about state governors and mayors, even higher up, very much higher up.

There isn't a politician in America who wouldn't be tarred and
feathered if the people found out the truth of what goes on in politics.
Bribery and favors are at the root of the American political system.
They're at the root of human nature, if you accept the proposition that
human beings are political animals. They have to form social groups
to survive and those groups have to organize themselves politically to
keep the members from exercising their basic instincts and clubbing
one another to death to gain property and territory.

Money is the medium, in a so-called civilized society, that serves as
a club. I have no illusions any more about what people will do for
money if they think they haven't got enough of it – and how many
people think they've got enough? Probably no more than a hundred
men in the entire country. Half of them are multimillionaires and the
other half are in the insane asylum getting fed through a nipple. Every
man has his price, and the worst part of it is, if you pay that price, he
raises it.

I could be wrong about what I said, about the people – that they'd tar and feather a man they'd elected to office if they found out the truth. They probably wouldn't do that at all. They'd raise the usual fuss and feathers and then when it died down they'd clap the man on the back and forgive and forget, because they'd know deep down he wasn't any worse than they would be if they had the same opportunity. They only make the fuss in the first place because they're sore that this guy had the opportunity to do what they would have done if they were in his position, only they're ashamed to admit that because they've fed all this crap to their kids – you know, that you have to go through life on the Boy Scout oath and never lie, never steal, never take advantage, never covet thy neighbor's goods or thy neighbor's wife.

Who really ever lives that way? Hardly anybody. And the few who do are usually sicker than the rest because they're so frustrated. People are so tangled up in lies – spouting lies day in and day out to themselves and their friends and their dear children, their dear children who are going go grow up and be the same fountains of crap – that it breaks my heart to think about it. I know you think I'm an old cynic, but I wasn't always this way. The world made me this way – and in some ways I'm not that way even now. It breaks my heart. It used to break my heart even more, but now it just makes me feel sick.

I'm not telling you all this to make myself out to be any sort of angel in the dungheap of humanity. That's obvious. I'm telling you exactly how much I lived in that dungheap. If I tell you I had a Mayor Poulson of Los Angeles on my payroll it doesn't reflect much credit on him, but it also certainly doesn't reflect much credit on me.

But I don't care, I'm above all that now. I'd be overjoyed if people would admit what scheming hypocrites they are, and tell the truth about what really goes on in life. We certainly wouldn't be any worse off than we are now, with things the way they are now. Life seems to me a hopeless proposition sometimes. By the time you're old enough to get from behind your mama's apron strings and out from under your father's heel, you're in such a mess, so godawfully indoctrinated... how can you win? How can you achieve any personal honesty?

When I hear a man say, 'I did a terrible thing, but I'll never do it again,' you know what I say to myself? 'New Year's resolutions. Crap.' I don't believe it. And I'm not ashamed to say what I've done in my life because there are very few men who would or could have done better in the same position, and a great many who would have done worse.

Let's just say that political bribery is at the toot of any political system, whether it's a democracy or a republic or a monarchy. Recorded history proves this time and time again. In Mexico, for example, they make no bones about it. They accept bribery as part of social life and they hand a man cash, and that's that. The only difference in this country is that they do it more secretly, the money gets funneled through dummy corporations, and so forth.

How high up did you go on the political ladder to get men, as you say, on your payroll?

Just as high as I could go. They wouldn't always take it. Tom Dewey turned me down once. You remember him? They called him 'the little man on the wedding cake,' because he had a funny mustache and that's what he looked like. He was governor of New York State, and then he ran for President in 1948. That's where the Luce people really fell on their ass, putting him on the cover of their magazine and saying, 'The next President of the United States crosses Niagara Falls,' or whatever he was doing. He should have taken my money, it might have helped him.

I'd given some money to Harry Truman as well, because I liked him and I had a hunch he'd win. I gave it to him personally. He was stumping out in Los Angles and I went to the Biltmore Hotel with Neil McCarthy, my attorney, and told Neil to give it to him. There's a sequel to this, but I'll save it for later. Anyway, Neil came back to the lobby, where I was waiting in a corner behind a potted palm, and said there had been several people in the room and he'd just handed Truman the envelope.

And I said, 'Jesus Christ, my name's not on the envelope, and he may not have known who you were, that you were my attorney.' I mean he may have known Neil was my attorney, but not necessarily have known that Neil was handing him *my* money.

So I ran right upstairs and got Truman into a corner and said, 'That envelope the guy gave you – the cash inside it is mine. It's from me to you.' I stressed that.

I thought you said you tried to give it to Thomas E. Dewey. Wasn't Dewey running against Truman in that election?

Of course. I figured I'd better play it safe, so, later on, probably a month before the election, I sent Noah to the guy who was running Dewey's campaign, Harold Talbot, and told Noah to give him $25,000, which is what I'd put in the envelope for Truman.

Talbot turned it down, and he was very insulting to boot. Dewey must have found out that I'd given the money to Truman also, and Dewey thought he was a shoo-in by then and he didn't want to be obligated to me, especially since it was Eastern money that was backing him, and they hated my guts.

Dewey lost the election. Served him right.

This was my money we contributed, which meant it came out of Toolco. It was illegal for a corporation to donate funds to a candidate or an officeholder, but it wasn't illegal for a foreign corporation to donate. Our money flowed through subsidiaries in Toronto and the Bahamas which had exactly enough cash flow to pay the bills for the various congressmen and governors and mayors and vice-presidents I had on the payroll.

Did you just contribute to campaigns, or did you keep paying them when they were in office?

Mostly before they got into office. Sometimes afterward. I didn't start the system of political contributions. I was just doing it to create good will, which I needed a lot more than most businessmen. I often gave some of these guys free flights, in some cases private planes, when they were stumping. And I'd hate to tell you how many hundred-dollar-a-plate dinners I paid for, and bar bills, and hookers. I think after a while I got the reputation of being an easy touch. The list of people was very long.

They got the bill, of course, either at the time of their election or later on. The bill came to Richard Nixon. But I'll tell that story in its time and place.

I had my troubles with RKO – couldn't get the damn thing off the ground. I took an axe to the fat, lopped that off and got it down to a backbone staff. This was in the first years I had it, 1948 up through 1951.

I shot my mouth off a little too much at first, said we were going to make forty pictures a year. But we only made about fifteen or twenty a year in the first few years – I was in Ethiopia then and later in Mexico and, as always, I overburdened myself with work. I put Noah in as Chairman of the Board, but he didn't understand the movie business and he made a total mess of it. I wanted to do another picture with Jane Russell, because everybody associated Jane Russell with me as a result of *The Outlaw*, and I figured we were a winning combination.

Overall, the studio was losing money, but I can't break it down for you picture by picture. I do remember we had trouble with *Jet Pilot*, took a lot of cutting and dubbing and cost us $4 million. And we took a bath on that Bergman-Rossellini thing, *Stromboli*. I did that one personally – I went out of my way to do it. I did two pictures with Ingrid Bergman. Walter Wanger talked me into the first one, *Joan of Arc*. Wanger had gotten booted out of MGM and I picked him up right away, and just about that time I had a vision that Ingrid Bergman was the finest actress in the world, and box-office besides.

I put them together, Walter and Ingrid, and they made *Joan of Arc*, and in the midst of it, or just about when they finished shooting, it all came out about Ingrid and Rossellini and the illegitimate kid.

This was 1950 or thereabouts, and the world was not quite as much of an open sexual circus as it is today. People still blabbed about morality. I said to myself, 'Well, that kills *Joan of Arc*.' But I got talked into one of the worst mistakes you can make – I threw good money after bad. Rossellini wanted to make *Stromboli* with Bergman, and somehow I figured out that if we were absolutely blatant about it, if we had Ingrid in a very adult film made by her lover and the father of her illegitimate kid, we'd have a smash.

I made *Stromboli* and I lost my shirt on it, or at least my left cufflink, in a manner of speaking, and then I said, 'Okay, release *Joan of Arc*,' which also fell on its ass.

At this point the studio was losing about five million a year. I let Noah watch the bookkeeping. I finally decided that I'd made a mistake and the movie business was just taking up too much of my time. It represented no more than ten to fifteen percent of my holdings, and Noah pointed out I was spending 85% of my time running it.

That's not to say that I was physically there at the studio. In fact, I was never there. Not once. Oh yeah, once, early on, I put on a suit and a wig and took the guided tour, just so that I'd know the physical layout of the place. I had my office over at the Goldwyn Studios and if I wanted anything done, I got on the pipe and told the man running that particular section what I had in mind. And once I flew over the lot and saw what condition it was in, and I said, 'Paint it.' Other than that, I never once visited it except on the guided tour.

But I kept in touch with things. I had my men working there who reported to me directly. I've always run things at a distance and I've been criticized for that all my life, and unfairly. It always seems to me that you can get a much better perspective if you're not up to your neck in the daily crap that's going on around a place. If you stand a little bit aloof, let the thoughts and information come to you, then you can see better than the men who are buried up to their armpits in the action.

To give a perfect example of what I mean, I wrote a memo when we were doing another Jane Russell picture. I treated Jane like a problem in aeronautical design, and I'm not talking about the bra I designed for her in *The Outlaw*, I'm talking about another picture. It was *Macao*, a film I made for RKO about that place off the China coast. I wrote a memorandum to a man named Tevlin who was in charge of Jane's breasts.

Now you may think when you read it that it's trivial that I should spend four pages discussing the shape of her nipples underneath her bra. But that's what makes movies, that's what catches the public eye, and if you're dealing with a property like that, you've got to deal with it realistically.

By that time Jane's tits weren't what they were cracked up to be. This was long after *The Outlaw* – she was a little older and she had begun to sag a bit. That's natural. The human body doesn't have struts, the pectoral muscles fortunately are not made of aluminum. One day I called Jane to my bungalow and asked her if she'd be kind enough to strip down to the waist, because I wanted to see for myself what kind of design job we had to run. She understood, and she did it. I looked at her from all angles and made a lot of notes. She was wonderfully patient. A lot of women wouldn't have stood for it, but Jane was a pro.

When I told her I was satisfied and she could get dressed, she said, 'What do you think, Howard?'

'I think they're terrific, Jane.'

'Really?'

'Yes, really.'

She said, a little sadly, 'They're not what they used to be, Howard.'

'Nothing ever is, Jane. If anyone is living proof of that, I am.'

What I didn't tell her was that the one thing I felt that we had to have in *Macao* was pointed nipples, and she didn't have them anymore. I don't know how most men feel about pointed nipples, but I feel that pointed nipples are very exciting. And so I explained to Tevlin exactly what I wanted in *Macao* in the way of support and image. Here's the memorandum, the part that deals with Russell. This will show you what I mean by 'attention to details.'

July 25, 1950 from: HOWARD HUGHES to: C.J. TEVLIN
IMPORTANT COMMUNICATION

Herewith are my comments on the Macao tests.

I am sending to you 1 copy of these comments ex these opening explanatory paragraphs and ex the notes on Jane Russell's wardrobe. This copy is for Sam Bischoff. I want him to carry out my instructions fully, and correct all the faults I have observed.

I am also sending you 1 copy of my comments pertaining to Harry Wild's photography.

This copy I want given to Wild directly by you, or by Bischoff, with the request that he correct the faults I have observed.

In addition, I am sending you 2 copies of my notes with respect to Jane Russell's wardrobe.

I want you to give one of these copies to Bischoff and the other to whomever I have instructed on this subject. I believe it is Perry Lieber and I believe he has assigned one particular wardrobe girl for this special job. If that is the case, then the copy of my notes mentioned above should be given to Lieber and he, in turn, should confer with the wardrobe girl so assigned and let her read my notes in his presence and see that she understands them thoroughly.

These notes pertaining to Jane Russell's wardrobe are vitally important. I want Bischoff to have a copy so that he can make the necessary changes in over-all wardrobe, and also that he can follow through and make doubly sure that my requests in connection with Russell's bosom and brassiere will be followed exactly. However, I am sending you the 2nd copy of my notes on Russell's wardrobe with the desire that it reach directly through Lieber to the wardrobe woman in charge of the Jane Russell bosom situation. I want to be very sure that the faults I have observed in this connection will absolutely be corrected.

The 2 copies of my notes pertaining to Russell's wardrobe I want to be returned by Bischoff and Lieber (or whomever I instructed to handle the Russell bosom situation) after they have made sure that my desires are fully and completely carried out. However, at that point, and when the mission is fully accomplished, I want the 2 copies of the Russell wardrobe notes returned to you and thence to me because I do not want these notes lying around in the files anywhere.

In further clarification of the disposition of my notes on Jane Russell's wardrobe, I want Lieber (or whomever I instructed in this matter) to call in the appropriate wardrobe girl to whom this responsibility has been given and make sure that she reads several times and digests thoroughly Russell's bosom situation, but I do not want these notes taken out of Lieber's office by the wardrobe girl as I do not want any possibility of her inadvertently allowing someone else to see them.

1. I want Harry Wild notified that I feel the photography of Jane Russell's nose was disadvantageous to her, and the defects of her nose which I discussed with him were quite apparent in this test.

2. I think Russell's wardrobe as displayed in this test is Christ awful. It is unrevealing, unbecoming, and just generally terrible.

There is one exception, and that is the dress made of metallic cloth. This dress is absolutely terrific and should be used by all means.

However, the fit of the dress around her breasts is not good and gives the impression, God forbid, that her breasts are padded or artificial. They just don't appear to be in natural contour. It looks as though she is wearing a brassiere of some very stiff material which does not take the contour of her breasts. Particularly around the nipple, it looks as though some kind of stiff material underneath the dress is forming an artificial and unnatural contour. I am not recommending that she go without a brassiere, as I know this is a very necessary piece of equipment for Russell. But I thought, if we could find a half-brassiere which will support her breasts upward and still not be noticeable under the dress, or, alternatively, a brassiere made of very thin material, so that the natural contour of her breasts will show through the dress, it will be a great deal more effective.

Please make very sure that you do not misunderstand me. She must wear something to support her breasts upward and all I want is that it be something which will not appear artificial through the dress.

In addition to the brassiere situation, it may be that the dress will have to be retailored around the breasts in order that it will more naturally form to the proper contour.

Now, it would be extremely desirable if the brassiere, or the dress, incorporated some kind of a point at the nipple because I know this does not ever occur naturally in the case of Jane

Russell. Her breasts always appear to be round, or flat, at that point, so something artificial here would be extremely desirable if it could be incorporated without destroying the contour of the rest of her breasts.

My objection to the present setup is that her breasts do not appear realistic in any way. The over-all shape is just not realistic and at the nipple instead of one point, which would be very desirable and natural, there appears to be something under the dress which makes several small projections, almost as if there were a couple of buttons on the brassiere or under the dress at this point.

One realistic point indicating the nipple, if it could be incorporated realistically into the brassiere and show through the dress, would be very fine. The trouble with the setup now is that where her nipple is supposed to be there is more than one projection and it looks very unnatural. Also, the balance of her breasts from the nipple on around to her body appears to be conical and somehow mechanically contrived and not natural. This is difficult to explain, but if you will run the film I think you will see what I mean.

What we really need is a brassiere of very thin material which will form to the natural contour of her breasts and, if possible, which is only a half-brassiere, that is to say which supports the lower half of her breasts only.

This brassiere should hold her breasts upward but should be so thin that it takes the natural shape of her breasts instead of forming it into an unnatural shape. Then, if something could be embodied in the dress itself at the point of the nipple to give it just one realistic point there (which Russell does not have) and if this could be accomplished without putting anything into the dress which will disturb the contour except right at the point of the nipple, this would be an ideal solution.

You understand that all the comment immediately above is with respect to the dress made of metallic cloth. However, this comment is equally applicable to any other dress she wears, and

I would like this instruction followed with respect to all her wardrobe.

Regarding the dresses themselves, the one made of metallic cloth is OK although it is a high-necked dress because it is so startling. However, I want the rest of her wardrobe, wherever possible, to be low-necked (and by that I mean as low as the law allows) so that the customers can get a look at the part of Russell which they pay to see and not covered by cloth, metallic or otherwise.

3. In the test, both Jane Russell and Joyce McKenzie were chewing gum. If this was inadvertent and Russell merely did so because she considered it a wardrobe test, I suppose that is of no consequence. But, if von Sternberg intends to play these girls in the picture chewing gum, I strongly object as I do not see how any woman can be exciting while in the process.

Sincerely, Howard Hughes

20

Howard is sued by his stockholders at RKO, has a fling with Hedy Lamarr, and confesses to a sex experience under the eye of his father.

RKO JUST WASN'T working out as an investment, so I put it up on the block. I'd had it for more than half a dozen years and it was time to cut my losses. In some ways I'd made a mistake – I'd bought the wrong studio. I should have bought Columbia Pictures. I tried to at one point, right after I bought RKO. I don't mean that I would have bailed out of RKO. I would have kept them both. Columbia was just up the street – very convenient.

And then in 1956 I bought about a quarter of a million shares in Twentieth Century Fox. But that was because I got a tip right from Spyros Skouras himself, and he was the head of the studio. He knew the stock was going up, so for me it was a straight plunge – in and out.

We'd done some business together, but more than that – this is usually the case – I had something he wanted. It was a Greek artifact from Turkey, a figurine of a warrior, and I'd been told that it dated from the time of Alexander the Great. It was given to me many years ago by Estelle Sharp, Walter Sharp's widow.

Spyros saw it a few times and he had his heart set on it. Anything Greek, he loved. He wanted this statue but I didn't want to sell it. For me it was something from the old days, from my youth in Houston. But when this thing came up with the Fox stock, Skouras tipped me to a fat profit. And then he said, 'If you want to show your appreciation, Howard, as I'm sure you do, you can sell me that little Greek soldier.'

I said, 'Jesus, take it. If you want it that badly, it's yours.' I don't know what the statue was worth, but it damn sure wasn't worth the two-million-plus I made on the stock. So I was happy to do Spyros a favor.

RKO, however, brought me one thing more than anything else, and that was lawsuits. I've been in court plenty, but I've never experienced anything like the barrage of subpoenas that came at me from my involvement with RKO. I was sued by the stockholders – that was the biggest suit, but it came last – and before that the first major suit came from Jean Simmons and Stewart Granger.

I don't like lawyers, I never have, and I don't trust them. The last man on earth I trust is my own lawyer. I know that probably sounds odd to you, but I can tell you – watch out. You just have to think about how these people can get the goods on you with this 'privileged information' crap. They've done things behind by back, time after time, by misrepresenting my wishes – and worse. They're in business to make money and I don't kid myself about that. I call them vultures.

Didn't Gail Ganley sue you, too?

For half a million dollars. Her father put her up to it. Her father stood there outside of my offices on Romaine Street and was taking photographs of the girl. We had her under contract, but I gave orders that she should not be allowed into Romaine Street. She would break up the place. She threatened mayhem, and she was capable of it.

I gave orders that when she came round to pick up her paycheck she shouldn't be allowed in the building. The money was lowered out of a window on a string to her, in a basket. She had to sign a receipt and that would be attached to the basket and pulled up to the people who were lowering the money. And her father came round to take photographs of that, as if it meant anything, as if it proved that I had cheated her in some way.

Don't you think that was a strange way of paying the girl?

She got paid, didn't she? It was cash was coming down, it wasn't spaghetti. I couldn't send her a check. She didn't believe in checks. She was a redneck country girl. And a lousy lay, I might add. Tore up my back with her fingernails and made a lot of loud noise, to the point where the people at the next bungalow in the Beverly Hills Hotel, some

English businessman and his wife, complained. She never saw shoes before I set her up with a contract. Finally I had to settle with her, but for a small amount of money, around a hundred thousand dollars.

Now don't get me wrong – I don't think $100,000 is a small amount of money. The value of money is directly proportional to the intelligence of the man who has got it. I'll give you my formula. *E=MC squared* – with apologies to Mr. Einstein. *Ego equals Money times Confidence squared.*

But in any case the settlement was a small amount of money compared to what Ganley was asking.

The actress Ann Sheridan sued me too, and we were friends, and had been lovers. I can't even remember what she sued me for, or why, but I liked her, and so I said, 'Ann, withdraw the lawsuit, or your lawyer will take most of what I give you, and I'll give you a private payment of cash. I'll give you every penny you're asking, because I like you.'

To finish up with the lawsuits, the big one came from the RKO stockholders. That was a lulu. They started pretty early on, around 1951, mostly because the stock had gone down to around three dollars a share. Nobody wants to admit they've made an error of investment judgment, and so they often try to pin it on management, which in this case was me.

You can do things right for forty years, you can have the golden touch, but the moment you do one thing wrong, or even if it just *looks* like you've done one thing wrong, they're lying in ambush to get you. The hammers are always cocked. I wasn't even an officer of the company, you understand. I had no official position at RKO. I just ran the studio. I made the major decisions. That's what control means.

I didn't take the suit too seriously. I was so used to being sued that it was like another bowl of Rice Krispies for me – I expected a new lawsuit on my breakfast table every morning or evening, depending on when I ate breakfast.

But eventually it got a little too serious – it got up to about $40 million worth of different lawsuits from different stockholders, and it was also getting annoying. I was used to having my name smudged, but I didn't like to have it colored black-and-blue the way these people were doing. They sued me for mismanagement, driving the studio toward bankruptcy, and also for putting actresses on the studio payroll for my own personal sexual pleasure, which, if you've listened to anything I've been saying to you, you'll know is horseshit.

First of all there was a fuss about Gina Lollabrigida. In 1947 she entered a beauty contest and was chosen Miss Rome. I saw a picture of her in a bikini and, as I think I told you before, I invited her to Hollywood for a screen test. I sent a TWA plane to Rome to fly her over. My people met her at the airport, bundled her in a car, and put her in a hotel room in Malibu. She said she was locked up there, but that was nonsense. She received English lessons, saw a slew of RKO films, and rehearsed for her screen test. Later she claimed that she was badgered by lawyers who wanted her to sign a contract written in English that she couldn't understand. And she said that for six weeks I came by at one o'clock in the morning, hired the hotel orchestra and danced with her for several hours in the hotel's ballroom. Well, why not? I thought I was being romantic. She was great in bed, when she was in the mood.

After six weeks of this she signed a contract and flew back to Italy, where she stayed. I never put her in a picture because she was too temperamental. The stockholders sued me for wasting all that money on her.

Then they said I'd signed Merle Oberon to a fat contract, $125,000 a year for six years, and never used her in a picture. That was true. I'd made a mistake. No mistakes are allowed. And there was a ballerina, Zizi Jeanmaire, a French girl, who I wanted in a picture about ballet. I hired the troupe as well, the Ballet de Paris, and the stockholders thought that was extravagant.

Was there any justification to these lawsuits? What part of all these accusations was accurate? I don't know. Half the time I didn't know where half these people were or what they were doing, and the other half of the time half of them didn't know where I was or what I was doing. I didn't know who was responsible and nobody else did, either. All I knew was that I wanted these stockholders' lawsuits off my back. That was accomplished, in the end, very easily. I simply bought all the stock. If the stockholders sold all their stock and weren't stockholders anymore, there would be no more stockholders' suits. I'd be the only stockholder.

I certainly wasn't going to sue myself.

And they sold it all to you?

Of course they did. If you appeal to people's greed you can't lose. The stock was selling at three dollars a share, and I made a tender offer at six. Noah suggested five, but I said, 'Come on, let's give them six, because then each little guy will say to himself, 'Yippee, I'm doubling my money overnight!' and psychologically that's better than him just thinking he's making seventy percent.' I owned about 25% of the stock then – I think there were about four million shares outstanding, and I had well over a million. It cost me $16 million and it saved me forty million in stockholders' suits, not to mention the legal fees. But the public gobbled it up like pigs at a trough.

You were buying a company on the edge of bankruptcy. I understand that you got rid of the lawsuits, but what else did you have then except a white elephant?

I had a beautiful tax loss, a carryback, a tax credit I could have used any way I wanted to. Toolco and the Aircraft Division were making money hand over fist. I had the physical assets of the studio – the lot, the sound stages, the equipment, a corporate shell. They were valuable. And I had a backlog of movies I could dump into the television market for ten or fifteen million dollars if I wanted to hang on and wait for the right bid.

I had plenty – but you're right, it was a white elephant and I was tired of feeding it gold peanuts. I wanted to get out. So I put her up on the block, one fat old white elephant for sale. Well, pretty soon some syndicate boys came along with an offer. What's commonly known as Cosa Nostra, Mafia, Organized Crime – you name it. Gangsters. Their money is as good as anybody else's. Well, it's as green as anybody else's.

I accepted their offer of roughly seven and a half million dollars. But I couldn't go through with that sale. The newspapers got hold of the background information on these syndicate guys, the spotlight turned on them and things got too hot. They had made a down payment of a million and a half. It was generally thought that they left this behind when they got out. But I'm sure you know nobody leaves behind a million and a half dollars without a good fight, and that was the case here. These guys were not the kind of guys to get out and just shrug their shoulders, and I was not about to expose myself to retaliation and revenge. I had enough enemies in my life without taking on the Mafia.

So I quietly and immediately paid these people back their down payment. And in some ways that was one of the best investments I have ever made. Because later, when I bought into Las Vegas, those men were invaluable. They opened doors for me, they gave me contacts I could never have had any other way.

After the deal with the syndicate boys fell through, I still wanted to get rid of RKO, but I was goddamnned if I was going to take a thumping on it. Things diddled and fiddled off and on for a number of years, during which I was involved with many other things. Toolco was in trouble. TWA was in bigger trouble. I had to spend a tremendous amount of time, energy, and sleepless nights dealing with TWA – I poured the sweat of my life into that airline. I had a big break with Noah Dietrich. But I still had to make time to get that albatross off my neck. That's what RKO turned into – first a white elephant, then an albatross.

Finally Manny Fox put in a bid for the company. I knew he had it on his mind, but one or two things had put him off, and then one day I was driving him to Los Angeles International Airport. He was going off to Europe. Without warning, he made me an offer on the way. He offered me twenty-two million and that was enough so that my foot went down on the brake without even thinking about it, and we nearly went up on the sidewalk with a big screeching of tires. He was all shaken up.

We pulled up in front of a luncheonette and I jumped out of the car and ran inside and called the airport to cancel his reservation. Fox didn't know I'd done it until I came back to the car and said, 'I canceled your reservation on the plane.' He couldn't understand why I did that in such a hurry, and I said, 'Well, you just offered me $22 million. We've got to talk.'

He said, 'But you nearly killed us there! You nearly broke my neck just to save the price of an air ticket!'

'Manny,' I said, 'watch out for the pennies and the dollars look after themselves. The twenty-two million is just cash in the bush, but the $500 air ticket is a bird in the hand.'

But that deal fell through, too. Eventually I sold RKO to General Tire. They wanted to be one of those big conglomerates. More than that, they wanted our film library for television. And more than that, I'm positive that some of those executives up at General Tire wanted to hump the film stars. That, as you realize, is the main reason why all those guys running the conglomerates have bought the various movie studios. They're rarely money-making operations. They may be tax write-offs in some instances, but as far as business goes, they're year-round headaches and crapshoots. But they give these guys access to the starlets. It's a free call-girl service.

I exempt myself from that group. With me it was more a matter of availability. The movie stars just happened to be where I was. And it's not true, not in all cases. I was attracted to a woman physically because – well, it's no secret that I used to have an eye for a well-turned calf. I'm a leg man. Some men like breasts, but that never meant anything to me. Others go for behinds. I myself have always liked legs and wrists. There's something about a nice slim wrist that really appealed to me.

Being out there in Hollywood I inevitably met beautiful women, either in the movies or trying to get into the movies. Every one of them wanted to get me into bed. Not that I was such a beautiful specimen, or a sexual maniac – I was anything but that. But I was Howard Hughes, the famous billionaire eccentric who'd been seen with beautiful women all over. They didn't realize that in most cases that's all there was to it. But there were exceptions, and one of them was considered to be one of the world's great beauties – Hedy Lamarr.

You're always trying to dig up dirt – I'll give you a little dirt. I'd put Hedy up in one of my rented cottages in Bel Air. I had her under contract at the time. The problem was that in my opinion she was a lousy actress. She may have been a decent actress when she started out, but she had become passé. Her acting technique didn't measure up. And I couldn't really find anything for her, so I just kept her in the bungalow.

I used to visit her every now and then, and spend the night with her. Beautiful woman – smooth skin, white like talcum powder. Lovely accent when she spoke English. But she was a very peculiar girl. For example, she was caught for shoplifting a few years ago in Los Angeles. And she stole me blind in that house. By the time I got her out of there the silverware was missing, and a few precious knickknacks – an ivory elephant, for instance, with a broken trunk, a present somebody once gave me. And my favorite golf ball. She didn't only take things of value – she was a kleptomaniac.

She also had some peculiar sexual notions, which I wouldn't go along with. She was A.C.-D.C, and she had a certain perversion which – let's say only a behind man could have gone for it. I refused. I'd just as soon stick my pecker in a wet loaf of bread.

*   *   *

These interviews leave me washed out. Why don't you talk for a while? Tell me about your life, about your pleasures and your mistakes. You must have some good stories to tell – you've led a full life for a comparatively young man.

I've told you a lot, here and there.

Tell me some more. See how it feels.

What's the matter with you tonight?

I'm all in a turmoil inside. Got a cat sewed up in my gut. I'm sorry to be getting at you that way. The point is that I haven't told the whole truth a number of times. I've been thinking about this. I told you on two occasions what I thought you wanted to hear instead of what I knew to be the truth. Maybe it's your fault, because you seem to expect a certain macho attitude from me.

I guess I've also told you a lot of things that I didn't intend to tell you. But it's just so difficult for any man to sit down and tell the whole truth about himself. There's too much that galls. Especially the unpalatable truths that we all have to face. And mine, I assure you, are as unpalatable as anybody else's.

You're referring to something that happened with Hedy Lamarr?

No, just other personal things we've talked about, I felt a sense of shame, because I've been trying to impress you in some way. This is what I meant when I said it was your fault, because you seem to be so interested in sex – you believe that sex motivates people far more than I believe it does. And I don't understand why I should feel I have to impress you, or anybody.

Just the other day I asked myself why I was doing this. Because it's going to be published? It will be published only if I allow it to be.

Nevertheless, it's depressing to recount all this and see your life being swallowed up by a tape recorder. It seems to me, as I've spoken to you, the life I'm talking about could be viewed as an unbroken record of things half accomplished, gestures made for God knows what reason. And I mean particularly on the very personal level, and at this stage of my life that's all that really interests me. Someone very close to me once told me that the unexamined life isn't worth living. I'm examining my life now, and I don't like it – and even an examined life, in this case, sometimes seems as if it was not worth living. I feel it all the time these days, and that's the reason for my being glum, since you asked.

In what ways do you feel you've failed?

The simplest thing I can say is: I haven't measured up to my own image of what a man should be. That image was based on my father. I suppose every man-child grows up with that idea in mind – that he's got to outdo his father, and I was no exception.

You told me you'd licked that father-image when you took the Hercules off the water.

I licked it in the sense of physical challenge. I outdid my father. I'll put it to you this way. I know it's common to every man, but I only live in my own skin. Your problems don't interest me. That's probably a terrible thing to say, but it's true. Maybe most men feel that way, and won't admit it. I do admit it. My own problems are what concern me. If you have insights into them, good for you, but it doesn't help *me*, because it's me who's got to have those insights. And the insights have to be comforting, not unpleasant.

So many times in my life I've had flashes of understanding – flashes that gave me tremendous hope, and made me think, 'Yes! Now I see what I have to do.' It may have been something that someone said to me, or just a moment when I had some communion, some osmosis with whatever is going on around us, whatever spirits are in the air – the Great Spirit the Indians talk about – and those flashes really elevated me.

And then day-to-day existence wipes them out, and a week after you've had that wonderful moment, you stop, and you look, and you say, 'Shit, I'm doing exactly the same things I was doing before. No better.' New Year's resolutions.

I'm on the wheel of life. That phrase, when I read it, made not much sense to me. But I understand it now. I understand something else, even more depressing, which is that people don't change. More hundreds of times than I care to remember, I've said to myself, 'Well, I've learned my lesson, I'll never do *that* again' – only to find myself doing exactly that, whatever it may have been, within hours sometimes. How do you escape from that? What's the answer? Do you know?

I don't know the answer. I have the same problem and so does almost everybody I know. I've done the same thing. I've got myself into a situation where I behaved badly, mostly out of cowardice, because I was afraid to hurt someone, and therefore hurt that person twice as badly by being dishonest. When the mess and shouting were over, I swore to myself I'd never do it again. And yet I did precisely the same thing again.

Well, this may sound callous, but that's encouraging. It means I'm not alone in this way, as I sometimes thought I was.

The problem is that the learning process is such a slow one that we don't have enough time. And it's not even a matter of willingness to change. It's a matter of ability. I think that the mold we're cast in goes back to our genes and from then on we're in the hands of destiny.

I've been in a state of depression, and the reasons for that are still with me. And those reasons were – to be blunt – the one or two lies I told you earlier. One in particular. You remember I told you about how I fixed up the Gotha and flew north and broke down on the beach near Monterrey?

Yes. You and Frank Clarke, when you were shooting Hell's Angels *in 1928.*

I've been thinking about that story and it's made me squirm. Because, although we did fly up north and did come down near Monterrey, and we did spend the night in Tortilla Flat, with those two girls – for my part, nothing happened.

The four of us were there. Frank was a little drunk and I was sober, but Frank had to screw them both. I couldn't do anything with mine and she despised me for it, and I despised myself for it.

Howard, all men have bouts of impotence, and the fact that you didn't tell me the truth about it is common.

Well, I meant this to be an honest revelation of myself – to set the record straight once and for all, so that when I die there will be someone left behind who's recognizably Howard Hughes, not the figment of some hack's imagination.

If that's the only lie you've told, it's not bad at all.

There are more. You asked me once if my father interested himself in my sex education. I don't remember what I told you, but whatever it was, it wasn't the truth. Because that's a sore that's been festering in me all these years. It's nothing terrible, nothing I'm ashamed of. And if I tell it, it may make you understand how crude my father was, and what a sad man. And yet also how he loved me, in his way. Well, maybe love isn't the right word. This goes back a ways...

My father had a little cabin on the coast between Houston and Galveston. Closer to Galveston. He used it as a kind of base of operations for fishing – or that's what he told my mother.

He used to go down often there for weekends, and of course I knew what he was doing down there. Jesse Jones was down there a couple of times too, and not with his wife. I don't care about that – that didn't horrify me in any way. That was just something that my father did, and I considered it his business, not mine. He was a man – I'm really not trying to criticize my father – he was a man with too much energy. He needed too many things. He needed other women, and he never hesitated to go out to get them. He didn't go out of his way to hide it from me, and I guess for the most part I accepted it.

That's what this little cabin was used for. On these fishing weekends he and his cronies would have two or three girls along to spice up the party.

Once they'd run out of booze, and I had to deliver it. This is when I was about fifteen years old. I drove down on a Saturday night. They were playing Red Dog and the girls were sitting around. I intended to turn around and go right back to Houston, but my father said, 'Stick around, Sonny. Bring me luck.'

So I hung around. When the card game ended I wanted to go, but my father insisted that I drink whisky with him. I think that may have put me off drinking for the rest of my life. I had a few drinks. Most of the men disappeared, went off somewhere. This one man, Hastings, had another cabin nearby. The girl my father was with seemed old to me at the time, but I don't suppose she was more than twenty-two.

The girl's name was Colette. It didn't really fit her. She looked like a Jane or a Mary – do you know what I mean?

My father took me off in a corner. He said, 'I've had too much to drink. I'm going to sleep it off. You stay with Colette and take care of her. I think she's tired, so show her the spare bedroom.' He wasn't crude, although the purpose was obvious.

I was certainly willing. I'm not trying to pretend that I protested, or anything. I got very excited by the whole idea.

I was a virgin, and Colette was a very pretty girl. Long, dark hair, lovely body, and green eyes. I went off with her into the bedroom and she threw off her clothes and then undressed me. Now I'm not trying to tell you some heart-throb of a story that I was impotent and couldn't hump her. I could, and it was no problem. I enjoyed it. I was fifteen years old and my brains were in my prick. At least that night they were.

I jumped on that girl and away we went. I know she liked it, and when I finished I was lying there on top of her, getting my breath back. Then I realized there was someone else in the room. I turned around. Daddy was standing in the doorway, leaning against the door with a little sweet smile on his face, proud. He'd come in during the action and I hadn't noticed. He'd been watching, to see how well I did it, and whether I would do it.

I don't know if the point of it makes any sense to you, but for a long time, every time I was in bed with a woman, I was looking around to see if my father was watching me. I felt he was always there in the corner, leaning against the door, looking at me, and judging.

That time in the cabin near Galveston, did he say anything to you?

He was drunk, and he slapped me on the back, and he said something about me being a chip off the old block. He wasn't unpleasant to me, wasn't dirty or anything. He didn't laugh at me, but I can't begin to tell you how ashamed I felt. To think he was there the whole time, watching me! If I have any dominant picture in my mind of my father, it's that moment.

I try so often to recall him in other situations, but he's always standing there in the door, watching me on top of that girl. For a long time in my life it was a very unnerving thing to remember.

Poor Daddy. He had so much going for him. You know, I don't think he was an unhappy man. I'm sure he was happier than I was, I mean happier than I am as a man or happier than I was at his age. I've lived a lot longer than he did, and that's a miracle of sorts.

I don't know why I say, 'Poor Daddy.' I suppose if he could see me now he'd say, 'Poor Sonny.'

You've spent time in Texas, so you know the way they speak. I worked hard for a long time to get rid of that southern accent. But what I wanted to say is this, about his name. I told you they called him Big Howard, which pleased him no end, because the way they talked down there, it came out Big Hard. You see?

Yes, I do see. It never occurred to me.

As an adolescent, it was made quite clear to me. His friends made a point of saying it that way, and leering at me in case I didn't get the point.

It bothered me. And yet, as I said, he wasn't an unhappy man. Far from it. And people loved him. They don't love me.

27

Howard is rebuffed by President Truman, regretfully sacrifices a friend, manipulates TWA stock, and defends Hughes Aircraft against felony charges.

NOW I WANT to talk about TWA and the beginning of my real involvement, because RKO was just a sideshow.

Jack Frye and I were running TWA together and we were doing a good job. By the end of the war TWA stock was selling for more than $70 a share on the New York Stock Exchange. I had bought it in 1939, I think I told you, for $8 a share – then it went up to seventy-five in 1945.

By 1948, however, it dropped to nine dollars a share, which was not just a drop, but a crash. That stock was heading for the pavement and you would have been able to scoop it up with a shovel – or a sponge.

In wartime, planes were flying full. You had to have a priority to get on a commercial airline. Jack Frye made the mistake of assuming that this situation would continue after the war, and he committed my airline to a buying program which nearly broke us.

My mistake was that I had given him carte blanche because I was busy with other projects like RKO. However, I trusted Jack and we got along well. Unlike me, he was a man who knew how to ingratiate himself. He spent a great deal of time in Washington – although our head offices were located in Kansas City – entertaining and making friends with politicians. He was an influential man in Washington by the time the trouble started in 1948. He had a place in Chevy Chase, near Washington – I've never owned a house like that in my life. He had an estate on about eighty acres of parkland.

To explain how Jack operated in TWA's interests, I have to remind you that I had contributed $25,000 to President Truman's campaign when he was running against Dewey. Perhaps that doesn't sound like a substantial sum to you, but Truman wasn't a rich man – sometimes these guys take whatever they can get, and they can be damned grateful for it.

As it turned out, it wasn't enough. Shortly thereafter, TWA had some overseas route applications pending with the CAB, and Juan Trippe was trying to stop them from going through. He had friends in Washington too. So I told Jack Frye to have a talk to Truman about the routes, and push them through. And if he had to, he could remind the President that I'd personally contributed a substantial sum to his campaign, shoved it right in his hand in the Biltmore Hotel in Los Angeles.

Jack got himself invited out on the President's yacht, in the Potomac. Clark Clifford was on board that yacht. He'd been a naval captain during the war and he handled the yacht, made sure Harry Truman didn't fall overboard without a life preserver. Clark told me later he didn't really like Truman. Truman wasn't classy enough for him. Also, Clark Clifford liked shrimps and Truman hated them. Truman said, 'That's rich man's food,' and he wouldn't eat them. Clark worked for me later on – he was my lawyer in Washington, but he was really a lobbyist for TWA. He was paid $50,000 a year to see that things went right for TWA, but I can honestly say – and I'm not being vindictive – he earned about fifty cents of that money.

Anyway, while Jack Frye was with Truman on the Potomac he reminded him about the money. Jack said, 'I was lucky I didn't have to swim home. The President almost kicked me off the yacht.'

That was one time I felt I didn't get my money's worth. Perhaps the mistake I made was I should have given him four hundred thousand, as I did later to Dick Nixon.

I tell you all this background to show you that Jack Frye, although he didn't make any headway with Harry Truman, was a well-placed man. At least he could get on the yacht. He knew everyone who was anyone in Washington, which was an advantage to me at one time, and proved a terrible disadvantage at another.

Then TWA stock just fell over the precipice after the war, crashing down to nine dollars a share. The airline was on the verge of bankruptcy. Lee Tallman, the treasurer of TWA, said they needed $17 million to get it off the ground again. I disagreed. I think they were afraid to deal in large numbers. My estimate was that we needed forty million.

That's when Noah Dietrich came into the picture, and I want to give Noah all the credit that's due him, despite our later differences.

'Go to New York,' I told Noah. 'Go to the largest and most powerful brokerage house – Merrill Lynch, Pierce, Fenner and Smith. Talk to Maury Bent, because he's the man who swings the weight up there.'

Noah talked to Maury Bent, and Maury talked to a man named Parkinson, head of Equitable Life Assurance Company. It turned out, by sheer coincidence, that Equitable Life at the time was keen to make a major investment in one of the airlines. They had liquidity, and they were looking for a growth-oriented situation in a progressive company. TWA filled the bill. Equitable, within three days of Maury Bent's approaching them, came up with a guarantee of $30 million cash on a debenture, with a reserve of ten million.

There was a little hook on it, though, which played an important role later on. None of the money was to go for deficit financing. It all had to be pumped into capital assets.

So we had what we needed. And Jack Frye pissed it away. Most of the money went toward salaries and operating costs, but some of it found its way into deficit financing, which was Jack's mistake. I can't call it a misinterpretation of the terms of the loan. It was dire necessity, and that thirty million vanished like sweat from your forehead in the desert. That year we lost $20 million.

There was no question in my mind as to who was responsible. Jack was down in Washington entertaining politicians and screwing Russian ballet dancers, and he didn't have his finger on the button. Some people, like me, are able to control a large corporation from a distance. Jack couldn't.

There was only one solution: Jack had to go. This pained me deeply, because I knew Jack and I knew his wife, Helen – a lady in every sense of the word. She had married one of the Vanderbilts, and then she married Jack, and I was very fond of her. I think I worried even more about what this would do to Helen than to Jack.

The problem was, Jack didn't want to go. He had fought like a gladiator when the board of directors of TWA tried to get rid of him in 1938. I had bailed him out then. Now I was playing the role of the board of directors, and Jack put up the same kind of fight that he had in 1938 – only tougher. And this is where Jack's contacts in Washington worked against me.

The airlines, even today, are in the grip of the government. The airlines carry the mail, and that mail is awarded on contract. The way you get those contracts is to have friends on Capitol Hill. Jack had those friends. He'd done a lot of favors for them. Not just cash – other things too, like call girls, and even call boys. When the crunch came, and it was Jack Frye against Howard Hughes, Jack Frye had his allies. They didn't want to offend him, because he knew too much. As soon as I realized that he wasn't going to step down meekly, I decided I had to fight this as best I could, and with whatever weapons I had at hand.

The major weapon I had at hand, as usual, was money.

So I went to Mr. Parkinson at Equitable Life and said, 'TWA is in trouble – therefore your forty million is in jeopardy. I'll bail out the operation, personally, through Hughes Tool. And I'll pump another ten million into the airline. I have one condition. I want Jack Frye out.'

Parkinson didn't know whether he could arrange that, but Noah came up with an idea. Because Jack had used some of that money for deficit financing, Equitable could throw the loans into default, which would force Jack out.

Again we faced a problem, which was that until Equitable received the next quarterly financial report from TWA they couldn't legally default the loan.

Time was of the essence, because Jack and I were already at loggerheads. Christ knows what he would have done in the remaining three months of his tenure. I didn't wait until that next report came in. I wouldn't put in my ten million until Jack Frye was out on his ass. This, you understand was to save the airline, because I loved the airline. I believed in the airline. There was nothing personal in it. Jack Frye was a friend.

Parkinson made a tactical mistake, which you can't blame him for. He put the proposition to Jack and tried to talk him into leaving for the good of the airline. Next thing we knew, practically all of Washington was lined up against us. The Tong wars in Chinatown are like snowball fights compared to what happened next. This is one of those inside battles that never gets into the headlines, because it demonstrates the possibility of corruption in the government, which of course, as you know, is nonexistent.

The postmaster-general himself, Bob Hannigan, was a friend of Jack's, and he called Parkinson and TWA.

He didn't mince words. 'If Jack Frye goes, your airmail contracts go too.'

Once again the solution was to fight fire with fire. Parkinson, at my instruction, sat down and wrote letters to every member of the board of directors of TWA. He said to them, in effect, that if they turned down my offer of ten million, which meant that Equitable would fall on its ass with their forty million, he was going to pillory every single one of them, hold them responsible, and run them out of American business.

You understand that all this time the airline was losing a fortune every day under Jack Frye's mismanagement. A few more months and TWA could have gone on the Canadian Stock Exchange, where they trade penny stocks.

Then we got the biggest break we could possibly have had. The pilot's union decided to strike against us. They didn't know what was going on behind the scenes, and neither did the newspapers. We couldn't even meet the payroll of TWA at that time, and then the pilots came along and threatened to strike, which would have shut down the airline.

Naturally I gave it out to the newspapers at the time that I was extremely upset about it – you can't very well tell the newspapers that the strike is sent from heaven. I think if the head of any large American corporation ever told the truth to the newspapers he should be given the Congressional Medal of Honor by the government and thrown into a mental home by the stockholders. It's the First Commandment of business: 'Thou shalt not tell the truth to the public, ever.'

I made the usual statements, that we were willing to arbitrate and we were immediately going to make an effort toward negotiations, and I convinced the media people that the strike was going to cripple us and we wouldn't recover for another five years.

This was unadulterated crap, because behind the scenes we were thanking God and the pilots' union. And we shut down the airline. We furloughed all TWA employees for the entire duration of the strike.

That convinced the Board of Directors of TWA that they had to accept my offer or the whole goddamn airline would go up the creek without a paddle. And they booted Frye out, took my ten million, and enlarged the board of directors with a number of my people on it – and from that time on I was the undisputed boss.

But that was not quite the end of it. Because it bothered me all the time that Jack, who was one of the few friends I've ever had, and poor Helen, should have to bear the brunt of all this. He'd made mistakes, but it just didn't seem fair that a man like that should be thrown out on the streets like a common bum. This is where I made what I consider to be my first major management mistake.

Jack called me, and we sat down in one of my cars on a side street in Kansas City. I said to him, 'Jack, this is killing me, that you're out.' He said, 'Howard, it's killing me too.'

I came up with the idea that Jack would still work for me. Because of his influence in Washington, he was an invaluable man. We didn't have anyone in Washington at the time who was what you might call a lobbyist, and I figured Jack would fill the bill perfectly. But he wanted a salary of $100,000 a year, and a plane at his disposal, and an expense account – which Noah quickly pointed out to me, when you figured that Jack would undoubtedly run the expense account up to the sky, came close to three hundred thousand. I didn't care. Money was not the important thing. The important thing was to do right by Jack. Because Jack had done his best. It wasn't good enough, in fact it was awful, but it was his best.

Then came the moment of truth. With Noah it was always *our* money; probably deep down he figured *his* money. He was older than I was, but I think he believed that one of these days I was going to kill myself in an airplane crash and he would take over and run the whole business, and so he was saving the nickels and dimes. Three hundred thousand dollars a year was a lot of nickel and dimes.

Noah hadn't liked the idea of my hiring Jack to do this job in Washington. He sent me a telegram: 'It's me or Jack Frye. You can't have us both.'

I mulled it over, made my decision, and my decision was my mistake. I chose Noah Dietrich over Jack Frye. I called Jack and said, 'It's no good, Jack, it won't work.' I turned down a good man, a friend, for Noah Dietrich, who was nothing more than a glorified bookkeeper. And that's one of my deepest regrets. I thought at the time I needed Noah more. I made an unsentimental business decision and it was the wrong thing to do. Business decisions are to make money or save money. But why did I need to make more money or save more money? I was rich beyond most people's understanding. Money was already beginning to corrupt me and I was too blind, or too stubborn, or already too corrupted, to see it. Jack Frye never spoke to me after that.

The $10 million that I then put into TWA was one of the best investments I ever made. That gave me total and absolute control of the company. Not just through my owning more than half the stock, but also through the fact that more than half the guys on the board of directors worked for me. There was one little hook in it – which didn't seem important then, but made its impact felt years later – and that was an indication that if for any reason TWA got into financial trouble due to my control, Equitable Life could ask me to appoint them as trustees of my stock.

But the big problem at the time was that my $10 million wasn't a straight loan. There was a clause in the agreement that gave me the right to convert the money into TWA stock at any time I wanted – that is to say, during a specified period, at the current market price. In other words, I had a three-year option, similar to a warrant, to convert $10 million into stock at average closing market price the ten days before my actual conversion. When TWA was selling for nine dollars a share, my ten million would have brought me well over a million shares of the stock. But I didn't buy. Like an idiot, I waited.

Once I was in control, TWA began to improve. We captured more of the passenger and freight traffic, expanded our routes, pioneered in research, and we made money. Well, when that happens, what happens to your stock? It goes up. By the time it got to fifteen dollars a share, if I wanted to convert my loan then, I wouldn't have gotten more than six or seven hundred thousand shares of stock. I suddenly found myself caught in a bind. The better the airline did and the more money we made, the more intelligence I applied to improving it, the less my loan was worth in terms of stock and a percentage of ownership. Every time I got them a new route, I was cutting my own throat – not financially, but managerially, which to me amounted to the same thing. My mistake was that I didn't cover immediately when the stock was at nine dollars.

I want to tell the truth about things even if they put me in a bad light, because truth and not self-glorification is my goal. There I was, in a bind. The stock was moving up on the New York Stock Exchange. I hadn't looked at the financial pages since 1929, but now every day I grabbed the paper – TWA plus an eighth, TWA plus a half, TWA up a quarter, and every eighth of a point meant that I was losing potential control of my airline. I got gloomier and gloomier about the whole thing, and nobody could understand why.

I conferred with one of my top financial wizards about it and we came up with a time-honored solution – I suppose you can say, reminiscent of Jay Gould and J.P. Morgan. Jesse Livermore would have been proud of it. Jesse Livermore was the king of the Wall Street pirates – they would hire Jesse to drive the price of a stock down so they could buy it cheap, then Jesse would turn around and manipulate the price of the stock up and they would sell it dear.

That's precisely what was under consideration in 1948. We thought we might open some brokerage accounts in the East, in New York,

Washington and Philadelphia – in other names, of course – and then begin to sell the stock short. That is, sell what we had at below the market price and sell other shares short, the purpose being to drive the price down so that I could convert my ten million at a reasonable price.

The price of the stock had gone to twenty-three by then. I finally realized that if we followed this procedure and got the stock down a few points, for every point we got that stock down, I would have had to sell shares, and suddenly I realized I would be robbing Peter to pay Paul. And I was Peter and I was Paul. So I got together with my financial wizard who put me in this predicament, and we came up with another plan, based on some precedents that had recently been set by some other company that offered a new issue, a secondary issue of stock, and had given the rights to certain stockholders to buy that stock at a few dollars under the market price. What I wanted then was to convert my loan at fifteen dollars a share.

I talked to Maury Bent about it. Maury said he thought it might work, except that my conversion rights would be so enormous that the stock issue might have a hard time finding an underwriter, and he tried to press me into converting right then and there.

We were eighteen and a quarter at that time. It had dropped that far. Of course I had an ace up my sleeve – actually, a full house. And that was that those guys on the board, the board of directors of TWA, were Toolco people on my payroll. We'd done just about all the cute maneuvering we could. That had served its purpose, but in the end it came down to simple old-fashioned muscle.

A few telephone calls were placed. Maury went to the board of directors and the proposition was put before them. A little lobbying took place and, lo and behold, it came time to vote and they said, 'Howard Hughes is our benefactor! Without Howard Hughes we'd have no airline! We're going to give this man the right to convert his $10 million, that saved our necks, at ten dollars a share.'

You mean you managed to get it for what you could have got it originally?

No, I could have gotten it originally for nine and a half. I had to pay ten. But I'm not complaining. And I didn't waste any time, I converted and I got over a million shares, because of course there was interest on the loan. I got an extra 40,000 shares in interest. Since I sold that stock eventually – which is another story – at over $80 a share, those million shares had cost me ten million and I made a profit of seventy-three million. That's not what I call chopped chicken liver.

*   *   *

In many ways 1948 was a critical year. Apart from that Jack Frye business, Hughes Aircraft got into serious difficulties. Several of my employees, high-ranking people, were indicted on fraud counts by the United States government. One of them was Glen Odekirk, who was assistant then to the president of Toolco, about as high as I could get him up there, and he made a damned fool of himself in this operation.

At the end of the war there were a lot of surplus airplanes around, and Hughes Aircraft wasn't doing much of anything at the time except working on the Hercules. Other than that they were buying scrap planes and converting them into luxury craft for executives. Then someone at the Aircraft Division got the bright idea of using veterans' priorities to buy these planes cheap and make himself a nice pile on the side. Veterans could buy surplus C-47s for next to nothing, the idea being to get them started in small businesses. Government paternalism, which almost always backfires because of the nature of the beast – corrupt.

This doesn't reflect credit on me, and it reflects even less credit as the story goes on. But I promised to show you Howard Hughes, warts and all.

This all started in Honolulu, where we'd picked up six planes for $100,000 through two veterans, and paid them $2,000 each for their trouble. The six C-47s were worth at least half a million dollars. The story leaked, and our men were indicted.

I got on the pipe to Noah and said, 'This won't do.' I arranged to meet him somewhere north of San Diego.

Did you have an office down there?

My office, then as now, is in my hat. I was only in Romaine Street twice in my life – once to check the wiring system on the alarm buzzers, and the other – I don't even remember why I went the second time. Oh, yes, wait, I do. I was driving around talking to Spyros Skouras about some business deal and we both suddenly had to take a leak. I realized we were only a few blocks from Romaine, so I said, 'Come on, Spyros, I haven't visited my office for ten years. Let's go there and take a leak' – which we did.

Anyway, I had one of my Chevies parked in Solana Beach, north of La Jolla, and I met Noah there, and I told him I wanted that indictment dismissed. I didn't want Hughes Aircraft's name blackened by this kind of thing. This applied to me also. Because I had specifically told my people *not* to use veterans' priorities, and once I gave an order I figured that was that. Noah said it would cost plenty of money to get the case dismissed before it came to trial, and we couldn't possibly get Odekirk and the others off the hook, since the veteran in Honolulu had blown the whistle loud and clear.

But I said to him, 'I don't give a damn what it costs, I want my company cleared. Try to save our people too, but I'm sure as hell not going to have the Hughes name tarred and feathered with this kind of thing.'

We worked it out and figured the only way to do it, as usual, was go right to the top. That's the way to solve a major problem.

I sent Noah to Washington and I told him he had half a million dollars from the political fund at his disposal. I didn't care how it was used, but I wanted Hughes Aircraft cleared. Noah spoke to someone at Democratic Party headquarters and, being Noah, he didn't offer the half a million. He wanted to get it as cheaply as he could, so he told them he'd give them $100,000 in the form of campaign contributions, $5,000 each to any twenty men they picked.

But there was some backtalk from the Justice Department. The Justice Department had a hot case and naturally they didn't want to drop it. Someone had to lean on them.

The man from the Democratic Party headquarters said, 'Listen here, my friend, you're running for public office' – the Justice Department official he was talking to had announced his candidacy for a high post.

'If you want to be elected, if you want the Democratic Party to back you, you better play ball.'

He played ball, and the company name was dropped from the case. And when it finally came to trial, two of the Toolco employees had to plead *nolo contendere* – no contest. They were fined a few thousand dollars each, and that was that.

I was personally exonerated by the United States Attorney. I wasn't accused, but I wanted a more positive affirmation. The United States Attorney got up in court and said that Howard Hughes had had no knowledge of this and had nothing to do with the fraud. My hands were clean.

22

*Howard offers his empire for sale at a Greek gin rummy club,
saves the CEO of Lockheed from shoplifting charges, founds a medical
institute, and makes a killing in California real estate.*

THE NEXT ITEM on the agenda – as they like to say in the board of directors' meetings that I never attend – is Hughes Aircraft.

In some ways this was my most successful business venture. Toolco was the backbone of my fortune, but that was my father's doing, not mine. I made it into a multimillion dollar company, but he founded it. On the other hand, Hughes Aircraft was my baby.

I originally started it way back in 1934, but it was just a workshop. I needed some space to develop the planes I used for my assaults on the various records, and then later of course we worked on the Hercules there, and we also did these conversion jobs on the surplus planes which got me into that legal mess I told you about. And during the war we made feeder chutes for ammunition.

What really got us off the ground was the electronics revolution. I saw this coming, and I backed up my hunch with a big stack of chips. I hired the best scientific talent around, built up a team of topflight R & D men, brought in a couple of retired generals into the top management spots – Ira Eaker and Harold George. They weren't particularly knowledgeable in research and development, but they had knowhow in administration, and they knew the right people, which was even more important.

Ninety-five percent of our business at Hughes Aircraft was done with the Air Force, and both my top men, Eaker and George, were ex-Air Force generals. I could never get along with Eaker personally, but he was a good administrator. What I couldn't stand about him was that he was a warmonger. You know I'm anything but a hawk, and this guy Ira Eaker was a screaming eagle. He would have torn a poor hawk to shreds, would have made it look like a sick pigeon.

We had a few discussions about politics and the Korean War, and after that I said, 'Look, let's just talk business or we'll have a terrible argument.'

Years later this guy wrote a preface to a book about the bombing of Dresden during the Second World War. More civilians were killed in Dresden than when we dropped the atomic bombs on Hiroshima and Nagasaki – it was a totally defenseless city with no war industry, just civilians – and Eaker said yes, it was terrible and all that, but it wasn't *so* terrible, it was justifiable if you remembered that Germans were using the V-1s and they'd started the war in the first place. If he had written this piece when he was working for me at Hughes Aircraft, I would have fired him on the spot.

As for Harold George, the only thing I held against him was that he spread stories about me that I was a pennypincher, that I borrowed dimes from him for telephone calls and never paid him back. Here's a guy who was making a hundred grand a year and he begrudged me a few dimes. He used to give me an accounting every month or two of the dimes I'd borrowed from him. He loved to twist it around and say I was a cheapskate. Who was the cheapskate, him or me? I borrowed the dimes and he complained that I hadn't paid them back to him. So who was the cheapskate?

But they were generals, so they knew who to talk to when contract time came round. Our R & D team was headed by Dr. Ramo and Dean Woolridge, top-flight scientists, and they really produced. Hughes Aircraft made fire control systems for the F-86 and F-94 jets, and then around 1950 we came up with a sophisticated system which the Air Force accepted for the F-102 supersonic interceptor. We beat out General Electric for that one. We built a new plant in Tucson to make the Falcon air-to-air guided missile. And we got deeply into solid state physics. We make the finest germanium diodes in the United States. By 1952 we had over half a billion dollars in contracts. We had about 90% of the Air Force business in all those fields.

Ramo and Woolridge got up an expansion plan, felt they needed more laboratory space, more men to handle the flood of stuff that was coming in from the Air Force. We were in the Korean War at the time. I saw the need for this expansion, but I wanted a new plant to be built in the Las Vegas area, where I was starting to spend a lot more time, and where I could be in closer touch with it. I felt Las Vegas was a coming section of the United States, an area wide open for development, whereas Culver City was already pretty well sealed off.

Ramo and Woolridge balked. They said it would be destructive to expand the R & D section into Las Vegas, separated from the main facilities. And they were backed up by the administration, by Eaker and George. They argued with me like they were the Longshoreman's Union, only they were management.

There were other problems, too, but they were largely Noah's doing. Hughes Aircraft was more than he could cope with. It was making lots of money, far more than Toolco in its palmy days.

You mean that in 1952 Toolco wasn't the backbone of your business empire?

This was part of the trouble. Toolco had fallen into second slot. Noah felt he had to take control in California – he felt he was in second place, which was true, and he hated it. And he precipitated the showdown. One year, for example, he wouldn't pay any bonuses to the executives, and the company at the time was making a small fortune. He called it an economy drive.

I held off making any decisions. There's a lot of talk about the ability to make snap decisions, but it's the ability to *not* make decisions which can be even more important, on my level. I found that often if you just sit quiet, the problems disappear all by themselves. What's vital today, if you keep postponing it, eventually becomes irrelevant.

At the time – with all that trouble brewing – I decided I'd better find out just how much I owned in Hughes Aircraft: how much it was worth. This was just in case I decided to bail out completely, in case I decided it was another albatross like RKO.

I don't know if you're aware of this, but there's no one you can call in and ask, 'How much is my company worth?' You can, but they'll lie to you, tell you what they think you want to hear. If you want to find out how much something is worth, you've got to find out how much someone is willing to pay for it.

For that reason, I had put Toolco on the block back in 1948. I went to Fred Brandi at Dillon Read, the New York brokerage house. Dillon Read was just starting to make inquiries when it leaked from someone and got into the papers. The people at Toolco were very upset –they wanted to know if their jobs were still safe. Apparently they liked working for me, and I was upset and embarrassed. I had to make all sorts of announcements that no one would be pushed aside if and when the new management took over.

We never could agree on a price. The Dillon Read group was offering around a hundred fifty million. It was supposed to be the largest sale of a company since the Dodge widows sold out to Chrysler. But, as I said, I had no intention of selling. I was just trying to find out what the company was worth – I think, in the end, they would have come up with about two hundred and twenty five million.

So again, in 1952, on the pretext that I was thinking of selling Hughes Aircraft, I opened up negotiations with Westinghouse, and General Electric, and Bob Gross at Lockheed.

Poor Bob, I drove him all over the desert around Las Vegas, night after night and day after day. I was used to the heat and he wasn't. I almost always keep the windows of the car shut tight, and I stuff any cracks with Kleenex. I did that with Bob Gross in the Nevada desert. It didn't bother me at all but he sweated like a pig, while we talked figures. We started somewhere around $35 million and I goosed him along night after night and got him to, oh, around fifty – and this was just for leasing Hughes Aircraft. I still would own the property.

Bob finally realized that I had no intention of selling, and he said, 'Thanks for the midnight view of the cactus, Howard, but I've got work to do.'

But he couldn't really be angry at me, because during these bargaining sessions I saved him from a terribly embarrassing incident.

The first night, in Las Vegas, we'd stopped at a little drugstore for coffee. Bob had coffee and I had a glass of milk, and when we left, Bob stopped at the counter to pay the bill. I was looking at a magazine rack at the time, and I remember, just as he paid, as the woman took his money and turned away to the cash register, I saw something – well, I couldn't believe my eyes. I saw Bob Gross – he was president of Lockheed Corporation, one of America's biggest corporations – reach out and stick a candy bar in his pocket. He stole it.

When we got out outside I couldn't contain myself. I said, 'For God's sake, Bob, what in the world are you doing stealing that candy bar?'

He turned red for a minute. Then he laughed and said, 'Well, every once in a while, it's a kick. It's more fun than paying for it. You ought to try it some time, Howard.'

I was totally flabbergasted. He told me he did this, not every day by any means, but whenever the impulse moved him. Never anything of value, you understand, not diamond watches or sable coats – a candy bar, that's all.

But this is just background. A few nights later, Bob and I gave up negotiating, and at about nine o'clock in the morning we were driving back to Los Angeles. We passed through one of these little crossroads towns and I spotted a 7-11. And I felt a yen for some Mallomars and a container of milk. You know, Mallomars are those puffy marshmallow chocolate cookie. Unfortunately it's getting harder and harder to find Mallomars. The damn fools at Nabisco had a winner and they went to sleep on it. I've had men go out and scour the stores to find me Mallomars, and they had to go to half a dozen stores before they found them. It's the Cadillac of cookies – at least for me.

I stopped the car. This was in the midst of a lot of publicity about me and TWA, and I didn't want to go in, so I asked Bob if he'd do me a favor and go in and buy me a package of Mallomars. 'If you can't get Mallomars,' I said, 'I'll take plain butter cookies or graham crackers. And a container of milk.' Bob said he'd be glad to do it.

So he went in, and I waited, and I waited, and no Bob. I thought, 'What the hell's going on ?' Finally, ten minutes later, I got out of the car and went into the 7-11. Inside, one man had Bob by the elbow, and Bob was talking hard, talking for his life, it looked like, to another man.

He'd stuck those damn Mallomars inside his windbreaker and zipped it up. That's not a candy bar – a package of Mallomars is bulky. And the damn fool had got caught.

Did he try to steal the milk too?

No, he'd paid for the milk. That must have been against his principles, to steal milk.

I stood there. What could I do? Go up there and say, 'I'm Howard Hughes and you must let this man go. He's the president of Lockheed Corporation.' I don't know whether Bob had identified himself as Robert Gross, president of Lockheed, and I didn't want to embarrass him, and I didn't want to be hailed into court as an accessory to a Mallomar theft in a supermarket. That would have made page one everywhere.

How far had he gotten with the Mallomars?

They grabbed him on the outside, near the door. They always wait, I understand, until you're past the checkout, otherwise you can sue them for false arrest.

I soon realized that Bob didn't want to identify himself as one of the leading corporate executives in the United States. He wanted to pay these people off get out of there as quickly as possible. That's what he was trying to do when I walked into the supermarket. But he didn't have enough cash with him. He had maybe ten or fifteen dollars, and that wasn't enough to get these hick-town people off his neck.

Didn't he have a checkbook?

Of course he did, in the car, in his briefcase, but how could he give them a check and sign it Robert Gross? That would have allowed them to blackmail him for the rest of his days. He needed more cash. You don't buy yourself out of a situation like that with ten dollars.

They had posted a man at the door, some beefy young guy in a T-shirt, to see that Bob didn't scoot out. Bob sidled up to me and told me what had happened and that he had to have something substantial to pay these people off. 'Howard, I've got to have a hundred dollars.'

I don't carry that kind of cash on my person, of course, but I did in the lining of my hat. I had my hat on the back seat of the car. They let me go – they had nothing against me except that I was the friend of the thief, and I went out to the car, tore open the lining of my hat, found a hundred-dollar bill and brought it back in.

I thought you said that you only carried thousands and singles in your hat.

I was lucky this time, or Bob was lucky. I had a few hundreds. If I'd only had thousands it would have cost Bob a thousand dollars, because I'm sure they wouldn't have made change for him. They probably would have had him arrested for passing counterfeit money. I gave Bob the hundred-dollar bill and he gave it to the store manager, and they examined the bill a long time and finally said, 'Okay,' and let him go.

We went outside together. He was red in the face and sweating. He said, 'Here's your damn Mallomars. Next time go in and buy them yourself.'

'I didn't tell you to steal them, you goddamn idiot.' I made him a long speech: 'You ought to know that crime doesn't pay. You should be grateful I had the money to bail you out of this. I could just as easily have turned tail and run and let you go to jail. How would it look if I was associated with a shoplifter? It would ruin my reputation.'

And that's true: I doubt very much if Equitable Life would have loaned me $40 million if I'd been involved in a shoplifting scandal, even for a package of Mallomars. But of course, mostly I was just kidding Bob, and he knew it. On the way to Los Angeles we laughed about it, although it was kind of a strained laugh on his part. I often wondered afterwards if he went on with his candy stealing, or if that was the high point of his criminal career.

Anyway, the following year, 1953, I became involved in another selling attempt, which was chiefly the result of a misunderstanding between me and Spyros Skouras. I'd been talking to him in a Greek gin rummy club that he frequented, and I said I was interested in expanding my medical institute, and I might sell out everything in order to do it. What I meant was that I might transfer all my assets to the medical institute once it got going, but he misunderstood and thought I wanted to sell everything I owned and become a philanthropist. Spyros didn't speak English perfectly and I couldn't understand half of what he said when he was talking fast, and maybe I didn't hear some of it and just nodded – you know how that can happen. You just nod and say, 'Yeah, yeah, sure.' Your mind is somewhere else.

Next thing I knew, Spyros called me and said, 'William Zeckendorf, the urban developer and the owner of the Chrysler Building in New York, and Laurance Rockefeller, the family's venture capitalist, want to come out and visit you. They're interested.'

'Interested in what?'

'Buying you out. You told me you wanted to sell, didn't you?'

'Oh, sure,' I said. 'Send them out.'

Now, I thought, I can get a free price on the whole thing – Toolco, the aircraft division, RKO, TWA. I even threw in the brewery. Spyros arranged a meeting. I gave them the full treatment. I didn't want anyone to know that I was meeting with William Zeckendorf and Laurance Rockefeller, because that would have provoked all sorts of rumors, so I told Zeckendorf he was to meet my people at such-and-such a street corner and then transfer to another car. We talked there for a while. Then I thought they might like a plane ride. I flew them down to Las Vegas in my B-19 bomber, which I'd outfitted with a bed and big easy chairs, a bar, even a partners' desk.

Sometimes I use this so-called eccentricity of mine to my advantage in business dealings. If you move people around enough, make a cloak-and-dagger operation out of it, that throws them off balance. I was also concerned that we were being spied on in Los Angeles, and therefore Vegas would be safer. So I told them to meet me at Santa Monica Airport at one o'clock in the morning on a runway, and wear dark clothes. White shirts are very conspicuous at night.

Was there a deal in the works by the time you arrived in Las Vegas?

There was an offer. They were serious, except that Zeckendorf wanted to make part of the payment with California real estate, and I already had plenty of that. They started out around a billion and change, and eventually I worked that up to around a billion and a half.

I said, 'I'll think about it.' I wanted to see if they'd jack it up to $1.8 billion which is roughly what I figured it was worth – what I *hoped* it was worth. But one and a half wasn't bad, either. It got bogged down somewhere up around there. They went back to New York, and finally I told the switchboard at 7000 Romaine that if Zeckendorf called, I couldn't be found. I think it was around then that I went to Cuba to see Ernest Hemingway.

Zeckendorf yapped to the newspapers – he was insulting, said it was unpardonable of me, and I was a man without a conscience for having changed my mind that way. That was a baldfaced lie, because I'd never changed my mind – my mind was made up from the beginning that I had no intention whatever of selling. As I said, it all sprang from a misunderstanding on the part of Spyros Skouras, because he was a Greek and couldn't speak English very well and I got bored listening to him and just nodded and said, 'Yeah, sure.' Zeckendorf must have known about the Dillon Read deal falling through in 1948. He wouldn't meet my price, and I certainly didn't feel sorry for him. It was me who paid the hotel bills in Las Vegas.

After Zeckendorf and Rockefeller had made their offer, I realized that I owned an exceedingly valuable property, and I certainly wasn't going to sell it, despite the fact that this would have pleased my managers, who didn't like the Hughes method of doing business. They wanted a more conventional establishment. They didn't realize it was the unconventionality of my approach that made Hughes Aircraft possible. I had given these men free rein, they had put together a highly productive team, and now they were going to smash it all up.

Things really came to a head when Noah Dietrich found that the inventory accounts were overcredited with several million dollars worth of parts and we were unintentionally defrauding the government by overcharging them. Profits were supposed to be limited to 11% of our cost, and if our cost figures were way out of line, then we were making more money than we were entitled to – it was a matter of only five million bucks.

Eventually we paid up, and the government got their money. And eventually I managed to piece together the true story – because, as it turned out, that $5 million repayment to the Air Force was only the first installment. That was a repayment on one contract only.

The full amount of the repayments eventually totalled $43 million, and Noah Dietrich called in a team of auditors from Haskins-Sells. They got to the heart of the trouble. A couple of the top people on the managerial end got bonuses based on the profits of the company, so that if Hughes Aircraft could make an additional $43 million they were in line for bonuses of close to two hundred thousand each.

I knew nothing. I was in Cuba at the time. It all split apart when Noah reached over the generals' heads and fired the comptroller, Then George quit; he was the administrative head. Tex Thornton quit. Woolridge left, and Simon Ramo, and a whole flock of their top men with them, and it looked as though the company was coming apart at the seams.

The Secretary of the Air Force, Harold Talbott, asked for an appointment with me. I had to grant it, and we met in my bungalow at the Beverly Hills Hotel. Talbott had a bad temper and he gave me the rough side of his tongue. Of course each time he said something I didn't like, I pretended I didn't hear him. He threatened to put me out of business. The Air Force would cancel all our contracts, every goddamn one of them.

I kept saying,'What? What? I can't hear you,' because I figured that after a while he'd cool down.

But he didn't. The best I could get from him was ninety days to straighten out the mess. Talbott insisted that at the end of that time I'd either have to sell to Lockheed or I'd have to accept a new management appointed by the Air Force. I finally accepted the new manager. They put in William Jordan, who had been president of Curtis-Wright. They had to make sure these fire-control and other devices kept coming off the assembly line – we were in the Korean War. It was tapering off, but they knew they would have to find another war to take its place, and they were already casting their eyes on Vietnam. Without a war every now and then, those goons are out of business.

They had me so scared they were going to take the business away from me that Tom Slack, one of my lawyers, came to me one day with an idea. He said, 'Howard, you want to make a safe haven for the aircraft company where the government can't get its hands on it.' It was his idea that we create the Howard Hughes Medical Institute and turn Hughes Aircraft over to it. I thought at the outset to start this up in Texas, in Houston, where that big medical complex existed already, and for a while that was under discussion. But it leaked to the papers, and everybody was talking about how Howard Hughes was going to give $125 million to the Texas Medical Complex. They were drooling at the mouth in Houston. But by that time I was fed up with Texas, and I felt that the last place I would put my money would be with those people who threw me out of the state.

I may be exaggerating. They didn't throw me out of the state. But they didn't want me back. They wanted the jobs I could provide. But they didn't want me personally. I was too funny a duck to paddle around in Texas among those beautiful Texas swans. I was the ugly duckling, even though I laid the golden eggs. And so my lawyers and I organized the Hughes Medical Institute in Florida and put the Hughes Aircraft company under its wing.

This had one drawback, which didn't turn up until later. Noah explained that if I needed money at some time in the future, I couldn't use the aircraft company assets for collateral or put them up for sale, because it was now a public trust. But I didn't think a situation like that would come along, and besides, I had plenty of money stashed away by then in Switzerland and similar places, for a rainy day. But from that point on I stayed out of the aircraft company's affairs. All my ideas get funneled into the company through Toolco and various people. We've got an order backlog of close to a billion dollars and this year, as I understand it, we'll sell another billion dollars worth of equipment. It's the finest company of its kind in the United States. We just developed something called the Lasermatic. That's a laser beam, controlled by a computer – it cuts cloth. Sold them to Genesco, and that's going to revolutionize the garment industry.

What about the Medical Institute? The Patman report accused it of being a tax dodge.

Don't parrot back that garbage to me. The Institute's done some fine things. They've sent research scientists to Harvard, Yale, Johns Hopkins, everywhere, and I've never gotten any personal benefit out of it in the way of treatment. I've never even been there. Never laid eyes on the place. They never even gave me an aspirin.

Then as far as you're concerned it's not a tax dodge.

It's every man's privilege to avoid paying taxes. That's the European attitude and that's the one I subscribe to. I don't want to discuss it anymore.

Early on, when you were talking about Zeckendorf, you mentioned that you had real estate in California. Does it amount to anything?

It amounts to quite a lot – in value, at least. And it also at that time amounted to a headache. In the middle fifties, Los Angeles wanted to build the Playa del Rey Marina, and they needed land. I had twelve hundred acres adjoining the site – the last big chunk of land in the Los Angeles metropolitan area. I had bought it many years before. I own hundreds of thousands of acres of land, in all parts of the United States, that I bought at various times. I don't know where half of it is.

I'd bought this land in California for about $1,500 an acre. That's cheap. And by 1955 it had gone up in value considerably, but I thought it was going to go up still further and I didn't want to sell it.

I told Noah, 'Don't sell any of it to those marina people. I'm not interested.'

'But suppose they offer a good price? How much would you consider selling for?'

'Not for less than fifty thousand an acre,' I said.

I hadn't kept in close contact with land values. I only named that price because I didn't want to sell the land. It was a ridiculous price. But they pulled a fast one on me. The city filed condemnation proceedings against me in order to force me to sell them the land they needed for the marina. It's the same as if you have a house in the middle of a proposed highway route; they file condemnation proceedings and that's it. You take what they give you, and you get out. I was in the same position.

Meanwhile I'd gone out of sight, and my lawyers were holding up the proceedings by employing the usual delaying tactics. It would have taken a good long time before anything would have happened with the condemnation procedure, but in the meantime Noah continued some quiet negotiations.

Finally he came to me and said, 'Howard, I had to sell them an acre and a half, just to keep them off your back a while.'

'For Christ's sake,' I squawked, 'I told you I didn't want to sell any of that land for less than $50,000 an acre. How much did you get?'

'I got $62,000 an acre,' Noah said.

That took the wind right out of my sails. 'All right, an acre and a half. But don't sell them any more. Got to pay taxes on all that profit.'

However, once the thing got going, it was like a snowball rolling downhill, and I sold them about 120 more acres. I realized after a while I must have taken a screwing when they bought the first lot for sixty-two thousand. I operate under the principle that if a man accepts my offer I must have offered him too much, and if a man agrees to pay what I ask him for something, then I've set the price too low. So I wound up asking $77,000 an acre. 'Take it or leave it,' I said.

They took it. That's not bad, is it?

23

*Howard receives a black eye from a football star, evades
marriage with Lana Turner, and reveals a dark secret from his
love affair with Billie Dove.*

MY PRIVATE LIFE during those years was a swamp of complications.
I was swimming as best you can when you're in a swamp – from
woman to woman, getting involved and then getting uninvolved, and
it sapped a good deal of my energies. There's no satisfaction in that
way of life, and certainly no salvation.

I had an affair at that time with Terry Moore, the movie star. It started
in 1950 and it lasted quite a while. It was interrupted when she married
Glenn Davis. He was the West Point football star, the Mr. Outside of the
combination that won all those games for Army. Mr. Inside was Doc
Blanchard. Terry wasn't really interested in Davis in spite of the fact that
they got married. It was one of those harebrained things that happen,
particularly in Hollywood. And later, when she came back to Los Angeles,
we took up where we left off. That is, back in the sack, making whoopee.

Things worked between me and Terry. She had a straightforwardness
which I appreciate. The problem was her husband, Glenn Davis. After
she left him and came back to me, he arrived ranting at my bungalow
in Malibu. When we opened the door he walked up to me and belted
me on my ass without another word. I'm tall, but I was skinny – I wasn't
a football player – and he knocked me flat on my back. I walked around
with a big black eye for days afterward.

He accused me of breaking up his marriage, which was a lot of
horseshit, because the marriage was broken up long before that night.
I didn't bring Terry at gunpoint, she came to my bed all willing. So this
obviously wasn't my doing.

What other women did you know in those years?

There was Gene Tierney, the actress, a beautiful woman – that was another time I got hit. I met her at a party given by William Randolph Hearst; he was always giving big parties up at San Simeon and throwing women at me. Gene was married to Oleg Cassini, the designer, and one afternoon when I brought her home from a walk on the beach Cassini was hiding in the garage waiting for us. He leaped out and clipped me. I ran away. The next time I saw him was at a Hollywood party and he threatened to brain me with a cut-glass decanter. I had to hide in an upstairs bedroom and call for help. Ginger Rogers was another one, although I can't remember who she was married to. At least he never jumped out at me. I stopped going to parties after the Cassini assault. It was too dangerous.

Did you get a kick out of involvement with married women?

The truth is, I didn't hunt for them, they hunted *me,* and I guess during that period I enjoyed the company of attractive and witty women and I didn't duck their attentions. Obviously none of them was in what I would call a good marriage. And in one sense it was safer than an involvement with a single woman who was looking for a husband – although as I've mentioned, there were physical risks.

Before Terry and Gene and Ginger, and after, I was involved with Lana Turner. A story went the rounds that Lana had her sheets embroidered H.H. because she thought I was going to marry her. I was supposed to have said, 'Well, go marry Huntington Hartford.' But that wasn't true. I would never be so crude. I just told her, 'In a pinch, you can always sell them to Huntington Hartford.'

There were plenty of women who were under the impression that I wanted to marry them, although I never said so or even hinted. For a while I was taking out some of these society girls, and they'd announce to the papers every other week that wedding bells were going to ring in the spring. That's what they would say – really – that's how their minds worked. 'Wedding bells may ring in the spring for Howard and me.' I'm talking about Gloria Baker and Tim Lansing and Meg Lindsay, and a few others. There was nothing really happening there. I suppose I did see Gloria Baker somewhat more than the others. I flew her once from New York to Los Angeles, and by the time that flight was over and she'd chewed my ear for fifteen hours I thought, God, I'd rather hear wedding bells in the spring with a female baboon than this girl's voice every day of my life, and I ended the relationship right there at the airport.

Usually I let these girls think whatever they wanted to think. I never put anything in writing. My father once told me: 'Do right, and fear no man. Don't write, and fear no woman.' That was wise advice and I followed it, especially the last part. You know, they'd say, 'Wouldn't it be wonderful, Howard, if we were married?'

And I would say, 'Uh, uh, uh... yes, maybe... who knows?' And if they ever got more serious than that I'd complain of an earache.

With Tim Lansing once, I had trouble with her parents. I had met her in Palm Springs and her parents came down to get her out. I think it was all a plot on her part to get me to marry her. They said she'd told them I'd told her I was going to marry her, and we'd even set a date.

I said, 'I don't remember it. You know I'm deaf. I obviously misunderstood.'

They didn't pressure me any further. I don't think they thought I was such a great catch. They thought I was a little crazy. That's another reason why they'd come down to rescue their daughter.

What did it mean to you to have such a succession of quick affairs, on and off, as you put it?

My behavior was based on one of those fallacies that are common to most men's lives. When you're young, assuming you're not a fairy, you think that women are essential to your life. You waste an awful lot of time wooing them or putting the make on them. This is a hangover from adolescence, I suppose, when you're yearning for a girl and you can't get one because you don't know how. My adolescence, and yours too, probably – although maybe not the adolescence of the kids today.

But I went through that as a very young man, and then as a grown man, up to thirty-five or so, and then the physical thing, which had never been very big with me, tapered off. But the habit didn't. The habit of seeing women, squiring them around, and the apparent need for feminine company. In those years when I had solved most of my problems with women, when I was supposedly a mature man, I still had this hangover from the earlier years, this habit of wanting women around, of wanting their company and treating them ultimately as sexual objects rather than as people who happened to be female.

I finally cured myself of it. With Terry and Lana and the others, I just saw them from time to time and went to bed with them rarely. It was reassuring to know they were there and that they liked me, but I didn't do it out of deep need. I don't think that's anything to be ashamed of. I'm sure it's common to most men. Only most men never see what they're doing. Fortunately I did, after a while.

And even then I made mistakes. Just about that time some actress I was going out with got pregnant. It's probably the only time in my life I've ever gotten a woman pregnant, and I was using every possible precaution and so was she. But the superficial evidence pointed to the fact that it was my responsibility. Neither of us wanted the child and I didn't want to get married to her. That was out of the question. And so I got in touch with Verne Mason and he took her over to a clinic in France for an abortion. They flew TWA, of course.

I suppose I'm a little bitter about it because I did feel that this girl was trying to trap me into marrying her. I don't trust women – that's a fact, sad to say – and I have trouble communicating with them. I have the disquieting notion that the female of our species is as foreign to the male as a lioness is to a bull moose. I've never understood women. I don't even understand my own involvement with them, and my need for it. There are times when I felt that I was punishing myself – in all instances but one. If you knew what I'd been through, you'd understand.

Who's this other person you talk about? I have a feeling there was someone else in your life besides your two wives.

You're badgering me to death and I see you'll never let up, so we better get this out of the way.

I've revealed more to you than I have to anybody for a long time. I've opened up these windows to my past – not only for you, but for myself. It's strange. My original idea in this whole thing was to give you my ideas and views, to talk about the present, and I find myself going deeper and deeper instead into the past. Oddly enough, I see myself sometimes with your eyes. You have very hard eyes sometimes. Well, that's neither here nor there. It's been a very strange experience, this telling the story of my life. Not always so good for me, though. I think sometimes you take advantage of me, try to make me the donkey. You've picked that up. And I don't guard against you, which I should do.

But we're at a critical point. I don't want to sound poetic, but I'm peering in at a window that I've kept locked for many years. So let's open it.

I've told you about Billie Dove, the woman I loved in Hollywood in the early Thirties. Billie and I very likely would have married, and almost did, but for a horrible thing that happened, which I suppose, has colored my relationships with women ever since. What you call my 'germ phobia' may stem in great part from what happened to me with Billie Dove.

She gave me the clap.

At that time it was not a laughing matter. This was before penicillin, and I went through the agonies of the damned. I thought my pecker would fall off every time I took a piss. While that creature, who gave me her social disease, walked around as though nothing had happened. You have no idea what lengths I had gone to for this woman, what favors I had done her. She and her husband, Irving Willatt, were estranged, and I paid him $325,000 in cash, in thousand-dollar bills, to get out of her life, to open the way for us –

Now, wait a minute. Let's start at the beginning.

Well, the beginning – what is the beginning? The classic movie plot. Boy meets girl, boy buys off husband, boy gets clap from girl, boy leaves girl. I don't mean to be flippant – I'm not telling you this to provoke laughter. You're leading me into that. This was a serious matter for me, and don't be misled by my temporary jocularity.

I didn't know where Billie got the clap. I never did find out. But it terrified me, as well as making me sick. First of all I had to undergo a nasty period of treatment. This was in Hollywood, in 1931. I was twenty-five years old, a man with a limited sexual experience. I was in love, and I took sex very seriously. I still had the deepest idealism regarding women. Billie shattered that, and it was a long time before I entertained serious thoughts about a woman again.

Billie and I would certainly have been married if it weren't for my getting sick that way. That terrified me. When I learned what I had, I went through my house – we were practically living together on Muirfield Road – and I gathered all my clothes, everything I owned, even including the towels and the rugs from the bathroom floor, and I packed it all into burlap bags, like mail bags, and I gave them all to Noah Dietrich and I told him to burn them. Burn everything! Including the shirt off my back. I found out later he gave it all to the Salvation Army.

I didn't leave the house for days. I ordered a fresh supply of sheets and towels until the rooms were fumigated. Then I had some clothes brought in to me and started life over again. The delivery people came to the door to deliver the clothes and sheets – I was stark naked, had to hide down behind a chair to cover myself and hand them the money for the sheets and things.

Billie then went on to have an affair with George Raft, who was in all those gangster movies. I always wondered if she passed the disease along to him. He might have had her rubbed out.

You can imagine, having corrupted myself in such a way that I would actually pay money for her, to have had this other thing happen to me, crushed me for years. It almost emasculated me.

After that I never made love to a woman without using a minimum of two contraceptives. And even then I felt unsafe. I had worshipped Billie, I had never dreamed that she could be carrying such a disease. After that I felt: what woman is exempt?

My sexual needs were never very strong – I had the reputation of being a ladies man, but it was undeserved. I married Ella, and that didn't work out. I made a certain show out of being a ladies man, because I thought that was what the world expected of me. I suppose I was trying to follow in my father's footsteps, if you want to put it simply – something I could never do. Very often I would take out a woman, and always a beautiful woman, and when the time came to perform, I felt I couldn't. I'm not trying to say to you that I was impotent. I wasn't at all. If I got into bed with a woman I did what had to be done, what she wanted.

But I remember, time after time, I would drive someone home and she'd say, 'Aren't you coming in for a cup of coffee?' – and I had a vision of myself being unable to perform or getting bored and I would almost always say, 'No, I'm sorry, I have a business appointment. You know I keep peculiar hours.'

Or I would arrange when I was out with a girl that a telephone call would come to me just before midnight, just about the time we were supposed to leave the club, wherever we were, saying my presence was urgently needed somewhere else.

I look back on it now, from the vantage point of sixty-five years, when such problems no longer plague me, and I have nothing but pity for myself as a young man. Pity because of the problem that I had and because the image of me that people had, even my closest friends, was so different, that I didn't dare tell anyone. How could I go to Glen Odekirk or Jack Frye or Bob Gross, men who loved me and would have done almost anything for me – and say, 'I'm afraid to go to bed with a woman for fear that I can't perform or that I'll be bored?' I didn't have the vocabulary for that, and I lived with this ridiculous feeling of shame. I lived a terrible life.

Part of this was this Texas thing we've spoken about, and which still very much ruled my thinking. I thought of myself as a Texan, Big Hard's son. Still today, to come from Texas, to be a Texan, you're supposed to be a big-balled son of a bitch. And frankly, that wasn't me.

Despite my terrible disappointment with Dr. Schweitzer, that I never got through to the man, and that he brushed me aside like some insignificant creature from out of the bush, I still felt that there were men in this world who had put their feet on the right path early in their lives and never left it. They were following a clearly marked path through the jungle that human life resembles.

I knew that I had my share of achievements, but when I added up everything I had done, I could see no focus. I'm talking about the early 1950s, when I was a man in my late forties. I could see I was not on a clear track that progressed from one stage of development to another. It was what seized my imagination at the time, and yet when I analyzed it in rare moments of introspection, I could see no progression. And when you can't see progression in your own life, no clearcut advance from one goal to another, leading to major goals, then you can't see your Self, which is blindness. That sort of blindness is worse than any kind of deafness.

And then I found the man I believed I was looking for.

24

Howard flies to Sun Valley under a pseudonym, swims naked in the Caribbean with Ernest Hemingway, is invited to buy Cuba, and contemplates ending his life.

ERNEST HEMINGWAY AND I had met briefly in Hollywood when I was making movies. It was hardly more than an introduction at a party in some bungalow in that crazy place he was living, the Garden of Allah. But Hemingway impressed me, and I thought I would like to see him again. I felt the tremendous force of his personality more than even the power of his work, although I had read and admired his novels very deeply, especially *The Sun Also Rises.*

The occasion arose, just after the war, sometime in the winter of 1948, when I went out to look over Sun Valley, Idaho, with the idea in mind of buying it and making it into a popular resort area. I flew out there in my bomber, a converted B-25. I knew Ernest was there with his family and he was hunting, and so I found out where he was living. I did something wholly uncharacteristic. I marched right up to his door, and knocked on it. He opened it.

I hadn't gone out to Sun Valley as Howard Hughes. Traveling under the name of Howard Hughes is the kiss of death. The people who owned Sun Valley would have jacked the price up fifty percent just on that knowledge alone. I was using the name Tom Garden. I knew a Tom Garden very briefly once. I met him out in Ethiopia in 1946. He was a young Englishman who wanted to go exploring in the Danakil part of the country. A lot of really savage tribes in that neck of the woods, and the emperor, or the court, or whoever gave such permissions, wouldn't give it to him. But he went anyhow, and he was never heard of again.

I don't want to convey any idea that I felt any kinship of any sort with this wanderer who vanished. But the story had impressed itself on me, so that was the name I gave to Ernest Hemingway in Sun Valley when he opened the door.

I must say I was struck by his reception. I myself – well, the occasion would never arise where some stranger would come up and knock on my door. First of all, nobody knows where my door is. Second, if they do know, there's a guard out there, a guard outside and a guard inside. It would certainly never occur to me to open the door myself.

But there Ernest came out to the door, looking like a middle-aged tramp, wearing beat-up corduroy trousers and a lumberjack shirt open nearly to the waist. Come to think of it, I was not a hell of a lot more respectable. It was winter and I had on a couple of old sweaters.

I introduced myself and Ernest said, 'Come in and have a drink, Tom.'

I came in, excused myself from the drink because I don't drink, and we talked for a while. He immediately showed an interest in who I was and why I was there. Understand, I passed myself off as a member of a real estate group in California that was interested in Sun Valley. I didn't say that I personally, even as Tom Garden, was going to buy it, but I suppose no matter how you dress, the smell of money doesn't leave your skin. And Ernest cottoned on very quickly to the idea that I was rich, and he was fascinated by rich people. He took a great interest in my proposal for the valley and the surrounding area, asked me all sorts of intelligent and perceptive questions about how I was going to go about it.

The extraordinary thing is that I'd been in his house no more than fifteen minutes, and I was sitting in an armchair and talking as freely and easily as I'd talked with any man in my whole life. Writers often give you this feeling – it may be genuine, it may be phoney – you tell me – but they give you the feeling they're interested in you, and in what makes you tick.

But Ernest had that quality of making you feel immediately at home. We spent a very pleasant couple of hours. We talked about practical things mostly, more than about either of us personally. We talked about them in a very straightforward way that I wasn't used to, except with pilots.

The thing is, at the time, I didn't want anything from Ernest and he didn't want anything from me. I had read a couple of his books, but I hadn't dropped in to see him as a writer. It was more that I had in mind a certain image of Ernest Hemingway as a person who had gone through adventures and rough experiences, and he'd had a dangerous time of it and he'd come out of it whole, tough. Toughened, I mean. Not only did I respect him for that, but I was fascinated, and I wanted to know how and why.

We spent a couple of hours talking, and I invited him to take a spin with me in my B-25 next day, which he was delighted to do. The fact that I had my own bomber tickled him pink.

I told him I was doing a geographical survey on this flight. The purpose was just to get an over-all picture for myself of the valley and its potential. I flew around, in and out, through the canyons of Idaho. Ernest was in the co-pilot's seat, and asked me a hell of a lot of questions about what I was doing and why I was doing it. That was a routine flight for me, so I could fly and answer his questions at the same time. He told me afterward that it was one of the most lucid and cogent explanations of flying that he'd ever heard.

And not only that – he couldn't get over the fact that I could fly and look around and maneuver and at the same time maintain a running conversation with him about anything in the world. That really impressed him. I was so involved after a while, however, with what I was looking for, that I broke off the conversation and just concentrated on flying. The flight was a bit low, I suppose, and looking back on it now, dangerous. The wingtips were not too far from the canyon walls a couple of times. This was no Cessna 180, this was a B-25 bomber.

Ernest loved all that. On the way back he turned to me – there was a touch of awe in his voice – and he said, 'Tom, you're a hot pilot.'

'You better believe it,' I said. I wasn't shy about my flying skills.

I left soon after that. We saw one another briefly the following day, and then I was off – had to go. But it was a rich encounter. Ernest wanted to write to me about something, as a matter of fact, but I knew I wouldn't answer, and I didn't want to create that sort of situation, and so I told him some story that we were moving offices, and as soon as I had an address I would write him. It was a lot easier for me to get in touch with him than for him to get in touch with me.

I didn't see him again for nearly nine years. It wasn't a matter of deliberate waiting. I was so embroiled in affairs, I had no chance. Sort of like a drowning man – I'd draw my head up out of the water and I could see Ernest along the shore from time to time, but I was sucked down again before I could even call out to him. And he was off on his own affairs in Europe, Africa, Key West, and Cuba.

Cuba, as a matter of fact, is where I saw him the second time.

When you met him that first time, how did you get along with him politically? Did you know he'd been involved in the Spanish Civil War on the Loyalist side?

Except for that brief anticommunist phase of mine in Hollywood, I've never been a political person. I've only voted twice in my life, and that was for Franklin Roosevelt, and it was a long time ago. I've always made sure that I had members of both parties on my payroll, so that no matter who won, Hughes Tool and Hughes Aircraft didn't lose.

During the Spanish Civil War, from 1936 to 1939, I was involved in my flights and designing airplanes and I was about as apolitical as you could get. Moreover, from what I could gather, politics was never Ernest's major interest, either. Strictly secondary. I've always had the feeling he went to Spain because there was a war on and he wanted to see men in action. That turned him on. Naturally his sympathies were with the Loyalists rather than with the Fascist side, because he was that kind of man. He had a sense of justice and a love for common people.

But he also had an obsession with death and how men faced it. He asked me a great many questions in later years about my accidents, how I had felt about them, and I answered to the best of my ability. He was the only man I ever knew who was almost as banged up physically – broken bones, and wounds – as I was. I often wondered if he ever used that stuff I told him in any of his books, or whether there's some unpublished novel of his that has quotes from me or some incident from my life in it, because later on his questions were endless, about how I felt in the various crashes, and how I felt when a plane was in trouble. Danger made him feel like a bigger person. That's why he liked that ride in the B-25 so much.

Anyway, nine years later, in 1954, I was in Florida, where I had planned to build my own jet aircraft factory. I was already thinking of a short take-off and landing jet – the STOL – combined with an element of vertical take-off, what's now called a VTOL. I was looking ahead to the future and intended to sell the first twenty-five planes to TWA – that is, to myself. Del Webb and I got together on it, but it fell through. And on the spur of the moment, that time in Palm Beach – I knew Ernest was in Cuba – I hopped over from Miami to Havana on a commercial flight.

First I went to the Floridita, that famous bar downtown, because I knew he spent a lot of time there, but he wasn't there. It was empty at that hour of the afternoon.

So I took a taxi out to the finca. I didn't remember the name of the finca, didn't even know it was called a finca then. I just said to the cab driver, 'Hemingway,' and he said, 'Ah, *Papa!*'

I said, 'No, no, I don't want Papa. I want Hemingway.'

He said, '*Sí, sí, Papa, Papa!*' By then we were halfway there, and Papa turned out to be Ernest.

I was let in without any ceremony. The maid at the door didn't even ask my name. Ernest was sitting around the pool half-naked with a few other people, and I hadn't had time to change. I was still wearing a business suit. I had taken my tie off, stuffed it in my pocket. I walked up and Ernest was sitting there with his pot belly hanging out, and he peered at me over his glasses.

The first thing he said was, 'Don't stand there with the sun behind your back. I can't make you out, and that makes me nervous. Move around this way.'

I did as I was told, so he could see me. He looked at me with a grim expression – like, 'What's this?' And then suddenly his face broke into a big beautiful smile, and he said, 'Goddamnit, Tom, it's great to see you!'

I felt wonderful, that he'd recognized me after all those years and welcomed me so warmly.

Ernest had that quality of welcoming, which is so rare. The house was full of people, apart from his family. There was his wife – at least some little woman running around that I thought was his wife. And some adoring blonde girl, who as I recall, the wife didn't like very much, no doubt because Ernest was humping her. A bunch of servants, too, and some children, his own and others. And some college kids from the United States. They'd come down there and thrust themselves upon him with their manuscripts, expecting that he'd help get them published. He read their work with great patience, and I remember that when one of them left he asked Ernest for money because he didn't have the fare back home, and Ernest gave it to him. That's the kind of man he was.

Did you keep masquerading as Tom Garden?

I was afraid to tell him my real name. It was such a good relationship that I didn't want to run that risk. We sat around the house and just talked. Ernest wanted to know what I'd been doing all these years, and I made up a few stories that paralleled my life. The events may have been different but the general content was the same, so that I wasn't lying to him in any meaningful way. I stayed almost the entire first day at his finca, and then he drove me back to my hotel in Havana, the Nacional.

The next day I was out there again with him, and on the third day we went fishing. I had taken Ernest up in my plane, and now he wanted to take me out on the fishing boat, to show me *his* specialty. I was not a sportsman; I played golf but I never went hunting, and I seldom fished anymore. I didn't really know what to expect.

There were a couple of Cuban helpers, one who was steering and one serving drinks. Ernest knew by then that I didn't drink, so he had a bottle of milk along in the ice chest for me. I think he drank tequila or daiquiris, and he had a couple of thermoses full of them, and each time he'd take a belt he'd say to his barman helper, 'Get out the milk for Señor Jardin.' And then he would crack up laughing. It broke him up, that I drank milk.

I was taken aback to begin with, when about fifteen minutes after we left the dock, there was Ernest at the helm of the boat, wearing a jock strap. Nothing else.

The fishing was poor. Ernest said it was the fault of the tankers that had been torpedoed there by German subs during the war: the garbage that had spewed out of them had killed off most of the big game fish. And he grumbled, and then it got hot, and he said his jock strap was itching, and he peeled it off.

He said, 'Come on, Tom, you're going to get prickly heat. Take off your clothes.'

I checked over in my mind what I remembered of Ernest's sexual habits, and I figured it was safe enough, so I peeled down to my skivvies. I've always been a little shy about being naked with other men, or women for that matter. Many times when I used to play golf, in the locker rooms all the men would shower together, and I waited till they were out of there before I would shower. Crept into a corner of the locker room when I had to change my clothes. I'm sure it harks back to my childhood, being tall and awkward, but I could never put my finger on the exact reason.

After a while Ernest said, 'Let's go for a swim. Bareass, Tom.'

I peeled off my skivvies and we dove over the side into the Gulf, which was perfectly flat and beautifully blue. That was an extraordinary experience for me, because we were grown men – I was forty-eight years old, and Ernest was somewhat older – and there we were in the water, naked, and Ernest started playing games. He would dive under the water and come up under me and tip me over by the ankles. One of us had to be a shark and the other had to be a killer whale, or a swordfish, and we would fight. Yell, shout, warn each other – 'Watch out, whale, here I come!' Splash around like children.

And it was marvelous. It was a broiling hot day and we were two middle-aged men splashing around like kids in the middle of the Caribbean Sea.

It gave me a curious view of Ernest. I saw something in him which I now know is a common element in many great men: the capacity to play, to remain in some respects childlike until they're too old to do it. I haven't got that capacity, sad to say – never did. It's a naturalness that men have when they're not ashamed of themselves and of what's buried inside of them.

It was an absolutely fine day. I felt more relaxed with Ernest than I felt with men I had known all my life. We just took each other for granted, and I was terribly impressed. With myself, too. Mind you, I wasn't conscious of this at the time. A lot of it came to me in thoughts afterward. But I was conscious of it to a certain extent, because I knew that this was not the way I usually behaved. And I was happy.

Then I made a bad mistake. We had such a good relationship growing up between us that I felt ashamed of myself for deceiving Ernest by calling myself Tom Garden. It suddenly seemed ignoble. And so I said to him, 'I have to tell you something. My name isn't Tom Garden.'

He took a gulp of his drink. 'Then who the hell are you?'

I said, 'My name is Howard Hughes.'

He looked at me for a minute, downed his drink, and said, 'Goddamn! I should have guessed. That's why you flew so well. I should have known it. Howard Hughes! Goddamn! I've always wanted to meet you, and here you are, bareass naked with me in the Caribbean!'

He kept on chuckling, and I was relieved at his reaction. I thought everything was going to be okay.

But it was a mistake to have told him. In subtle ways his attitude began to change almost at once. The first thing that happened is that he wanted to know all about me – that is to say, about Howard Hughes. He asked me a hell of a lot of questions. That's when we got on to our long discussion about my crashes and wartime experiences, and that was all right – but then he started asking me the same sort of questions that reporters had asked me for years.

I had developed a habit, the moment these kinds of questions were posed to me, of instantly ducking into my shell and being brusque. And that's what happened to me then. When we went back to the house I said to Ernest, 'The one thing I beg of you is not to tell anyone else who I am, because that ruins everything for me. People treat me differently and I don't like it.' I wanted him to pick up the hint.

He said he understood. He wished that he could be anonymous sometimes, but his face was too well known, the big beard and everything. In retrospect I don't believe him, but that's what he said then.

But his attitude had changed. He had always been fascinated by rich people, and he confessed that to me, and he began to talk about money.

Money is not a subject that I'm shy about. Money's played an important role in my life. I'm hardly alone in that: people will lie, beg, borrow, steal, do damn near anything for money. It's played an exaggerated role in my life because I've had more of it than almost anybody else. If you're a man seven feet tall, like 'Wilt the Stilt' Chamberlain, it's bound to be important in your life that you're taller than anyone else around. You stand out, and people are going to gawk at you. People have always gawked at me because I've had more money than they have. They treated me like a freak, which is one of the reasons I've always hid from them.

And so I didn't want Ernest pumping me about how much money I had, how I got it, and what I was doing with it. But obviously I couldn't avoid the subject altogether. He wouldn't let me. And the more I talked – I guess when I talk, I talk about a million dollars as most men talk about a hundred – the more Ernest became almost deferential to me. He was awed by all this.

The worst thing that happened was that just before I left, he became aware that he had been deferential. Because he was a perceptive man and he was, I think, aware of his own attitudes as few men are. Once it dawned on him that he was being deferential – I may even have said something to him, not meaning to insult him, but said, 'For Christ's sake, don't pull that with me, that's what I get from flunkies' – he was ashamed.

He turned against me. He became surly and difficult. Although when I left, we had one very good moment. He threw his arms around me and said, 'I don't care whether you're Tom or Howard, I'm just delighted to know you, and I want you to come back and I look forward to seeing your skinny ass again.'

And so everything was okay when I left.

Did you see him again?

I waited a long time. Much too long, in fact, because we had a good friendship, and if I had continued it I think I would have been the better for it. Ernest could have been the kind of friend I always needed. Different from me, although I don't think that would have made a barrier.

But those were the years that I got so terribly involved and embroiled. 'My son Howard the Billionaire is drowning!' I was drowning in details and deals, and I was sucked down into that morass of suits and counter-suits and financing – the whole horror story of TWA.

Did you and Ernest correspond with each other?

No, he didn't write letters and I rarely do. I did go back, though, to see him about five or six years later. That was sometime in 1959, and the Cuban revolution had already been accomplished. And this time I went deliberately – I had no business in Florida.

I went straight to Cuba to see Ernest, because it was a time in my life when I was completely fed up with everything, and I had nothing but good memories of Ernest and the times we had spent together. I regretted that we'd been out of touch. I had read in the papers that Ernest was back in Cuba, and that was what prompted me to go. This was not meant to be a two-day visit, or a three-day visit, or anything. As happened again later, I was willing to burn my bridges behind me. I felt that Ernest and I had a great camaraderie, and there wasn't much more I needed in life at that point other than one close friend. So when I went back it was with the idea that I would stay as long as I wanted to. It could have been for the rest of my life. I had no time limit in mind.

You were married to Jean Peters then, in 1959. You mean to say you and Jean would have moved down to Cuba?

I don't know what would have happened. Things had started to go a little sour by then in my second marriage. In fact, long before then. But if I had stayed on in Cuba, and I was free to do so – all I had to do was throw over my entire industrial empire, so-called – I probably would have asked Jean to come out, give it a try to see if we could live together again.

When I arrived and went out to Ernest's finca, it was a terrible disappointment. It threw me completely, because everything had changed. Ernest had become an old man. And I don't mean just old physically, old in appearance – he always had that big white beard – but the vitality had gone out of him. And some of the intellectual honesty had gone out of him too. He was crotchety and difficult and he talked to me in an entirely new way.

The first day I was there, half our conversation had to do with Cuban cigars, because Castro had accomplished his revolution and Ernest was worried that Castro was nationalizing the cigar industry and the cigars would not be the same quality they were before. He said, 'Howard, why don't you buy the island from Fidel and go into the cigar business?'

He pursued that theme. I'd come to talk to Ernest about a possible total change in my life, and he kept saying, 'The cigars won't be the same if they're not rolled on the thighs of nubile Cuban girls, and you can make a good deal with Castro, you can buy in for a hundred million, and what does that mean to a man in your position, Howard?'

I hadn't come to discuss the quality of Cuban cigars. I was uncomfortable and a little impatient.

The second day was just as bad: I never got a chance to talk to Ernest alone. He got up late and he had a lot of visitors. We had a pickup of meal out at the finca and there were a bunch of Cuban army officers and political figures. He introduced me, thank God, as Tom Garden. He still respected my wish for privacy. But he and these officers and politicos chatted away furiously in Spanish all afternoon. Every once in a while Ernest would stop and throw a line or two of translation in my direction. I was bored.

By the time the afternoon was over, when they left, Ernest was drunk as a skunk. His head was falling on the table. I was embarrassed for him. This was a man who'd won the Nobel prize. I found it a pitiable thing to see a man of this power, this nobility of spirit, demeaned in this way. I didn't want to see any more of it.

I left. I was at the Nacional in Havana. It was empty, I had the whole floor to myself – and I hadn't rented the whole floor that time, as I did years later at the Desert Inn in Las Vegas. Matter of fact there was a parade while I was there and Castro himself came marching down the street. I watched it from my window.

I went back once more to see Ernest. It was even worse. I don't know what had gotten into his head, but naturally he wanted to know all about what I'd been doing in the past years. I didn't feel the machinations at Hughes Aircraft and troubles at TWA were the things that really would have fascinated him, but I gave him a brief rundown on it, and all he could do was criticize me, and harp on the fact that I was wasting my life on involvements with this kind of thing and the kind of people I had to deal with. Now I knew this. That's precisely why I had come to see Ernest. I was like a man who had a crippled leg, and I had gone to the doctor to see if he could cure me, and all the doctor could say was, 'Your leg is crippled, your leg is crippled.' What I was looking for was the cure.

Ernest offered me no suggestions, only harped on the fact that I was too involved with these people. I would say, 'Yes, I know that, but I want to become uninvolved, and how do I do it? And where do I go? How do I cut loose?' I may not have put it in such childlike terms as that, but it was clear that I was there for help. And instead of helping me, Ernest tried to bully me.

When you bully me, I vanish. Usually I vanish physically, but sometimes I just vanish mentally and emotionally.

I crawled into my shell, and the more I did that, the more Ernest tried to pry open the cover and knock holes in me. He still had a lot of the old charm, he wasn't unpleasant enough for me to pick up and walk out of his house, because every time he saw me getting really uncomfortable, he'd slap me on the shoulder and say, 'Oh, shit, it's good to see you, Howard, or Tom' – he called me both names. People in Cuba thought my name was Tom Howard or Howard Tom. Ernest had kept his promise, I think it amused him that he was the only one who knew.

We didn't go fishing this time. Ernest was in no condition for that. He was worried about whether the government was going to take over his farm and he didn't even want to leave the house. He was worried about his health. I remember the doctor came out and took his blood pressure right there at the table.

But there was still some of the old Ernest left. We drove into Havana together, and the car broke down halfway. Ernest cursed up a storm and started a speech about 'goddamn modern machinery,' and got out to open the hood. But I could tell what the trouble was from the way the motor had sputtered. I told him, 'You're just out of gas,' and that's what it was. His gas gauge was broken.

This was where the old Ernest popped up out of that crotchetiness. There was a car parked nearby, not far from a house or a few houses. Ernest took a length of rubber tubing from the trunk. 'Indispensable, Howard,' he said. 'Never travel without it.' He siphoned a gallon or so of gas out of this other car, sucked it up with his mouth, which made me terribly nervous. I shudder to think of what fumes went down into Ernest's lungs. And if the owner of the car had seen it he might have fired a shot at us.

Anyhow, we got to the city all right and filled the tank there.

It was a bad visit. It was a mistake. It colored the good memories of Ernest with an overlay of this unsuccessful meeting. What I most deeply regret is that I hadn't known Ernest as a younger man, and that we hadn't kept in touch. If I had known him during those years, let's say even from 1946 up to 1959, that might have changed my entire life. But events intervened, and you don't always see what's the right course to follow, and we had lost touch.

I never saw him again. I was deeply saddened when I heard of his death, that he'd blown his brains out. Not that I object to suicide. I feel it's every man's right to put an end to his life when it's become intolerable to him. But what preceded it – the sickness and the periods of insanity, the decline of a brilliant and fine man into a wretched shell – saddened me deeply.

What about you, in your life? Have you ever contemplated suicide?

I imagine every man has. The first serious time was when I broke up with Billie Dove. That was a totally demoralizing experience for me.

The other times were flashes of despair. But I have to tell you one thing, and then you'll understand a lot about my life, about these past years.

After my crash in the F-ll, when I was in the hospital and the doctors had just about given up on me, what saved my life was my will to live. And I'm not talking about an unconscious instinctive will to live, like the fox that bites off its foot in a trap – I mean a conscious repetition of my intense desire to go on living. I lay there in that hospital bed and I repeated it to myself time after time. 'You've got to live. You've got to live.' Not: 'You're going to live.' I said, 'You've *got* to live.'

That phrase burned itself into my mind, I had repeated it so often so that years later, when things were really bad and that flash of despair came to me, which I suppose is common to all men, it was always overpowered by an echo of what I had said to myself in that hospital bed: 'You've *got* to live.'

The only time I thought seriously about doing away with myself, other after the breakup with Billie, was during my last marriage. It came then from a deep sense of shame at having failed – I don't mean only in my marriage, but in my life. It was as if over the years, all the bad and wrong things I had done, the promises I had made and broken, welled to the top. I'm not just talking about promises where I said, 'I'll buy these planes from you' and then I didn't buy them. I'm talking about promises in human relationships, promises that are not given in words, but that you make by virtue of the obligations you take on. Time passes and you find you were unable to fulfil them because you've changed, the other person has changed, and life interferes. And yet, what it amounts to in the end is a mountain of lies and deceptions beyond your control. They pile up inside you – each one is a little hard stone that seems to grow. You feel the weight of them year after year as each one gets added to the pile, and there's no way to get rid of them. You can't vomit them out anymore because the weight is too great inside you.

And then I suppose a moment comes when you feel this interior heaviness at the mistakes you made, and these personal failures, so much so that you think you just can't go on. Cancer of the memory, you can call it.

But I went on – for which, all things considered, I'm grateful. No man can be certain of this, of course, but I don't believe I will ever commit suicide. I feel my spirit caged in this decaying carcass, yearning to get out. But I will do nothing to hasten that departure.

INCIDENTS AND OPINIONS

There's a story I heard about you from a friend. It has to do with a man named Bob Balzer and a house you rented from him on Mulholland Drive.

In West Los Angeles. Yes, I remember that I had a house up there. But I never met Balzer in my life.

Correct. Your lawyer told Balzer you wanted to rent the house for a year. Balzer said he had just built it and wasn't interested in renting it. Your lawyer said, 'But Mr. Hughes will pay a year's rent equal to the cost of the house.' Balzer said, 'Well… that offer is hard to resist.'

It was a beautiful house, unusually secluded – suited me perfectly. I told you I had several houses I was renting, a few bungalows and a couple of larger ones like this man Balzer's place. What's the point of this story?

Your lawyer met with Balzer at the Beverly Hills Hotel to sign the lease. Balzer said, 'I'll give you the keys tomorrow as soon as I've moved my things out, and then Mr. Hughes can move in.' Your lawyer said, 'Mr. Hughes has already moved in, and never mind the keys, the locks have been changed.' Balzer turned pale and said, 'What about my clothes?' Your lawyer said, 'Go buy a new wardrobe and send the bill to Mr. Hughes care of me.' Balzer got furious, and charged up to the house. He knew a way over the garden wall and in through the back door. He climbed over, but two guards grabbed him and heaved him back over the wall. They said, 'Mr. Howard Hughes is renting this house, we don't care who you are, get out.'

They never would have revealed that I was leasing it.

Balzer knew who he'd leased it to. He went out, bought new clothes, and sent you the bill.

In which case the bill was paid. I'm terribly sorry that the poor man was thrown over the garden wall. I had no knowledge that such a thing had happened.

There's a climax to this. A year later, a year to the minute that Balzer had rented it to you, he showed up at the front door with two bodyguards of his own, resolutely determined to get in and to throw you out on the dot. But the door was open, and his old locks had been reinstalled, and when he walked in, the house was empty. Not a soul there. He ran around, of course, inspecting for damage –

There was no damage. Whoever said that is lying.

Balzer didn't find any damage. However, he walked into the bedroom, where he'd slept exactly one year ago, and the cufflinks that he'd worn the night before, a year ago, were on the dresser, and the same yellow striped sheets he'd slept in were still on the bed. Nobody had slept there. The liquor cabinet, the kitchen, the living room, all were untouched. You'd never used the house, never slept there in the entire year, and it cost you, according to my friend, about $200,000 to rent the place.

It's not true – I did sleep there. People tell ridiculous stories about me. They exaggerate terribly. I slept there several times.

But the bed was untouched, they were the same sheets. Balzer's shirt was still hanging on the back of a chair the way he'd left it a year ago.

I didn't sleep in the man's bedroom. I slept in the maid's room. I don't need sunken bathrooms and a suntan machine. The servant's quarters were much more private and quite comfortable, and nearer the back gate. I slept there at least three or four times, maybe more. That's a while ago – I don't remember.

*   *   *

I was recently in Palm Springs to see my aunt. She knew you years ago. Her name is Beabe Hamilburg and her husband was Mitchell Hamilburg. Do you remember them?

He was a talent agent. And if I'm not mistaken, I met your father through Mitch.

That could be. Beabe told me a story that I wanted to check on. She said that you flew her and Mitch and the actress Mitzi Gaynor and Mitzi's mother down to Las Vegas for a weekend.

When was this?

In the Fifties. She didn't know where she was going and they had no clothes packed, and she said you kept her virtually a prisoner in the Frontier Hotel for a week.

Hardly a prisoner, since they had the best suite in the hotel and I made sure they had ample chips to gamble with. Besides, now that I'm recalling some details of this, they came down to Vegas inadequately equipped for a week, and I sent a big choice of clothes for them to pick over. And jewelry for your aunt. And they had a chauffeured limousine at their disposal.

But Beabe said she never saw you the whole time they were there. What was the purpose of your inviting them if you didn't see them?

I saw them, I'm sure, but the purpose of the trip, as you probably guessed, was for me to get into Mitzi Gaynor's pants.

Did you need Beabe and Mitch to hold your hand?

Maybe to hold Mitzi's mother's hand. I've always needed other people around. The point is that I didn't want to spend that much time with Mitzi. It was an interlude, nothing more. I wanted Mitzi occupied when I wasn't with her, because I had business down in Vegas at the same time. And if I'm not mistaken, your Uncle Mitchell was Mitzi's representative at the time. He introduced me to Mitzi. Very wholesome girl. I needed chaperons, that's another point to the way I did things. I had the mother along, as I've mentioned. Of course she knew what was going on. But I wasn't interested in marriage. I've said many times since, and at that time I said, I wasn't going to get married again until I was in my fifties. I had too many things to do.

*   *   *

During the war didn't you have sunken gasoline tanks in the San Fernando Valley?

Why would I do a thing like that? That's ridiculous. Who told you such a thing?

Gasoline was rationed and it was hard to get. I don't remember who told me.

It's not true. One tank, that's all – one five-thousand-gallon tank. That's reasonable, I think. I owned a lot of Chevrolets.

Over-population is the over-riding critical problem today and it's going to become more so as time goes on. And I don't see any workable man-made solution to this problem.

Do you think it's a possible solution to populate outer space? Other planets, or satellites?

No, I think that's quite hopeless. It cost us the better part of several billion dollars to send three guys to the moon. I know a fair amount about this, because my equipment, Hughes equipment, was used up there and was key to the project. It's a losing battle. I know that guy, Armstrong, the astronaut, said, 'One giant step for mankind.' One step forward, two steps back, that's about the size of it. Technology can't solve this problem. It will be solved by nature, but not in a way that we'll enjoy. New and virulent diseases can sweep away two thirds of humanity as they did in the time of the Black Death, before any solutions can be found and applied. I think that it's a historical necessity that something of this sort will happen. The deck is stacked against humankind. The world is only able to hold a certain number of people and we're fast approaching that limit. My vision of the world in a hundred years is one great big India. When I was out there I saw what could happen, and I know how horrible and frightening it is. And it could easily happen, even in the United States.

You don't think it's possible to colonize outer space, in any form?

Not for the next five to seven hundred years, that's my estimate. But there certainly are observers from other planets down here, checking us out, putting us into the scheme of things. UFOs, most of them, are not optical illusions. I have a copy of the Air Force's top-secret Blue Book that tells the true tale of the so-called flying saucers.

I'm sure there are, at the very least, hundreds of inhabited planets in our galaxy alone, not to mention how many thousands of other galaxies, and some of them have been inhabited for millions of years.

There is some doubt, at least in other people's minds, that the beings on some of these other planets have evolved to a higher degree of civilization than we have. Man doesn't want to believe it because for the most part he still thinks – not with his mind, but with his primitive instincts – that the earth is the center of the solar system and the solar system, our solar system, is the center of the universe. Never mind what he learns in school or what his common sense tells him – common sense is very much over-rated, it's rarely the important factor in thinking and decisions. The average man still says, 'the sun's rising' and 'the sun's going down,' and whether he knows it or not, he believes it.

I'm not in any doubt that these advance beings have been visiting us at irregular intervals for the last five thousand years or more. Observation trips, reconnaissance trips. Probably feeding all the information, from the rules of our wars and what we eat and the sounds we make when we screw, into some extraterrestrial computer about the size of a TV set. And maybe the only thing that's saved our bacon so far is that they still can't figure out what makes us tick. Because if you computerize everything about mankind, the computer still wouldn't be able to figure it out. Man is an insane animal. Hypocrisy and denial are his two outstanding attributes.

*　　*　　*

You once mentioned that Noah Dietrich had told a story about you regarding cookies. You said the story wasn't true, but you never said what it was.

Noah Dietrich, now that he no longer works for me, has told story after story about our past business dealings where he's twisted things around. Where I was the one who made the decision, he's told other people, 'I made it and Howard didn't know what he was doing.' Here's an example of one of the things he did. The story itself is trivial, but I'll tell it to you because you asked about it.

It was a long time ago, just after I had finished shooting *Scarface*. I was working with the cutting editor and hadn't slept for two days. At one point we sent out for food, but when we finished eating this guy was still hungry. I had sent out for milk and cookies, which was enough to keep me going. This man hadn't sent out for any dessert, and when I started to eat my cookies, he said, 'Mr. Hughes, could I have one of your cookies?' I gave him one. It's true that I hesitated, because I didn't want to start a precedent. Cookies were all I had to eat. These other people would go out and gorge themselves on hamburgers and french fries, while I drank milk and ate graham crackers. I kept them in the studio or the cutting room, wherever I happened to be working. But I gave him a cookie. Noah twisted this all around. He told somebody that I refused to give the man a cookie. That's absolutely not true. I gave him a cookie.

The sequel to this incident was that for weeks afterward men would come up to me on the lot, whenever I went off to a corner to drink my milk and eat my cookies, and say, 'Howard,' or 'Mr. Hughes, can I please have a cookie?' They were kidding me. But I couldn't very well refuse them, since I'd given this other man a cookie – so my cookie supply vanished before my eyes. I knew then that I was right in the first place, because if you give one man a cookie, you've got to give every man a cookie, and pretty soon you don't have any cookies yourself. And you're a poor man, cookiewise.

You may think that's funny, and I can see the humor in it too. But when you're hungry it's not funny. Besides, it might have been hundred-dollar bills next. I didn't want to get the reputation of being an easy touch.

*   *   *

Let me explain my personal theory on the structure of the universe. You know the structure of the atom, with a nucleus, protons and electrons revolving about it, and so on. It must have struck you that this is similar to our solar system. My theory is that there's a possibility for life in some form not only in the various systems in what we call outer space but in systems within ourselves. In other words, each cell within our body is composed of many atoms. I'm putting this very simply so that you'll understand. I know you're not a scientist.

I believe that within ourselves, in any given cell, there are systems that are similar to the galaxies that we can observe in outer space, and that within, let's say a cell that's part of my pinky, there may be a universe, or what's called a multiverse, and that perhaps in one of those miniature solar systems in my pinky there may be hundreds of planets supporting life in miniature – from our point of view. And right there, in my pinky, there may be a planet called X, but similar to our Earth in most details, in which two men are talking just as we're talking today.

There's no way we can investigate this. We're not advanced to that point. But it seems to me perfectly logical. And if you follow it through, as I have, you can come up with an interesting theory about disease.

Let's say that a nuclear device is detonated here on the planet Earth. That may be creating a cancer in the universe. It's possible that cancer in ourselves, and other diseases, may be caused by wars, or natural disasters such as famine, in these other universes within ourselves. Suppose a famine strikes India or two African nations go to war on one of these tiny planets in your abdomen, and that famine or war spreads to other planets, the other systems in your abdomen – this may be the cause of ulcers, for all we know.

I'm sure this sounds far-fetched to you, but if you think about it for a while, you'll realize that we don't really know the nature of disease – we may know the physiological reasons, but we don't know *why* it all happens, why the body decays. And if it's possible that the cellular structure of the human body is a replica of the universe, a microcosm as opposed to a macrocosm, then it's also possible that our own solar system may be an atom in some giant's lungs. And when we detonate a nuclear device...

He coughs.
Or worse.

*　*　*

There's something we've got to talk about, and we've slid over it somehow in these sessions. That's your phobia about germs. I'm not trying to offend you, but on various occasions you've mentioned precautions you've taken against germs – although I must admit you haven't taken any in my presence.

I dislike the word *phobia*. Anybody in his right mind would take the same precautions. And you're quite wrong about my not taking precautions in your presence. We haven't shaken hands very often, have we? Most men I wouldn't shake hands with at all. The first thing

I look at are someone's nails. The man who doesn't take scrupulous care of his nails probably doesn't wash his hands often, either, and will probably just use soap.

What do you use?

I use antiseptic sprays both in my throat and on my hands, and in my living quarters. I also have ultra-violet ray machines. I take large quantities of vitamins, especially vitamin E. That's one of the vitamins that have not been fully analyzed. However, it does tend to break up the quantities of foreign matter that coat the lungs. Heavy smokers like yourself, of course, are killing themselves, and vitamin E won't help them, but it will attack the normal particles of dust and crap that you take in from the atmosphere and which stick to the mucous membranes.

I have emphysema, brought on by the smog in California, and the vitamin E reduces the need for oxygen in the system and makes it easier for me to breathe. I've taken other precautions over many years. For example, the properties inherent in simple white cotton gloves are not widely recognized. All the documents, memos, and so on, that came to me in past years were typed by secretaries wearing white gloves, so there were no oils and germs brought into my presence. I used to buy the gloves wholesale from an undertaker's supply house.

Used to? The past tense?

I've modified my views somewhat, mainly because I'm not a well man and precautions of this sort are no longer of great significance. But there was a time, not long ago, when I was very careful about the people who came to visit me at any of my houses in California and Nevada. The places themselves were fully purified, the air cleaned and rendered antiseptic.

But that wasn't enough. I had to open the door for these people. Now please don't think I'm a maniac. I've been called a maniac enough times. I don't like to think that's your opinion. I don't believe it is, but I don't even want to see the suspicion on your face. A great many of the precautions I took were on doctor's orders. And if not doctor's orders, then doctor's suggestions, because of the damage to my lungs, and my skin condition, and my anemia, and various other ailments.

You went a bit overboard on it, didn't you?

I'm a man who always goes the whole hog. These places of mine in Vegas and L.A. were very well protected against germs. Nevertheless, people did come to see me, by invitation, and when I opened the door for them, I admitted untold billions of harmful bacteria.

To minimize this risk I had a little square chalked just in front of the door in exactly the right place. When someone came to visit me, I would make sure that the guard had him placed in the center of that square before I opened the door to admit him. In other words, that square was placed so that I could open the door the absolute minimum to allow him to come in. Once this happened with Charles Laughton came to see me. Laughton was a fat man, so I opened the door and it hit him in the belly. Knocked the wind right out of him. He went down to all fours. I had to help him up and apologize.

Why didn't you use something similar to a decompression chamber?

Are you making fun of me, Clifford? As a matter of fact, I did that once. But people wouldn't stand for it. That was in my bungalow in Las Vegas, years before I moved into the Desert Inn. I had a bungalow off the Strip, set well back into the desert. I also had a battery of ultra-violet ray machines set up in the entrance halls but people said it would give them cancer, and I finally had to drop it.

And you object to the word phobia?

There's nothing phobic about a man taking care of his health. I've gotten through to the age of sixty-five, and for a man who's suffered as much physical injury as I have, that's a triumph. A man with my ailments who hadn't cared for his body the way I have, and who let people push him around, would have been dead at the age of fifty.

I mentioned to you that the typists on Romaine Street end elsewhere wore white gloves, and so did the people who came on plane trips with me. But one pair of white gloves wasn't enough, I realized, especially for these people on the trips. They used two pair.

At the same time?

Yes. One pair, the one on top, was discarded when they got into the plane, at the top of the gangway, and the second pair which they wore during the trip, discarded when they left. And this way I got some measure of precaution against the hordes of germs that surround us.

You mean everyone who flew with you had to go through this?

Not everyone. Only the ones I didn't know well, and people who were obviously dirty. I had ratings for people, Class A, B, C and D. A file card had to be consulted by my people who would arrange the meetings.

I'm well aware that this attitude and my precautions leave me open to the charge of being insane. That accusation has been leveled at me for many years, and I'll take this opportunity to refute it. I'm not insane, but I am eccentric. Eccentricity is often a sign of a superior intelligence. I'm not trying to say that I have a superior intelligence, because the truth is I don't believe I do. My creative talents are limited to technical spheres. I'm a synthesizer, an enlightened opportunist. I'm a hard worker and I'm stubborn, and above all I'm a man of action. Any such man is eccentric by common standards.

Ridiculing eccentricity is the sign of an inferior intelligence. You told me about your wife's father, how he ordered food in restaurants – two French fried potatoes and six string beans. Now that was really eccentric, and the waiters probably thought he was crazy. That's why they were waiters and he was a rich industrialist. Does your wife think he was crazy?

She thinks he was a great man.

Exactly. My point – and I think it's of the deepest importance that I spell this out for you - is that my eccentricities are intelligent safeguards against the uncommon dangers of life. Every man would behave in a so-called peculiar manner – not necessarily my manner, but his own peculiar manner – if he had the courage.

And the money.

Correct. The money to indulge his wishes and to tell other people to go to hell if they don't like it. That explains in a nutshell why I'm odd. My oddness is the essence of my individuality, which I can afford to express whereas others can't or are too frightened to do so. And so the ones who can't express themselves look at someone like me – what they know of me – and they say, 'He's nuts.'

If you're rich you can structure your life to suit your deepest personal tastes, without fear of the consequences. And any man's personal tastes are – if he expresses them honestly – goddamn peculiar.

Artists are the closest, in this sense, to a man like myself. They have a highly developed sense of their own individuality and they don't mind telling the world to go take a flying fuck at a rolling donut, and I don't, either.

You were saying that you rated people from A to D in terms of cleanliness. What did the ratings mean?

Filthy, Dirty, Moderately Dirty, and Moderately Clean. Moderately Clean was Class A – that was the highest rating I would give.

How many people got Class A ratings in your system?

Very few. And there were other people, of course, who simply wouldn't stand for it, wouldn't wear the two sets of gloves. Too strong-minded.

Where do you rate me?

Look at your fingernails and make a guess.

*   *   *

When I started out in business, there were thousands of men far richer than I in this country. This proves, I believe, that it's not true that the man with the most money always has the advantage. Not if he's a poor business gambler. Then he'll lose his shirt. You have to figure the odds, and when they're in your favor you have to bet and bet hard. If you turn chicken, you're going to lose. I'm sure these are not the high-sounding tales you read in the Madison Avenue magazines about how the mighty men in American industry make their deals. But take it from the horse's mouth, that's the way it happens.

The coming thing in modern American business is the computer. Supposedly no decisions are made until all the data has been fed into the IBM 3600 or the Control Data monster or whatever is being used. But I know how these CEOs operate, and that computer is there like a court jester in the olden days – it's there to amuse the executives and to back up their gut-level decisions. Any businessman worth his salt makes his decision first, based on his gambler's instinct, and then assembles the necessary data to support his decision. And now, sometimes, just to satisfy his stockholders, he gets the bright boys who run the computers to feed all the data in and... well, you know the phrase: 'Garbage in, garbage out.' I heard someone say that ten million monkeys, working nonstop on a problem for a thousand years, could not make the same major mistake that a computer could make in one tenth of a second. In many respects the purpose of the computer is public relations.

I don't say that they're not useful. My companies use them in all our operations, but we don't use them to make decisions. Many of the finest businessmen I know had no more than high-school educations, and in many fields they were totally ignorant. They rose to the top of the business world because they were intelligent gamblers, able to act intuitively and swiftly, far more intelligently than any computer.

Do you think if you hadn't inherited Toolco, you'd still be the billionaire that you are today?

Of course not. But I still would have become a pilot, and I would have turned my energies at some point toward aircraft design. I would have made a lot of money at it. That was built into my genetic makeup. I don't know if I would have become a major figure – what I am now, in an odd sense – but I sure as hell would have created something of value.

I'm a creator, and I'm proud of it. I consider myself a man much maligned, a human being who has made a lot of big splashes but has missed the mark. My own fault. Life is a struggle, and the tools we've got are our muscles, our brains, our imaginations, our will to achieve something, and our ability to sniff out danger – that last is a sixth sense which we share with animals. If you don't use those tools wisely, and you fail, you have no one else to blame. 'The fault, dear Brutus, lies not in our stars, but in ourselves, that we are underlings.' I know that quote well. And not only underlings, but overlings who have missed the mark. In the darker moments, that's how I see myself. If this book has any value, I hope it will have the value of showing such a man. You can't live your life over again, so you might as well learn from it and make an example of it for the people who come after you.

25

*Howard makes a permanent loan to Richard Nixon, and whispers
in a Washington columnist's ear.*

I'VE MENTIONED RICHARD NIXON'S name several times to you,
and this is as good a time as any to tell the story of my involvement
with him.

I want to say at the outset that I have nothing against the man
personally, and in no sense is it my intention to cut him out of the pack
of politicians as a particular target. This just happens to be something
that happened in my life, and therefore I feel the obligation to tell the tale.

I've often believed that every man has the family he deserves, and
Dick Nixon is no exception. He's got the biggest jerk for a brother that
you can imagine. Early in the 1950s Donald Nixon was running a
glorified hamburger stand in the Nixons' home town, Whittier,
California. The restaurant featured the Nixonburger. That was nothing
more than a hamburger, and not a very good one at that.

Don Nixon would have done better running a soup kitchen for the
Salvation Army, or any other nonprofit organization, because,
Nixonburger and all, he was up over his ears in debt. His food
suppliers were dunning him and he couldn't even pay his light bills. In
1957, soon after Dick had been elected Vice-President under
Eisenhower, Don, with this white elephant of a hamburger joint on his
hands, needed $205,000 to bail himself out. And no bank or legitimate
loan institution in its right mind was going to lend two hundred and
five thousand United States dollars on a corner candy store operation
like that.

Dick Nixon would have given his brother the money, I'm sure, but he didn't have a plugged nickel at that time. Politicians make money after they get elected, not before.

It's important to understand that I didn't get wind of his brother being in trouble and make an offer to Nixon. I didn't know who the hell his brother was, and I cared even less. Nixon specifically asked me for the money. Clark Clifford, my lawyer, the man who had worked for Truman when he was president, called from Washington on a secure phone and spelled out the situation. Dick Nixon needed money to save his brother's neck and he wanted it from me.

There was no shilly-shallying about this, nothing cute. It was a direct request for a loan, and it was also pretty clearly an indirect request that the loan be a permanent one.

Why did he come to you?

We had met before and he had me on his list for an emergency. This was the emergency. I had a number of things pending before government agencies at the time – I'll get to those in a minute – and I figured $205,000 worth of juice ought to grease the skids. I agreed to provide the money.

The only security the Nixon family had for the loan was a vacant lot owned by their mother in Whittier, California. They wanted to build a filling station there. As a matter of fact, I own that filling station right now. I had to take it over, much to my annoyance, because it's a pain in the ass. A filling station has no place in the Hughes Empire. But at least I could gas up my car whenever I went to Whittier, and it didn't cost me a nickel.

I had to get this money to Donald Nixon sub rosa, because it wouldn't do, naturally, for the papers to associate a Howard Hughes loan with Dick Nixon's brother. They might think I was looking for favors from the government, especially since Dick was being widely called 'Tricky Dick' and had just barely saved his political skin when he was campaigning with Eisenhower in 1952. You way remember the famous Checkers speech that he made, when he had to explain why these big businessmen in California had him on their payroll at the same time he was a U.S. senator. That's when he cried on television. I always thought he had an onion in his handkerchief.

Anyhow, Noah Dietrich tried to kill the whole idea of the loan. Noah was a rockribbed Republican but he sensed that Nixon might be a little careless about covering up, and this thing could come out as easily as the campaign-contribution thing and we all would have a hard time explaining it the second time around.

Noah was so firm about it that he convinced me it was a mistake.

I said, 'All right, but you'd better go talk to Nixon personally. Explain our position. I don't need him as an enemy.'

Noah went to Washington and saw Nixon. The appointment was in Nixon's office, the vice-presidential suite. He and Noah had lunch together. Noah began to express his fears, but Nixon said that if any of it came out, well, tough titty, he could handle it. He'd been accused of worse things in his life. He said to Noah, 'Don needs the money. I put my family ahead of my career.'

He also dropped a little bombshell on me, via Noah. He said he wanted an additional $200,000, so that his brother could go into another business.

Noah asked him what that business might be, and Nixon said, 'I'll work that out.'

When Noah told him that he didn't believe that Mr. Hughes would want to put up any more money than the sum originally agreed on, if even that, Nixon said, 'Tell Mr. Hughes I'm going to be in U.S. politics for a long time, and there are a great many favors I can do for him over a great many years.'

Noah reported this to me and said, 'Don't do it, Howard. He's slippery.'

'Yes, and loyal to his idiot brother, and thoroughly dishonest. I can use a man like that. We'll give him the money.'

We worked it out and eventually resorted to various methods to get the money to Don Nixon. The full four hundred thousand. In for a penny, in for a pound, as the Brits say.

What did Nixon do for you?

The most important thing was a problem with the CAB, the Civil Aeronautics Board. They wouldn't let TWA deal directly with Toolco, because I owned them both. That squabble had been going on for twelve years and caused me no end of aggravation. A couple of weeks after the loan was made, the CAB lifted that restriction.

Did you specifically ask Nixon to remove the restriction?

I didn't ask Nixon anything. I just saw that a memo with a short list of my problems appeared on his desk. The other important item was that Toolco was involved in an anti-trust suit from the Justice Department. That was settled by a consent decree. And then we had another domestic route granted to TWA, and also we were allowed to stop in Manila on our Far Eastern flights.

In other words, I got my money's worth. About that time Hughes Aircraft received a number of defence contracts, but that didn't really have anything to do with it because the stuff we were turning out was of such superior quality that we would have got those contracts anyhow. Of course, if I'd changed my mind about the loan the way Noah wanted me to – who knows what would have happened? There might have been trouble.

Be that as it may, we covered up pretty well. But when you're dealing with Nixons, with second-rate minds who haven't got the brains to hire better than second-rate minds to work for them – there's no covering up. When someone craps on the table you can't wipe his ass for him. I mean it's too late – you can wipe his ass for him but it doesn't solve the problem. The pile of crap is still there.

We even tried to haul that jerk Don out of the hole he'd dug for himself and show him how to run a restaurant. We set up a committee with Pat DiCicco in charge. Pat had the feeding contract for Hughes Aircraft – brought in box lunches for the guys on the assembly line. He was supposed to know something about the restaurant business.

But Don Nixon didn't like to deal with committees. I can't blame him for that, although in this case it might have saved his bacon, or his Nixonburger, because the restaurant went out of business a couple of months after the committee pulled out.

Meanwhile, of course, we had given him the four hundred and five thousand. I hadn't dared to make it a direct loan. Most of it I passed it to him through a Los Angeles law firm, Waters and Arditto, which I used at the time. It was convenient, because Waters was a friend of Dick Nixon's – there was some tie-in through their wives. The money was sent to Jim Arditto, who did some work for my companies, and had actually taken care of the arrangements for me to get married to Jean in Nevada. And Arditto turned the four hundred grand over to Don Nixon's mother, who passed it along to Don. In return for this, Hannah Nixon, the mother, gave us a mortgage on the gas station, as collateral for the loan, and agreed to pay a monthly mortgage payment of a few hundred dollars. But the lot and gas station were worth, at best, about forty thousand dollars.

Someone had to receive that mortgage payment. We didn't want it to be Toolco, so the mortgage was transferred to an accountant in Waters' office, a guy named Philip Reiner. He was a dummy. I don't mean he was stupid. I mean he was a dummy for Toolco – he held the trust deed on the property in Whittier.

Reiner was a registered Democrat. Nobody seemed to think that mattered at the time, and of course I knew nothing about these details. But bear that fact in mind – he was a Democrat, and I don't think he made any secret of it.

Reiner received the rent checks, and kept them.

One summer day in 1960, three years later, while Nixon was just starting to campaign against Jack Kennedy for the presidency of the United States, an auditor going over the books down at Toolco in Houston found that $205,000 figure standing there all by itself, very lonely, on one page. The other $200,000, fortunately, came from an offshore source, a Mexican corporation that had a bank account in the Cayman Islands. No one in Toolco knew about that.

But the two hundred five thousand had been there on our books for three years and the auditor wanted to know what it was all about. It passed along up the line and it got to Arditto's office in Los Angeles. Arditto figured that the men in Houston were asking him to account for the rent money. He called in Philip Reiner, who been pocketing the few hundred bucks a month rent – by then the total was about ten thousand dollars. Peanuts. But not peanuts to the auditor at Toolco. And certainly the two hundred and five thousand on the books, which nobody could really account for, wasn't peanuts.

Arditto said to Reiner, 'I guess you'd better pay them back the ten thousand.'

Reiner walked out of Arditto's office in a huff. He walked straight to his lawyer's office and told the lawyer what had happened, and he mentioned the Hughes Tool Company. The lawyer looked up the mortgage property and found that it belonged to Hannah Nixon, the Vice-President's mother.

Reiner was a Democrat and his lawyer was a Democrat. Zing, they saw the implications of the whole thing, and the lawyer in Los Angeles sent Reiner to Washington to talk to another lawyer, a guy named McInerney, a close friend of Bobby Kennedy.

McInerney and the Kennedys got together. But they still had a problem. They didn't have any real evidence, and they knew nothing at all about the additional two hundred grand that had gone through the Cayman Islands. They only had Reiner's version of the mortgage story, but they didn't have any actual proof that Reiner was a dummy for Toolco, and Reiner didn't want his head on any chopping block. There was a notarized paper that spelled it all out, but Reiner didn't have it. He'd given it to Arditto as part of the so-called security arrangements, and Arditto had locked it in a safe, and for all the Kennedys knew had even destroyed it after the first phone call came from Houston saying, 'What's going on?'

Now comes a little ironic twist in this. Jack and Bobby Kennedy wanted Reiner to be as clean as possible in the event they could get the evidence and break the story, so they gave him $10,000 – or whatever the total of the rent money was that Reiner had received for holding the trust deed on the Whittier property – and told him to return it to Arditto. Reiner returned it, and eventually it made its way back to Toolco. The irony, if you boil the money trail down to its simplest elements, is that the Kennedys paid the mortgage on Dick Nixon's mother's gas station in Whittier.

And then – well, I've said this before but I'll say it again. The stupidity of intelligent, educated people never ceases to amaze me. Quite a while ago Arditto had Xeroxed the Nixon mortgage file, and put a copy in Reiner's filing cabinet. Why he did that we never found out. Reiner never knew it was there – it was buried in with a lot of junk.

A few days after he got back from Washington to Los Angeles, Reiner called Arditto to make sure the check for $10,000 had been received, and Reiner said, 'Oh, by the way, I left some papers in your office. Would you mind sending them over to me?' He was setting up new office space for himself in Santa Monica. So Arditto emptied out the desk and the filing cabinet – didn't even look what was in it – and sent it to Santa Monica.

Reiner casually looked through it before he put it in a new file cabinet. There was the copy of the Nixon file. Most important, there was the notarized paper setting him up to hold the trust deed.

I know that seems an incredible story, but it's really not so incredible, not if you accept the fact that intelligence is an ability, not a permanent state of mind. People don't seem to be able to use their intelligence more than a few minutes a day.

Arditto forgot to plug in his intelligence that day, and he just said, 'Get these files the hell out of my office and over to this guy's new office in Santa Monica.'

This was shortly before the elections. Reiner gave all the material to McInerney, who put together a reasonably accurate account of the whole deal and fed it to the newspapers.

But they wouldn't publish it. They didn't believe it.
But McInerney and Reiner had proof.
Proof is only proof when you're in the mood to believe it's proof. I think the newspapers didn't want to be accused of a last-minute smear campaign against poor Dick Nixon, who had been knocked from pillar to post already by Jack Kennedy. Maybe they figured it wasn't dignified. The only guy who would touch it was Drew Pearson, and even he said, 'Not until after the election.'

I watched from afar. Although Pearson and the newspapers

wouldn't touch the story, they did make a few inquiries to the Nixon people, and Nixon panicked. He must have convinced himself that he'd better scotch the snake before it bites. After all, he was paranoid, and he didn't know the newspapers didn't have proof or were reluctant to print it. *He* knew it was true and he couldn't be sure the newspapers didn't know it was true.

Robert Finch, his campaign manager, came roaring out and made a statement to the press that there had been a personal loan to Donald Nixon by his old friend Frank Waters, Arditto's partner, and Howard Hughes and Toolco had nothing to do with it, and Dick Nixon hadn't known anything about it, he was pure as the driven snow. They called it a last-minute smear attempt on the part of the Democrats.

Drew Pearson blew his top at this hypocrisy and decided not to wait until after the election, and he broke the story with all the details – in fact, quite a few more details than the accountant and McInerney had supplied him with.

That came about because I had come to the conclusion over the years that Nixon was not very bright. Cunning and wildly ambitious, but not intelligent. Not eccentric. Common. Vulgar. I'd watched him on television and he always looked to me like a vacuum-cleaner salesman who just knocked on your door and is trying to sell you an out-of-date model. I had decided that Jack Kennedy was the better man. I was fond of the Kennedys, especially Bobby, and I thought the country needed a president who didn't have a brother who made Nixonburgers. So the rest of the details leaked to Drew Pearson. Not all, not everything I've told you, but more than the file showed. Someone whispered in Mr. Pearson's ear where to look. Mr. Pearson looked, and Mr. Pearson found.

Finch tried to deny Pearson's accusation, but he had to admit, finally, that the money had come from Toolco. However, Richard Nixon hadn't known anything about it and no favors had been done in return for it, which any human being with even a quarter of a brain could see was a blatant lie.

There was a hell of a fuss. This was a week or two before the election

– a touch and go situation, if you recall. Nixon was already in trouble because he hadn't done well in the TV debates against Kennedy – too much five-o'clock-shadow, they said.

Some people say that loan cost Dick Nixon the presidential election. I never saw myself as a power behind the scenes in Washington, but I did my bit. Every businessman need friends in high places. I did my bit, and I saw to it that Jack Kennedy knew that I did it.

Did you tell Pearson about the second Cayman Island loan?

No one has ever known about that until now.

Can you give me some more details?

I've probably told you too much already. If that ever came out, Nixon would probably be impeached. I'm pretty sure that taking a bribe, even though he was only Vice President when he took it, fits the founding fathers' definition of 'high crimes and misdemeanors.'

But it's going to come out in your autobiography.

Let the chips fall where they may.

26

Howard makes promises he can't keep, buys jets he can't pay for, negotiates at a garbage dump, makes a grown man cry, fires his oldest employee, gets married again, and hunts for a missing cat.

I'VE ALREADY TOLD you about the beginning of my involvement with TWA. But it was a three-act drama, and now I'm going to tell you Act Two. I had dozens of lawyers and advisers on this case who were milking me dry, telling me: 'Don't do this, Howard,' or, 'If you do that, Howard, the jig is up.' Night and day they nagged at me. I felt like one of those experimental rats that keeps getting new charges of electricity shoved up his ass no matter which part of the cage he moves to: 'Let's see how long he can stand it, before he goes nuts.'

This all started in 1954, although the real crisis came later and lasted six years, from 1957 to 1963. If I hadn't loved that airline so much, I would have walked out and said, 'Let it go down the drain.' It took ten years off my life. What it did to my marriage and my personal effort to get my head clear, can't be measured in years or any other form of measurement. Of course in the end I have no one else but myself to blame for allowing it to happen, but you never see that when you're in the thick of battle.

The man I got to replace Jack Frye was Ralph Damon, who at that time ran American Airlines. He'd done good things with American, but they weren't going anyplace then and TWA was. So I made it known to him that I was interested in his meeting with me, with a view to his becoming president of TWA. This has to be done carefully, because it's not considered good form to go around propositioning the president of one airline to take over the presidency of another. Damon had to sneak away from his offices, and I had to take extreme security precautions at the time. As a result, Damon sat in a hotel room for four days in Beverly Hills waiting for me. I didn't know where he was and I didn't know when he was supposed to arrive, and he knew even less about my whereabouts. When I didn't show up he got annoyed. I don't remember who he was in touch with then, but he told them he never wanted to hear from me again.

Of course that wasn't true. We arranged another meeting, this time in Houston. I checked into the Rice Hotel under another name. But I forgot to tell Ralph Damon the details. So he checked into another hotel in Houston and we spent two days without either of us knowing the other was there or how to get in touch.

I was there in my room catching up on my sleep. You know, I can go up to forty-eight hours without sleep, but then every now and then I need a long stretch in bed, a good hard bed with a board. I can sleep for twenty-four hours. It doesn't happen often, but it happened then, and while it was happening Ralph Damon was running all over Houston like a chicken with its head cut off, and finally he left.

He said a second time, 'I never want to see that fucking Howard Hughes again.'

The point, of course, was that he had *never* seen me.

I never did get to meet him. Eventually I got Noah to arrange things, because Noah operated in a more conventional manner. Noah offered him the job and we signed him up for five years.

Ralph Damon was a fine president. He was able to act on my decisions as few other men have. TWA was the first airline to come up with the idea of the two-class service. That was my idea. I got hold of Ralph on the phone and I said, 'People are snobbish. If we divide that plane into two sections, quite a few passengers are going to pay a lot more money just to ride forward in the first class section separated from the cattle in the back, and the people in the back are going to feel they've got a bargain. It's a win-win situation. Sales will go up.'

Ralph grasped the concept, and did it. That put TWA on the map again as a pioneer. And that's become the standard system for airline passenger traffic.

But I tried to stay away from Damon because he was an excitable man. I heard once, and I have no reason to doubt it, that after a telephone conversation we'd had, he cried himself to sleep. I felt terrible about that, because I don't think I said anything to hurt his feelings. Maybe he had difficulty that time in interpreting my suggestions.

Unfortunately, he died while he was still president of TWA. Some people say that I drove him to his grave. It wasn't true. He had cancer of the intestines.

Did you have more TWA stock, at this point, than the original stock you'd bought?

I had been buying the stock all along. I'm a heavy plunger. I believe in putting all my eggs in one basket and watching them hatch.

The situation after the war was as follows. All the airlines were running piston aircraft, but the jet age was just over the horizon and you had to be blind not to see it. They thought the propjet, the turbo-prop, would bridge the gap for a while, but that was a mistake. The gap narrowed too quickly. In the early 1950s all the airplane manufacturers – Douglas, Boeing, Lockheed, Martin, and the Convair Division of General Dynamics – were scrambling to get jets into production. Everyone wanted a piece of the action. And all the airlines were trying to make up their minds which manufacturers to buy from.

A conversion like this meant huge loans, many hundreds of millions of dollars. The ones who were really licking their chops were the banks. You don't just say overnight, 'Okay, scrap the piston planes and buy the jets.' Not only was it a tremendous financial investment, but it involved retraining programs of pilots, mechanics, personnel of all types, changeover of hangar facilities and ground facilities. It was not something anyone plunged into. You could have been jumping off the diving board into an empty pool.

But anyone with a half a brain knew that the pool was filling up and the plunge had to be taken. I flatter myself that I've got half a brain. I went shopping. I decided right away that Boeing and Convair were going to make the planes to fit my needs.

Again, that decision was not so simple, because it's not like buying a vacuum cleaner from a salesman who comes in and says, 'See? This is our vacuum cleaner. Try it out. If you like it, buy it.' Unlike the vacuum cleaner, the planes didn't yet exist. And if we were going to buy a jet from Boeing, we had to tell Boeing precisely what our needs would be. To give you an example, each plane has a different seating potential. These planes were mocked up in the initial stages so that you could have a bank of three on the starboard side and a bank of two on the port side, or similar combinations. Dozens of other configurations had to be specifically arranged between the manufacturer and the airline.

With my attention to details, and you know what I'm talking about because you've read my memo about Jane Russell's brassiere, I think I drove those airplane guys up the wall. But they let me do it. The men are who run American business receive annual salaries that run into the tens of millions of dollars. And yet if their companies prosper, it's usually in spite of them, not because of them.

In 1955 I decided to buy jets from Jack Zevely, the boss at Convair. I was late making up my mind, but I finally did make it up. However, Jack thought I was a bit peculiar because of the way we started negotiations. I didn't want the other airlines to know which planes TWA was going to buy. Moreover, I wasn't sure that I was going to buy them at all. Beyond that, I wanted to keep the other manufacturers, like Boeing and Douglas, on the hook a little bit – so everything had to be done with the utmost secrecy.

I conducted my negotiations with Jack where I usually conduct my negotiations. I would instruct him to meet me in a specific remote area. One time we met at Indio in the California desert and then I drove him to a spot adjacent to the municipal garbage dump in Palm Springs. It was a hot night. Jack kept saying, 'Open the windows, Howard.'

I said, 'No, let's keep the windows closed so we can talk privately.'

'It's stifling,' Jack complained.

I finally opened them, with great reluctance, and then he realized we were next to the municipal garbage dump. The stink came through the windows of the car, and he yelled, 'For Christ's sake, Howard, close the windows!'

TWA didn't buy those jets from Convair, which disappointed Jack a great deal, because there had been protracted negotiations. The problem was that Ralph Damon had already made arrangements to buy another plane from Douglas Aircraft, and I had to back him up. He'd put his signature on paper – all I'd done was talk to a man a few times in a car. I chewed Ralph out for acting without my final approval, and I guess that's the time he cried himself to sleep. I called him a few nasty names. I thought he was a big boy and could take it, but I guess he couldn't.

I felt bad about breaking off the negotiations with Convair. They had plans to build a long-range jet, so I went to them and said, 'I want a dozen.' But they were slow. God, they were slow. Actually I worked with Jack Zevely on the design, and Jack has made statements since then that he never could have designed that plane without me. As it turned out, unfortunately, he couldn't sell that one to me, either, because the planning took so long that by the time we'd finished it, the prototype of the Boeing 707 was in the air, the Dash-80, and the Douglas DC-8 hard on its heels, and Convair was out in the cold. Boeing and Douglas had made better planes.

Convair blamed me for this. But Jack Zevely didn't have to do what I said. Any time he wanted to, Jack could have frozen the design and put that ship on the production line. He didn't have to listen to me – I wasn't God.

I started negotiating at one point with Lockheed, with Bob Gross. But he knew me too well and once I started making too many demands he turned the tables on me. One night at around 10 P.M. my private telephone rang. For once I happened to be asleep. I woke up quickly, alarmed, because no one who had that number would have called me at that hour unless it was on a terribly important matter. I grabbed the receiver and croaked, 'Hello? What's the matter?'

A voice said, 'Knock, knock.'

I was too befuddled to say anything except, 'Who's there?'

'Howard.'

I recognized Bob Gross's voice, but I thought I might be wrong, and I was still dazed, so I said: 'Howard who?'

Bob Gross said, 'Howard you like to go fuck yourself, you goddamn maniac!'

Then he hung up, and I couldn't get back to sleep – so he had his revenge for all those nights I'd driven him around the Nevada desert.

Meanwhile the Convair management was running around in circles. They abandoned the long-range jet and decided to go for something in-between, an intermediate. I still felt bad about what had happened, so I called Jack Zevely and found out what he was doing. I said, 'I have complete faith in you and Convair, and I want the first thirty medium-range planes that roll off the line. 'And let's paint them gold, not silver.' My engineers had developed a process to anodize aluminum so that it looked like gold, blazed in the sun, wouldn't pit or tarnish. I offered it to the Convair people at no charge and they were delighted.

They came up with the CV-880. But it was supposed to be a medium-range aircraft, and it turned out to be a long-range jet, which meant it had to compete with the DC-8 and the 707, planes that were already operational. The 707 was a tremendous success right from the word go. Not as fast as Douglas's plane, but handled nicely, a sturdy aircraft. She had problems, of course. Landing was one of them – they'd built the engine pods a little too close to the ground to keep them away from the fuel tanks in the wings, and on a crosswind landing you had trouble banking her, you could knock off a pod on the runway. And they'd yaw a lot if the damper wasn't functioning one hundred percent.

You see, the Convair people, from the very beginning, had made a mistake in the negotiations with me. When I go in to negotiate with a man, or a company, I assume from the beginning that everybody's out for his own interests, and from the beginning you've got to lean on the other guy. If he's worth his salt he's going to try and lean on you, and you have to get in the first push. So I started leaning on Convair from the beginning, and I leaned, and I leaned, and they fell right over without a whimper. They weren't donkeys, they were lapdogs.

I had a great deal of faith in the plane we were going to develop, the 880. I didn't want my competition using it – Pan Am and American and United. So Convair and I reached an understanding that they wouldn't sell the 880 to anybody except TWA and airlines such as Delta who flew other routes and weren't in competition with TWA. Now that, you must admit – to agree to a restrictive condition like that – was pretty dumb of them.

There was a time limit, of course. But by the time the time limit was up, United and American had committed themselves to planes from Boeing and Douglas, and Convair wound up holding the bag – the empty bag. They blamed me, but all I did was negotiate powerfully. If they had negotiated powerfully against me, we would have come to some more reasonable arrangement.

I knew Jack Zevely was under a lot of pressure, especially during these design sessions with me. He wasn't used to staying up all night. Moreover, I had an advantage in that I absolutely controlled my company. For all practical purposes I owned TWA, whereas Zevely and all these guys I dealt with were representing a bunch of stockholders and had to watch their step.

But I tried to do everything I could for the man. Once, after we'd been talking half the night, I said, 'What you need is a little pick-me-up, Jack, and I'm going to take you to the movies.' I arranged a private midnight showing of a new film at RKO – *Jet Pilot*. I got Janet Leigh to come down, and Janet sat next to him during the show and cuddled up to him. He fell sound asleep.

Jack Zevely made a very unkind remark afterwards. He said the 880 was not named after the eighty-eight seats it was supposed to have, but for the '880 ridiculous goddamnned conferences' he'd had with Howard Hughes.

I hadn't picked up these 880s yet, because the changes hadn't been made that I had insisted on. I decided I didn't want the planes. They hadn't styled them exactly the way I wanted them, but I said to myself, 'Jesus, I've got to give these guys a break.' And they'd come up with a new plane by then, the Convair 990, so I said, 'All right, give me a dozen of those.'

And you got those?

No. I had to cancel that order too. By then I'd bought Boeing 707s.

And I didn't have any more spare cash. You see, to start this financing program after the war, we needed $500 million. That's big money. I called Noah Dietrich one day and said, 'Noah, where the hell am I going to get this $500 million?'

'What $500 million?' he asked.

'Pay attention to your job,' I said. 'Get out the files and look and see what the goddamn TWA's committed itself to.'

He called me back two days later and said, 'Howard, where are we going to get the $500 million to buy these airplanes?' That was Noah.

Toolco had a hundred million in cash, profits from the expansion program that we had gone into recently. But that left us four hundred million short. Noah wanted a bond issue, because he wasn't sure that Toolco's profits would continue in the same way. The bond issue was meant to be a sort of insurance against the possibility of profits dropping off down at Houston. But he wanted not only a bond issue guaranteed by Hughes Tool, but a bond issue with a conversion clause – meaning that the bondholders could convert at a given point into common stock or preferred stock, whichever the hell it was. This meant in effect that they could take part of Toolco away from me, and I wasn't having any of that. I said, 'No dice.'

We worked out some sort of compromise, because we had to come up with the money. I got Fred Brandi of Dillon Read in New York to start the ball rolling – you need a syndicate, you understand, to float an issue of that size. Fred went ahead, and then the details filtered back to me and I realized I could lose my ownership of Toolco this way. That's what everybody wanted in the long run – they wanted to take Toolco away from me.

I called Fred and said, 'Forget it. Kill it.'

My father always said, 'Watch out for partners.' And what could be worse than being partners with several thousand greedy stockholders? They never care about the company, they just care about the price of the stock.

It was then that Noah Dietrich committed the most irresponsible act of his business life. I was buried up to my neck in the problem of trying to find $400 million, and he went off on a vacation to shoot a goddamn elephant in Africa. He said he was going on safari, but I have a feeling he just wanted to hide out down there. He said I had been so indecisive in the buying of the new jets that he couldn't stand it, and I wasn't taking his advice now, and he was going.

Don't you think it's true that you had been indecisive?

Because I kept changing my mind? That's not indecision. That was just an intelligent reaction to changing circumstances. The Convair people promised me they could do certain things and then when it turned out they couldn't do them, I backed away. Then they came up with a new set of promises, and dropped the ball there too. I knew what I wanted and they couldn't deliver.

Noah, however, called it indecision, and told me I was being irrational in the matter of raising the money for TWA, and he elected to flee. I did everything I could to stop him, not out of selfish reasons, except insofar as the company was in trouble and I needed Noah. I offered him six months' vacation if he'd just wait until the troubles were over, but he wanted his three weeks in Tanganyika. I telephoned him at Kennedy Airport in New York – had him paged. I pleaded with him. I got down on my knees – I didn't literally get down on my knees, because I was on the telephone – but verbally I got down on my knees. I said, 'Noah, please don't go. I need you.'

'Goodbye, Howard,' he said, 'I'll see you in three weeks.'

By the time the great white hunter got back I'd come up with an interim solution. For one thing, I stalled, and while I did that, TWA began to do better, so that it turned out we didn't need that much cash at all. I squeezed what I could out of Toolco and Equitable Life and the Bank of America and Irving Trust – maybe $30 million. I got it by means of short-term 90-day notes guaranteed by Toolco.

An incident happened there that seemed minor at the time, but if I'd had my thinking cap on I would have realized that it was a portent of the future. These 90-day notes were renewable, and the second or third time I wanted to renew them – this was a $12 million loan from Equitable Life – they balked.

How much did TWA owe by that time?

It wasn't so much a question of how much TWA owed, it was a question of our long-term commitments for jets. That, at the time, amounted to around $300 million. I wanted the loan to be renewed and the guys up at Equitable got a little stuffy and said, 'Give us the details on your long-term financing.' In other words, they wanted to know specifically how I planned to find the rest of the three hundred million. I said, more or less, 'It's none of your business. Do you want to lend me the twelve million or don't you?'

'Well, sure,' they said, 'we know you're good for it, or at least Toolco's good for it, but we'd like to have some guarantee for the future, and for our stockholders.'

This was just doubletalk. Then they got around to the point.

You remember that back in 1948 I loaned TWA $10 million which I eventually converted into stock, and that's how I first got control of the airline. Equitable Life had been mixed up in that, in the sense that they had also loaned TWA $40 million. They were my principal creditor, and one of the conditions they put on my conversion rights was that if TWA defaulted on its payments to Equitable, then my stock would be put into a voting trust controlled by them.

They brought this up again in 1958 when I wanted to renew the ninety-day notes. 'Sure, Howard,' they said, 'we'll give you the money, but if you don't complete the long-term financing within a set period of time, let's think about that voting trust possibility.'

This was said by a man named Oates, who ran Equitable. I got the drift, and I said, 'Thank you very much, Mr. Oates. I've decided I don't need your $12 million anymore. You'll have it back within a week.'

I dug into the till at Toolco and came up with the twelve million, plus interest, and paid them back. They said at the time I was gun-shy, and they were right. They didn't exactly stick a gun in my ribs, but I could see it bulging in the holster under their collective armpit, so I paid them back.

What I didn't realize then was that when the real tussle came they wouldn't just whip out a .38 caliber automatic, they'd come at me with bazookas and Sherman tanks, and if I ducked behind a wall to hide there'd be ten guys in gray suits and sincere ties waiting for me with switchblade knives. And I also didn't realize that these bankers and insurance company presidents were a gang. I made the mistake of assuming they operated semi-independently.

I bypassed Equitable and went to Ben Sessel at Irving Trust and borrowed $26 million from them. That was another major mistake, but I didn't realize it at the time.

Meanwhile I got another estimate of what Toolco was worth. I got it from Merrill Lynch and a couple of those other brokerage houses I was always using to find out where I stood. 'Fifty million,' they said. The way they came up with their figure was based on a formula – a price-earnings ratio. In this case they'd figured the company was worth about fourteen times net earnings. Now, this meant that if you can raise the earnings, then the value of the company is that much higher. For every million dollars more that the company could earn each year, it would be worth fourteen million more in its stock price.

So in the middle of May 1957, I decided I wanted Noah to go down to Houston again and work with Toolco, because I was sure we could get more money out of Toolco, boost its earnings and therefore boost its potential sales price. I asked Noah to stop by my bungalow in the Beverly Hills Hotel so that we could discuss it.

I had started to grow long hair and a beard around that time. I hadn't seen Noah for a month or two and when he came in the door he said, 'Howard, you look like a gorilla.'

'Noah,' I replied, 'if your knowledge of finance matched your knowledge of zoology, you'd be a poor man. A gorilla may have long hair, but as far as I know no member of the species has ever been able to grow a gray beard.'

'All right,' he said, 'you look like a Neanderthal.'

'The way I look,' I told him, 'is none of your goddamn business.'

This still had me annoyed when we got down to business, and then Noah said he didn't want to go to Houston. He said he was comfortable in California and he saw no reason for it.

'Hell, there's a damn good reason for it,' I said. 'We need more earnings because we need a higher valuation.'

He told me he needed to discuss it with his wife, that she was tired of his running off on errands so often. The next day he called me and said, 'I'll go, but on one condition.'

'What's that?'

He wanted more money. Half a million a year plus expenses wasn't enough for him. He had been nagging me for years for a piece of the company, stock options, and some way that his income could be capital gains. He was greedy, that's common enough. Each time he would nag me I would eventually throw some bone his way to make him happy.

He sprang this to me on the telephone. I said, 'You get the hell over here.' I was furious. He was trying to hold a club over my head.

I was still at the Beverly Hills Hotel. But by the time he got there I decided I didn't want to see him.

When he called me from the house phone in the lobby I told him to get to a public phone, which infuriated him. He insisted on coming out to the bungalow.

'Noah,' I said, 'there's absolutely no need for you to come out. I don't want to hear any more remarks about my gorilla-like or Neanderthal-like appearance, and we can talk more easily on the telephone. Just get to a more private public telephone. Any hotel employee can listen in on a house phone.'

I moved him around to a couple more telephones until finally he was at one that I considered safe. By then he was nearly out of his mind with fury.

'What kind of raise do you want?' I asked.

What he wanted was profit-sharing and a capital gains agreement – a slice of the apple pie.

'Noah, we've discussed this before and I said no. I've made you a rich man. Now you're pushing me.'

And then he said something which instantly severed both our personal relationship and our business relationship. He made a speech to me about how I had been promising him this arrangement for years. That was not true. He wound up by saying that he had finally come to the conclusion that I had no integrity and he didn't trust me. He wanted to send his lawyer to talk to my lawyer, and he wanted a decision within forty-eight hours.

'Noah, you're insulting me, and you're trying to hold a gun to my head. Nobody does that. You're fired. If you're in this hotel five minutes from now, I'll have the management throw you out onto Sunset Boulevard. If that happens, be careful. There's a lot of traffic.' And I hung up.

I called my people at Romaine Street and had the locks changed on his door and on his desk.

But you had such a long relationship with him – he'd worked with you for over thirty years. Didn't it pain you to lose a man who was in many ways closer to you than most people?

He was never really close to me. At least I wasn't close to him. And by then, not at all. There are other men who I've met more briefly, men with whom I've lost contact, or who have died, whose passing from my life I've mourned far more deeply than Noah Dietrich. He viewed me the way a stockholder views a stock he owns. He didn't care about me, he cared about wringing as much profit as he could out of me. He pushed me too far.

And you didn't miss him after that, as a business adviser?

I missed him all the time. I got into a lot of trouble because he wasn't there to keep me in check with his narrow and conservative bookkeeper's mind. I realize that all too well. But you have to draw the line somewhere. I drew it, and I took the consequences.

Who were you close to at that time?

Mostly Jean, my wife.

I'm glad you brought up her name. You've steadfastly avoided the subject of your second marriage to Jean Peters. Don't you think it's time you talked about it?

No, but I also think you'll make my life more miserable than it is now if I keep on successfully dodging the marriage to Jean, so I'm willing to deal with it – up to a point.

Do you remember Groucho Marx's famous remark when he was invited to join the Beverly Hills Country Club? He said, 'I wouldn't join any club that would have me as a member.' That's my feeling about marriage to me. I can't truly fathom how a woman in her right mind would want to do it. I'm not good husband material. I'm too fixed in my ways. I'm generous, and when I get involved with a woman I take a great interest in her, but there's too much else on my mind for me to satisfy a woman's needs. And I do have my quirks.

Having said that, let me also say that Jean is one of the most delightful and loyal human beings on the planet. And she's intelligent. Which makes me wonder why she married me. But she did, and that's a fact. Why I married her is of course easier to understand. I was lonely, and tired of messing around with all those Hollywood beauties who were pursuing their careers nonstop and, no matter how fond of me they professed to be, basically out for what they could get. Jean wasn't like that. She was a caring person. And I cared for her. I really loved her, respected her, and wanted the best for her. She reminded me a great deal of my first wife, Ella. Make of that what you will.

I thought, if I marry Jean, that will bring stability and common sense to my life. I won't worry so much about things like TWA and Hughes Aircraft – I'll go for walks in the country and watch a movie and sit down to dinner at dinnertime like a normal man with his normal wife. I'll have someone to care for me when I'm old and crippled, as I knew was inevitable after all the plane crashes I'd had and the damage I'd done to my body. If you damage the body, you also damage the mind. Mind and body are one. I thought Jean might stop me from losing my mind.

I proposed to her after many years of seeing her off and on, and she accepted. She loved me. She'd been married once before, to a businessman named Stuart Cramer III, but that didn't work out, and the funny thing is that after he and Jean were divorced Cramer married my old girlfriend Terry Moore. Maybe there's only a limited pool of women for every man and vice versa. These things are mysteries.

Jean and I were married in Tonopah, Nevada by a local justice of the peace, using other names to avoid publicity. That's legal in Nevada. We flew down there in January 1957 in one of my Connies and the whole thing didn't take more than three hours.

Where did you go on a honeymoon?

Right back to the Beverly Hills Hotel. I was too involved in the TWA horror to have a proper honeymoon. We didn't even live together at first, mostly because my living habits were so outrageous that Jean wouldn't stand for them. I intended to change them, and I told her so, but not just yet. We lived in separate bungalows at the Beverly Hills Hotel and we could see each other whenever we liked, but at least she didn't have to listen to me doing business on the telephone at three o'clock in the morning and raiding the fridge at five o'clock for a bowl of French vanilla ice cream, which was my favorite.

I had five bungalows rented there at the hotel. One for Jean, one for me, one for business staff, one for cooks and waiters, and one for storage of my ice cream supply, cases of Poland Springs mineral water, plenty of Kleenex and soft toilet paper, and a few cartons of white athletic socks. I can't stand the idea of running out of socks or soft toilet paper so I always keep a large supply handy.

We didn't really lead a normal life, that was the problem. When I wanted to divert myself from business I'd go over to the Goldwyn Studios with Jean and screen a few movies. I could watch two or three in a row but she would inevitably fall asleep. Then at one point I got tired of the facilities Goldwyn offered me so I found a producer named Marty Nosseck who was willing to let me screen movies in his private screening room on Sunset Boulevard. Actually, I moved in there.

Into the screening room?

Yes, Marty Nosseck was very understanding about that, and I paid him well. My needs were few. I had a bed moved in and a supply of Kleenex and toilet paper, and a few telephones, and that's where I conducted the TWA negotiations. I had a room there for my aides and my projectionists. I lived in the screening room for about three months.

What about Jean?

It was hard on her. Finally she put her foot down. She reminded me of all the promises I'd made her, especially that we would have a house where we could live together as man and wife. So on my fifty-fifth birthday, in 1960, I gave up the screening room and we moved into a house on an estate near Rancho Santa Fe in San Diego County. Jean wanted me to buy it, of course, but I said, 'Let's try it out first and see how things to.' I was a little frightened by the whole idea.

There was trouble right away. Not only couldn't I give up my nocturnal business habits, and my eating habits, and my quite considerable and realistic precautions against germs and harmful bacteria, but we had a problem with her cat.

You were able to live in a house with a cat?

I love animals. They're a lot cleaner than human beings. And a cat particularly is a clean animal. Jean loved her cat, which was a spayed female called Sweetness, gray and white and very friendly-looking. I often stroked her fur, which was like mink, and tickled her under the chin, and she purred a lot when I paid attention to her. I guess I was very fond of that animal.

And then one day it vanished. Just vanished. Didn't come home that night as it always did. I thought it might have been kidnapped but Jean said that was ridiculous. Nevertheless, she was deeply upset, and I went out of my mind trying to locate that cat. I had my entire staff combing the neighboring estates and all of Rancho Santa Fe, and I hired a team of local rent-a-cops to supplement them, including four men on horseback and a helicopter. I told my people,

'This is not the Everglades, this is not New York City with its dense population. This is a civilized bucolic area free of predators. Find that goddamn cat!'

And did they find her?

No, but she wandered in on her own a couple of nights later, a little the worse for wear – a cut on her nose and a patch of fur missing. Jean wept for joy.

That, however, was the end of our sojourn in Rancho Santa Fe. I knew the cat could go off again to meet with whatever cat she'd been hanging out with the time she vanished, and the plumbing in the house was lousy, so we moved back to Los Angeles where I rented a place in Bel Air. It was a large house and Jean and Sweetness lived in a separate part of it, although she - Jean, not Sweetness – visited me at least twice a day. I wasn't feeling well at this time. I was taking codeine for pain and Valium to calm my nerves. I was under tremendous pressure.

27

Howard learns that Time, Life, *and* Fortune *are out to get him, that his personal physician is trying to have him certified insane, meets with a banker on the beach of East Hampton, and is sued by his own company.*

NOW THAT WE'VE investigated my domestic life, I'll get back to TWA: Act Three of the horror story. Be aware that from this point on, I was without Noah Dietrich. No one except my lawyers was advising me.

TWA was flying at 96% capacity, which is phenomenal. Our net profit per day pole-vaulted to an average of $175,000. The airline under my guidance was making big money. But suddenly I got wind that the Luce empire had decided there was a crack in the Hughes empire, and this was the time to pour troops through the breech and batter down the gates. They used *Fortune,* their most prestigious and conservative magazine, to do the job.

This attack had nothing to do with journalistic ethics or the search for truth. It had to do with the fact that Clare Booth Luce still hated me for turning down *Pilate's Wife*, and she wanted revenge. So Henry Luce, her accommodating husband, did the job for her.

The guy who was going to write the *Fortune* story was a writer named Charles Murphy, who had already pilloried me once before, in 1953, when *Fortune* published an article about Hughes Aircraft. Now it was the turn of TWA.

Murphy had been around already talking to people, and he made no bones about what he intended to do. I did a lot of banking then with the Bank of America, and my man there was Keith Carver. Murphy had gone to Keith and told him he was going to pick up a literary axe and bury it in my skull.

I was still in Rancho Santa Fe when I called Frank McCulloch, Los Angeles bureau chief for *Time,* and the last reporter I ever let interview me. He was a good man, a fair man, and he could speak his mind to Henry Luce, the pope of Madison Avenue. I begged him to call off the wolves. I said, 'Frank, I don't deserve this. You people are doing an unfair thing.'

McCulloch went to Luce on my behalf. Luce turned him down. All my begging came to nothing. They went ahead and printed the article.

Aside from Luce, who was trying to cut my throat in public, there were plenty of men trying to cut it in private, and the foremost among them was the president of Boeing, William Allen. Mr. Allen had never forgiven me for holding off on my purchase of Boeing jets while I was dickering with Convair. When I was sitting out there at Palm Springs at the municipal dump with Jack Zevely, Bill Allen in Seattle wanted to know, 'Why doesn't Howard Hughes invite *me* to the municipal dump?'

My order for sixty-three jets was the largest in history, and thirty-three of those were supposed to be supplied by Boeing. That was a $186 million order, and I paid $39 million cash in advance in order to show good faith. And now they were dunning me for more money.

I staved them off a little bit because the Medical Institute owed Toolco $18 million, and after a little maneuvering we were able to use that to pay some of what we owed Boeing. But we were still short. In the meantime, the situation was that Toolco owned all the planes and was leasing them to TWA day by day. That was absurd. I owned both companies, Toolco and TWA, I had to take it from my left-hand pocket and put it in my right-hand pocket – but with all sorts of financial and governmental restrictions on it.

Considering that I needed money to get Boeing off my back, I'd just about make up my mind to go along with Fred Brandi of Dillon Read. He'd worked out a way to come up with $350 million where I'd still have a reasonable measure of control and wouldn't have to give up any part of Toolco. The only hook in it, and this had been proposed by Haggerty of the Met, which made me figure he was the villain of the piece, was a little rider in the financing agreement. That rider said that if there were any major adverse developments in the airline itself, or in its management, then the banks and the insurance companies had the right to pull out of the deal.

And there was a hook in the hook, which turned out to be more pertinent. Once the financing was completed, if there were any adverse developments in TWA's management after that date, they'd have to be rectified within ninety days or else my stock – which the syndicate was holding as collateral against the loan – would go into a trusteeship.

I considered stepping in and taking over the presidency of the airline. I thought that might be the solution. I tentatively suggested it to one of those insurance companies, I think to Equitable, and I was told if I did that they'd foreclose immediately – like I was a leper. Believe me, these lepers at Lambaréné got better treatment, more respect, than I did from these Eastern bankers. And they invoked the 'adverse-development clause,' which meant I had ninety days to pull a rabbit out of a hat.

What were your choices? What could they have done to you?

What they wanted to do was get me to turn my stock over to a trustee – namely them, or some guy who was fronting for them. The alternative was for me to find the money elsewhere so I could pay off my creditors. Or else I could declare TWA bankrupt.

While I was trying to figure all this out, suddenly, from out of left field, the Civil Aeronautics Board got after me. Not about TWA, but about Northeast Airlines.

What did you have to do with Northeast Airlines?

Somewhere alone the line I had picked up a significant share of a company called Atlas, a holding company, and kind of tucked it away into a part of RKO, and then it got transferred to Toolco. Atlas owned about 60% of Northeast Airlines.

The CAB got wind of this, and since they have to earn their salaries by poking into other people's businesses, they started another investigation. I controlled TWA, and the idea is that you can't run or control two major airlines. You can't do that because you might run a more efficient business that way and make more money than your competitors. But the alleged reason is conspiracy in restraint of trade.

The CAB wanted a voting trust established over the stock, they wanted me to appear, they wanted me to stand up before the board and sing *La Cucaracha* for them, which I only do for select audiences and certainly not for the CAB.

It dragged on forever, and during that time I pumped a lot of money into Northeast through Toolco and some New York banks. We did concoct some interim trust agreement concerning my stock in Northeast, but that was just a formality. The trust was revocable any time Toolco wanted to revoke it. The truth is, I owned Northeast Airlines and told them what to do, as simple as that.

At one point I timidly suggested we merge Northeast with TWA – then I'd only own one airline. The CAB howled and said that if I didn't divest, give up my Northeast stock, they'd cancel the Northeast route from New York to Florida. They don't fool around – there are no Marquis of Queensbury rules; it's 'You try that merger plan, and we'll take away your New York-Florida route to show you that we mean business. And that's just for openers.' It's the American way of business, which is the same as saying the American way of life. Dog eat dog. Who's the lion and who's the donkey, let's find out.

And who was the lion? Did they take that New York-Florida route away from Northeast?

They held that club over my head. I stalled, but it didn't work with them. Finally they said, 'Okay, Hughes, you lost the route.'

We went to court in Boston to the Federal Court of Appeals. I had friends there, meaning that they're friends as long as you keep their bank accounts fat. Finally we went to Congress –we got the guy from Massachusetts to get the ball rolling and a new law was passed.

It was meant to get Northeast out from behind the eight ball. It said that any carrier that had been flying a route since a certain date, even though it didn't have permanent authority to fly that route, under this law the route became permanent. That applied specifically and uniquely to Northeast Airlines and the Florida run and everybody goddamn well knew it, which made the CAB – in particular its chairman, a guy named Boyd, who hated my guts – go raving mad.

Still, that was just a sideshow. The main event was always TWA. Everybody was putting the screws to me. TWA still owed Irving Trust about $15 million, and Irving Trust wanted it. 'Pay or die,' they said. Worse, from my point of view, was that I personally had borrowed eleven million from Irving Trust, which was due around that time, and I'd pledged Toolco, lock, stock and barrel, as security for the loan. Of course I could have found $11 million without any difficulty, but that was only part of the over-all debt and it would have been like putting my finger in the dike when a tidal wave was coming our way.

We needed a total of $165 million. By that time I had about five business days to get it. The consortium of banks and insurance companies offered it, but they also slipped in a little proviso there – because, understand, if I borrowed $165 million to pull TWA out of the hole, theoretically all I had to do was pay back the money one day and I'd be out from under the thumbscrews. But they put in a proviso that if I wanted to pay back the money, I had to pay a 22% interest premium on it at the moment of payback. They call it a premium but any five-year-old would know that it's a penalty at 22% interest. That harks back to the days of Shylock – it's usury, but no one cared because it was Howard Hughes who had to pay it, and he deserves to have his wrist slapped, if not his throat cut.

And then in the midst of all this, something terrible happened. I had a Toolco lawyer named Ray Cook handling certain things for me, doing in part the sort of job that Noah did before I fired him. Cook decided that the way I was dealing with the TWA situation was proof that I was losing my mind. Behind my back, he contacted Noah Dietrich. Noah, to give him credit, just laughed. He'd heard this phrase many times before, relative to me, from people who didn't understand how I operated. But in this instance Cook happened to be serious. He wanted to start legal proceedings against me, on behalf of all the Toolco management and employees, to prove that I was incompetent.

Not just incompetent to manage Toolco and TWA – I'm talking about incompetent in the full and legal sense of the word. He wanted to have a guardian appointed to take care of my financial holdings while he milked me dry. He alleged, among other things, that in the midst of the most delicate and vital negotiations for control of TWA, I had taken three days off to organize a posse for a missing cat. That may have been true, but so what? I was just acting like a decent human being and that meant I was crazy.

Cook managed to bring Verne Mason, my doctor, into the picture. Verne Mason, who had been my personal physician for forty years, and was the head of my medical foundation, was going to help certify me as a loony and come to court and give all sorts of testimony about the crazy things I had done and my addiction to codeine as a painkiller. They wanted to take everything I had and put me in a straitjacket, lock me up in a closet. I'd scratch at the closet door like one of those poor people who are shut away in attics in the Ozark Mountains. It gives me the shakes just to think about it.

How did you find out?

A loyal employee in Houston tipped me off, and then I got some more information from people around Cook and Mason, and sure enough, those people came up with a copy of a secret memo from Cook to Mason that revealed everything – it was a list of people who would testify to my insanity and a list of psychiatrists who would offer affidavits, and also the names of some hospitals they were considering for me.

How did you stop them?

I had Ray Cook fly out to California and meet with me on the Santa Monica pier. I said, 'I know what you've been doing, you double-dealing son of a bitch. You want to have me put away.'

He turned white as chalk and he denied it, but finally he saw that I knew what I was talking about. 'Well, Howard,' he said, 'it would have been for your own good.' He knew already he was fired, he had nothing to lose by telling the truth then, and he tried to tell me it would have been for my own good. 'And you would have gotten well again. And when you were well you could have come back and taken over.'

I grabbed him by the collar and almost shoved him off the pier into the Pacific Ocean. But I restrained myself in the nick of time. That might have given them just the evidence they wanted.

Firing Cook right in the middle of the negotiations put me in a terrible plight. I saw everything that I'd worked for all my life about to slip out from under my fingers like an ice cube. My back was to the wall, and the entire Eastern banking establishment – that's a lot of muscle – had hold of the carpet and was trying to yank it out from under me. I didn't see how I could hold out, how I could win. My strength was giving out.

I got Greg Bautzer, a Hollywood lawyer, to take Cook's place. I sent Bautzer to New York to Merrill Lynch. Dillon Read was handling things but I thought I might get a better deal from Merrill Lynch. But everybody construed this the wrong way and thought I couldn't make up my mind and was stalling. Of course I was stalling, but my mind was made up. I had to get the money, and I'd do anything to get it, short of giving up Toolco and Hughes Aircraft.

Merrill Lynch wouldn't play ball and we went crawling back to Dillon Read. By then they'd come up with the final touches on that famous, or should I say, infamous, trustee agreement, which I consider the most unfair thing that's ever been done publicly to an American businessman of high repute and good financial standing. Shameless. But par for the course, the way they operated.

The idea was that three men would have control over my stock in TWA. Toolco could appoint one of them, and this consortium of banks and insurance companies would appoint the other two. This was a ten-year trusteeship agreement. At the end of the ten years I was supposed to get it all back. So they said. They appointed their trustees. One was Ernest Breech of Ford and the other was Arnold Oldman, former Chairman of U.S. Steel.

Now is this a horror story or isn't it? Lon Chaney never starred in anything to match this one. 'Howard Hughes, who brought you *Hell's Angels, The Front Page, The Outlaw, Toolco Versus the Relatives*, and *Hercules Versus the Dragon from the State of Maine*, proudly presents: *Trans World Airlines Versus the Wolves of Wall Street*. The plot: a simple Texas boy turned pilot, financier and medical benefactor, loses his head, and from his secret laboratory in the mountains high above Los

Angeles inadvertently looses upon the unsuspecting world a monster of his own creation. Is it a man? Is it a bird? No! It's TWA! But all is not lost. The heroes –Prudential, Irving Trust, and First National Bank of Boston – charge to the rescue to protect the American public from this raving monster. Battling singlehandedly against tremendous odds, with only $20 trillion in assets and a ragtag army of 7,500 lawyers to help them, they vow to achieve a just solution.'

That's the script they tried to play. I was desperate. And I felt I had to have a man on the inside to know what those guys were really up to. I had to sign by the last day of 1960. I stalled as much as I could until I could find someone who I knew was going to be on that board, someone I could trust, so I could get access to the private meetings of the board.

Greg Bautzer had power-of-attorney for me to sign and I had to get him to pretend he was sick. He was staying at the Hampshire House in New York and just before the signing I said, 'Greg, tell them you're dying. And if they don't believe you, if you feel that there's the slightest doubt on their part, check into some hospital.'

He claimed he had stomach ulcers and back pains. You can never diagnose back pains. He went into Roosevelt hospital.

Why did you have him delay in this way?

Because I was still trying to get to one of those trustee guys. I would never have agreed to the whole arrangement if I didn't feel that I'd know what they were going to be doing behind my back. I thought of Breech at first, because I'd known Ernie Breech for years. When I came back from my trip around the world there was some dinner in New York and Breech was the toastmaster and I remembered he had been very friendly to me.

I checked out his financial position and my men reported to me on his personal and family life, and I realized there was no leverage. I needed leverage.

That left Arnold Oldman. He was vulnerable, in his bank account. I don't mean to say he was a poor man, but for reasons of his own, which I won't go into, he needed money. There are only two things in the long run which will appeal to a man in a situation like this – one is money, and the other is the satisfaction of any perverse desires he may secretly harbor. As far as I was able to find out, Oldman was not a secret pervert. And in any case that's not my style. I won't stoop to that. But everybody needs a little extra cash, and if it's tax-free and out of the country, so much the better. Oldman was no exception. So we had a little talk.

Face to face?

This wasn't something I could do over the telephone or trust to Bautzer. I flew to New York in a private jet with a few of my aides. Oldman and I arranged a meeting out on Long Island one evening, at East Hampton. We drove around near Georgica Beach, where a high wind was blowing that kept anybody from eavesdropping. We came to an agreement. We both knew that he couldn't overtly function as my man on the board, that was never even suggested, but he could let me have word in advance of any moves that were planned and I could take steps to counter them. And he could help me that way.

How much did you pay?

A lot of money, in cash, deposited to a special offshore account.

A lump sum or spread out?

In this kind of deal there are no time payments. I don't reveal this to blacken Arnold Oldman's reputation. The reason that Oldman was willing to do this for me was that he didn't have the prejudices that all these other guys had accumulated over the years. I hardly knew him and he hardly knew me, and he was able to take me at face value for the man that I was. I probably could have gotten him on my side without paying him at all, but a man is worth his salt. In fact, let's say for the record that the money was not for services rendered, but in appreciation of his understanding of me. Because Arnold Oldman was a fine man.

And what did Oldman do for you?

He did a few little things, and then one thing which made the payment almost worth it. Well, it might have, but it didn't work out – we couldn't foresee that. He got word to me, in advance, that TWA's new counsel, Cahill, Gordon, Reindel & Ohl, had recommended that TWA sue me and Toolco for violating some obscure anti-trust laws – and that they'd do it if I didn't come up with some money right away. But Oldman let me know they were going to sue me. It gave me the chance, at the time, to make a counter-offer.

Unfortunately, my counter-offer boomeranged. They panicked. They had to sue before I paid them back. The last thing in the world they wanted was their money. They wanted control of TWA.

What else did Oldman do for you besides that?

The poor man died before anything else of major interest came up. The timing of his death was disastrous. By then TWA was suing me and I was suing TWA, and I was counting on Oldman, and he got sick and died.

Why exactly did TWA sue you?

All those banks and insurance companies had been telling me for years that I'd endangered the financial security of TWA by buying too many jets, and the first thing that the new management did was place an order for twenty-six new Boeings – that meant $200 million more debt – which they were going to finance through another loan of $147 million. The hypocrisy of these people was so blatant that I didn't know whether to laugh or cry. Three insurance companies were going to put up the money. You won't need three guesses; they were Equitable, Metropolitan, and Prudential. That was enough to make me see red, but then I found out – through Arnold Oldman – that one of the covenants of the new loan stated that if the voting trust of my stock was ever terminated the $147 million had to be paid back immediately in cash.

Of course that arrangement was completely against TWA's interests. It was aimed at me alone. I was still the majority stockholder. The purpose of the covenant was to keep me from making any legal effort at any time to terminate the voting trusteeship over my stock. Because if I succeeded, it would throw TWA into bankruptcy and wipe out my equity overnight. That's how far these people went to tie my hands behind my back. So I fought the expansion program. I got my lawyers to raise a stink – I said it would ruin TWA financially and the Board of Directors was acting out of total irresponsibility. If they wanted new jets, I said, why don't they buy the ones I'd already ordered from Convair when I was still the boss? I raised such a fuss that one of the insurance companies, the Prudential, got cold feet and pulled out. I went out on a limb, in TWA's interests and in my own, and that's when they decided to sue me.

The other reason – maybe the main reason, although it was never spelled out in their arguments, because it would lay them open to too many counter-charges – was that there was a merger in the works between TWA and Pan American, which I unalterably opposed. They feared that I could put a stop to this if I still had control. The only way to get me out was to sue me and vilify me. They sued me for all sorts of anti-trust violations, interlocking directorates between Hughes Tool and Hughes Aircraft and TWA, and they also claimed that I had personally mismanaged the airline to the brink of ruin.

That hurt me in the deepest way. Really, whatever was good about TWA was my doing. I countersued on the grounds that the whole deal they had set up was a conspiracy to defraud me and my companies of our rightful interests. I also accused Metropolitan Life and Equitable Life and Irving Trust of conspiring to gain control of TWA and make it a captive outlet for high-interest loans. The man behind it all, I believe, was Juan Trippe of Pan Am, who happened by coincidence to be a director of Metropolitan Life.

This all came to a head when I was supposed to appear in court in Los Angeles. I didn't show up, and that cost me $137 million.

The reason I didn't show up is that I was fed up. I didn't care about the money anymore. What had money ever brought me other than more money and more headache? I talked it over with someone whose opinion I respected, and that person helped me to see that it wasn't worth demeaning myself in front of these people in public. I could have fought and I might have won, but even that didn't make it worthwhile. As for TWA, by that time I was able to say to myself, 'It's only an airline. Just another company.' I was able to say that because many things had changed in my life. My marriage had become a failure. Jean had moved out. She was starting to say things like, 'Howard, you're losing your mind,' and, 'I can't stand this kind of life anymore.' So the handwriting was on the wall. I knew it was a matter of time before she filed for divorce.

And I thought, why am I involved in all this lunacy? I used to design planes, and fly them, and make good movies. My companies and I used to be creative. Now all we're doing is fighting to make money or borrow money or hold on to the money we've got. It's demeaning, it's destructive, it's disgusting. It's not what I want to do with my life, with what's left of it.

My view of the past had changed completely. This was partly the result of new feelings I had about my life, and new insights into life in general. It's time I told you about them, and how I acquired them.

28

Howard tells of the secret love of his life, tries to write a book,
and asks his biographer to cut him a little slack.

IT'S TIME FOR me to clear up a mystery of my own creation. I've
thought about it and really there's no reason for me not to, provided
that I exercise a little discretion.

You remember I discussed a woman I'd met once on a plane flying to
San Francisco? Woke up holding her hand? And then I told you that
when I flew with Cary Grant to Mexico in the winter of 1947, I was
meeting someone in Acapulco. That was my friend – the wife of the man
in the diplomatic corps, the one I'd met on the transcontinental flight.

I didn't tell the full truth about her, and I realize this story of my life
will be incomplete if I don't, just as my life itself would be incomplete
without Helga.

That's her name. Helga. She's of Scandinavian origin. We'll skip her
last name. Maybe Helga isn't her first name. Maybe it's a pseudonym.
Names aren't important.

I was seeing Helga fairly regularly until just about a year ago,
because she filled a special place in my life. She's not a famous person
and she's not a glamorous woman, not like the various movie stars I
squired around in my Hollywood years. She wasn't a beautiful woman
in that sense. In fact she has a slightly hooked nose and imperfect teeth
– I wanted to get her teeth fixed, I wanted to pay for it, but she said no.

Don't misunderstand me, I'm not implying that she's ugly or even
odd-looking. She's an unusually attractive woman, but she hasn't got
the conventional good looks that Americans usually associate with
being beautiful. I'd call her handsome and strong-featured. Great jaw,

great neck. Her blood is German and Norwegian; she's got dark hair and green eyes with small hazel specks.

She's an educated woman, far more educated than I am. Some of the ideas that I've had in recent years have in many ways been due to her influence. Helga has given me lists of books to read, from Plato to Tolstoy and up through Isaac Bashevis Singer, and for the most part I've read them and I've discussed then with her. She thinks clearly, which is a rare trait, and expresses herself simply, which may be even rarer.

Helga put herself through school in the face of great difficulties. You know, the Horatio Alger stuff, but in this case it was true, and I think even more admirable because she was a woman. When she was a teenager, one of her sisters committed suicide, hanged herself in the family garage. I tell you this just to show you the odds against such a woman making something of herself. But she did. She pulled herself up by her bootstraps. Right from the beginning he had this keen intelligence and determination. She worked her way through Columbia, and then she went to Europe for a year, lived in Paris and Mykonos, a Greek island.

At one point she wanted to be a lawyer but I'm not sorry that she didn't achieve that. I told her some stories about the vultures that made her realize it's not the noblest profession in the world. But she wasn't able to do that because she met a man and got married and raised two kids.

Lovely children, by the way. Now, of course, they're grown up, married, have children of their own. I knew them when they were very young, and I was very fond of them. In fact, it's the only relationship I've ever had with children.

Do you miss not having children of your own?

Well, for some years – because there were periods in her marriage when she was apart from her husband – I spent a fair amount of time with Helga and the children. And, as I said, it was the first real contact I'd had with kids. I gave the boy a few flying lessons and taught him a lot about aeronautical engineering. He didn't become an engineer or a pilot. He's in another business entirely, with a brokerage house, but not in New York.

What I'm getting at is that I enjoyed teaching him, and I can see the pleasure a man can take in seeing his children grow and playing a vicarious part in their lives and having the responsibility of shaping a growing human being. I had it, as I say, very briefly in my life, during this on and off relationship with Helga. So I wish in a way that I had children, because there's something missing from a man's life if he doesn't. It's probably one of the major experiences in a man's life. I missed it, and, yes, I'm sorry.

Mind you, in everything that I've seen, even with Helga's two children, there's so much heartbreak involved in the child-rearing process that I'm not sure the game is worth the candle. Those children have treated her very shabbily in the last ten years. For the most part they've taken their father's side in the obvious deterioration of the marriage. She wanted a divorce but he was a professional diplomat and he claimed it would ruin his career. She stayed married to him only under duress, with the understanding that when she wanted a period of independence she took it, which is something the children never could fathom.

But the general breaking away of children from their home – not just Helga's children, but all children – I should imagine is extremely painful to a parent. You don't like to invest your emotional capital and never get a stockholder's report or a decent dividend. Your children, Clifford, are much younger, and you haven't experienced that yet, but it's a good bet that you will.

And yet I sense that you would have liked to have had children of your own, despite this inevitable breakaway when they get older.

In the long run, yes. Any kids of mine would have had the best of everything, and it's a hell of a lot easier to be happier in life and considerate of other people when you have money to fall back on. The cold wind of poverty may be a fine instructor in the realities of life, but it's still cold.

But for me to have had children it would have been necessary to have a marriage that worked. The one thing I would never have done in my life is have children with a woman where I knew the relationship would end in divorce, as both my marriages have done. With my first wife, with Ella, I was just a harebrained kid, and the marriage never stood a chance. I knew that from the beginning. I've never been sorry we didn't have children because Ella would have got them and they would undoubtedly have looked at me as that crackpot in Las Vegas who sent them – or never sent them – a million dollars a year.

And with Jean – well, we tried, and nothing happened, and I'm glad nothing happened because of what I've already told you. We're divorced now, as you know, and she's remarried and it would have been much more painful if we'd had children. Not only because of the broken home they would have had, but because I'm getting to be an old man and I'd have been gone before they would have reached their adulthood.

But Helga is one of the main reasons I'm sitting here today. She planted the idea in my head to write a book.

This was years ago. I was up to my eyeballs in lawsuits. I said to her, 'I don't have the time.'

'Make the time,' she said. 'A man like you has to face up to himself and define himself, even if he does it badly.'

'I don't have to apologize for anything,' I said. 'That's what most autobiographies are – apologies and cover-ups, full of half-truths and wishful thinking. I don't want to do that, and I know I'm not clever enough to avoid the trap.'

'How do you know until you try?'

I allowed her to nag at me, because the challenge was appealing. That's my nature. Give me a challenge and I can't resist taking a crack at it.

One day I started to do it. This actually was when I was living in Marty Nosseck's screening room on Sunset Boulevard. I had an IBM electric typewriter of my own. And I started to write the book on my own. I knew plenty of journalists but I didn't trust a single one of them, except maybe Frank McCulloch, and he was hooked up with the Luce publications so that was too dangerous. I wrote fifteen or twenty pages about growing up in Houston and about my father. I waited a few weeks and then read them, and they were awful. I showed them to

Helga and she said, 'Yes, they're evasive, and there's an underlying anger. Wait a while. The right time will come.'

Now, as you know, it's come. I've faced my father. I've tried to see him in a clear light. I'm not angry at him anymore. I see that we are what we are, and what we do to other people is a function of our fundamental character. Almost unavoidable. That's very liberating to know.

Did you ever show those pages to Jean, your wife?

No, Jean was wonderful, but that was something I couldn't bring myself to share with her. Perhaps I should have, but I didn't.

How often did you meet with Helga during all the years since you woke up holding her hand on the transcontinental flight?

Oh, two or three times a year – sometimes less, sometimes more. It all depended. I saw her in Ethiopia, in Addis Ababa, when I was out there in '48. She was living in Europe then. Her husband was posted there. She was able to get away for a week, and I showed her the country. I flew her all over. In some ways that was the happiest single week of my life.

She also... well, I'm not sure if I told you the reason I went down to Lambaréné to see Schweitzer.

You told me something about having visited a leper clinic in Ethiopia, and that started you thinking about him.

That was part of it, but only a minor part. Helga had told me about Schweitzer. He was a man she admired enormously, and so I read one of his books. It may have been his only book, the story of his early life. Helga said, 'Why don't you go down and see him and talk to him?'

So I went. Not that time, but the next time. But it didn't work out, as I've told you.

On other occasions I rented a house on the outskirts of Oaxaca, in Zapotec Indian country in southern Mexico. That's the place where we spent the most times together. She took me to all the Indian ruins and gave me a crash course not only in pre-Columbian history but in archeology. In fact, it was to Oaxaca that she brought her children to meet me for the first time, although it was done very discreetly. She stayed in a hotel in town with the children. I was in the bungalow and she came to see me there. But she wanted me to meet the kids. She felt that our relationship was important enough that I couldn't understand her unless I knew her children and how she felt about them.

I went skiing with her once. She taught me. I fell down more times than I cared to, so I never became a real skier. I've never been fond of the snow or cold weather, but I went for many walks with her in the mountains. That was in Sun Valley. We kidded around, threw snowballs, and I was able to relax with her more than I had ever in my life with a woman. She reminded me of Ruth Elder. She was very much like Ruth, in the sense that she was interested in many of the same things I was interested in, and if she knew something I didn't know she wasn't overbearing or superior about it. In fact her belief, and mine too, is that the basis for any marriage is friendship of equals. Partnership. Sharing of knowledge.

Did you ever discuss with her the possibility of marriage?

It was out of the question. I came to the belief that the success of the relationship was based on the fact that we weren't married and only saw each other on rare occasions. After I married Jean, I wasn't free. And Helga was never free. Her husband would never have granted her a divorce. I didn't mean to imply that she hated her husband. They were friendly, just incompatible. He smoked in bed, which is a disgusting habit – got the ashes all over the sheets, smelled up the house. And he resented her intelligence. He wanted to be in command and feel superior.

Then too, I often felt that she really didn't want to get divorced, and if I'd suddenly said to her, 'Helga, get rid of that dumb son of a bitch and marry me,' she would have run for the hills. Because I would have been twice as difficult a husband as the one she was stuck with, even if I don't smoke in bed. I'm no bargain in the husband department. Ask Jean.

I don't have to. I believe you. Did her husband ever suspect that she was seeing you?

He knew that she was seeing somebody but I'm sure she never told him who. The kids found out after a while who I really was – you can't keep children in the dark for too long a time, they have better noses for ferreting out mysteries than adults do. This wasn't serious at first but unfortunately the kids were old enough to be, well, I'll call it thrilled at the idea that Mommy was seeing someone like me – and also, unfortunately, not old enough to keep their mouths shut. They gabbed and the word got around, at least in a limited circle of people. I think finally what kept it from being accepted as the truth was that everybody believed I was a total recluse and incapable of having a real relationship with a female of the species. Sometimes it pays to be a professional eccentric. But I would never have been surprised in those years to pick up a newspaper and see some gossip columnist asking, 'Who is Howard Hughes's new secret love?' or some sort of maudlin romantic crap like that. Thank God, it never happened. Helga herself was a completely discreet woman. She could arrange things on the q.t. almost as well as I could. Women often have that knack. If you care for a woman you call it discreet, if you can't stand her you call it sly. Most judgments in life depend on where you stand and what mood you're in when you make them.

Are you still seeing Helga?

If you don't mind, I'll save that story for its proper chronological place in this narrative – or maybe I won't tell you at all. A little mystery has its place in every man's life, don't you think?

Cut me a little slack on this one. We'll see.

29

Howard buys the French Impressionists, declines to show up in court,
and receives the largest personal check in history.

IN THE TWA case they'd been trying to subpoena me for six months
but they hadn't been able to find me. I know how to vanish, I've had
decades to practice. For the most part I was playing golf in Hawaii or
traveling with Helga, both activities under another name.

We went to Paris. Helga took me to all the art museums and I
developed a taste for the Impressionists. I even bought a dozen Monet,
Degas, and Renoir oils, not because I thought they'd go up in value,
although I suspect they will, but because I really liked them. I decided
not to hang them anywhere – I was sure someone would get wind of it
and try to steal them – so I wrapped them up in a lot of cardboard and
paper and crated them and stored them in a locker I rented in Orange
County, California. They're not even in my name. I arranged for a
bank to pay the rental forever, and I padlocked the storage locker, and
I have the key. If I died tomorrow, no one would know what lock that
key fit, and those paintings would sit there forever.

You'd better do something about that. You could be hit by a bus, and
the world would lose a dozen important paintings.

Yes, I will. Remind me, will you?

Anyway, during that period when I was dodging the lawsuit, and
Jean and I had separated, Helga and I rented a little house in France,
in a village just outside of Aix-en-Provence. I set out to learn French.
It's one of the few things in my life I've tried hard to do where I failed
miserably. One of the others is to become friendly with French people.
They're charming, and often cultured, but for a man like me they're

Martians. And, although they respect my eccentricity, in other respects they regard me as someone from Pluto.

Meanwhile the flood of subpoenas mounted, demanding my presence in court, and eventually I couldn't ignore them. From Marseilles I flew back to the States and conferred with my lawyers. It was a dollars and cents proposition in many ways. If I appeared I might be able to win the case, or more probably the judgment against me could have been reduced to ten or twenty million dollars. As it was, I knew that if I didn't appear it would cost me well over one hundred and forty million.

But at that point I rose to the occasion. I felt I had demeaned myself so much by this enormous involvement with the case, and with the fight for control of the airline, that I couldn't go any further without destroying myself. There was something in me, thank God, that really fought against this self-destructive process that had been the theme of my whole life, and I clung to that something like a drowning man clings to a plank.

When it came time, when I was subpoenaed, the horror of it finally got to me. I made a vow then that I would not only not go into that court, but never go into any court again in my life, either to defend myself or to attack anyone else.

I was fed up with the niggling, mean, unimaginative aspects of the business world. But I had visions of worthwhile things to be done in that world. There was nothing small-minded and petty about those visions, including what I tried to do in Las Vegas. But I'll get to that in its proper place.

The upshot of the TWA lawsuit, however, was that they got a default judgment against me for $137 million and they threw out my countersuit. It was a judgment with treble damages.

A bond was put up by Toolco. The issue is still in the courts, and it'll probably stay there as long as I'm alive. I don't need the money, but those bastards aren't going to get their hands on it. I've got that money earmarked for a nobler purpose.

The lawsuit, in any case, was totally unjustifiable. Of course they did their damndest to justify it. Ernest Breech made a public statement, just the sort of thing you would expect him to say, to the effect that as the new president of TWA he had an obligation to the stockholders and to the people who worked for the airline to sue me. He felt that was a cardinal principle of American business – the obligation to the stockholders to sue. It was a lot of doubletalk, because he forgot to mention that I was the principal stockholder and he was suing me with my own money.

After I went through the horrors of that lawsuit and the countersuit and the demands that I appear in court, I was totally fed up. I washed my hands of the whole thing.

But you held the stock.

I still liked TWA as an investment, and I liked it until 1966, when I sold it. Everyone has written that Ernie Breech and Charlie Tillinghast, who followed him, did such a great job of managing the airline and therefore made my fortune, or part of it. That's a lot of crap. Tillinghast did do a good job of managing the airline, but that's no more than you expect of the president of an airline, and the years between 1960 and 1966, when I was relatively inactive in TWA, using my weight here and there and holding the stock, were boom years in the American economy. Everyone prospered. I fail to see why such great credit should be given to Tillinghast and why everyone should demean me. If I had been running the airline, it would have prospered in exactly the same way, or maybe even better. They were also boom years in the stock market. That was the big bull market – with the exception of the 1962 drop it was just up, up, and away, until the spring of 1966.

I had taken my licking in the stock market back in 1929, just like everyone else, and after that I took the market a little more seriously. On my payroll I had what's called a technical analyst. A technical analyst doesn't just look at the value of a company. He looks at the movement and internal conditions of the market as a whole, and he looks at the movement of an individual stock, and he says, based on the price-and-volume movements of that stock, 'It's going to go up, or it's going to go down.' He doesn't care whether it's TWA flying around the world or whether it's some company in Dogpatch that makes toothpicks. That toothpick company – if the movement of their stock is healthy, then it's a buy. And if the price-and-volume dynamics of a stock like Xerox is poor, then no matter how good the company's prospects look, then it's a sell.

At the end of '65 and the beginning of '66, if you were at all aware of the internal condition of the stock market, you knew it was going to fall on its ass. In my view the market is a law unto itself. Stocks are worth only what people will pay for then. There are many old sayings about this: 'Don't fight the tape,' and so forth – meaning that if you buy a stock and that stock goes down, then you were wrong to buy it, despite the fact that everything may look good for that company and you can't understand why the price of the stock should sag. The fact that you can't understand it doesn't mean a thing, except that you can't understand it. I once had a talk with Bernard Baruch about this and he disagreed with me. But I've made a lot more money out of the market than Baruch ever did. And with him it was a full-time occupation.

In the beginning of 1966, people on the inside and the banks who fix the prime rate of interest knew that the market was headed for a terrific drop. And I knew it, too. Every single technical indicator confirmed it. That's when I decided to sell. Moreover I had other uses for the money. I didn't see any sense in it just sitting there in stock certificates when I had already formed a plan – more than a plan, a vision – about the Las Vegas area, for which I needed cash. I'd been thinking about this for several years already. So, to put things as simply as possible, I decided to sell out my block of TWA.

It was the second largest underwriting in history. Merrill Lynch did the job for me, palmed off a lot of the business on other people, spread it around and did a very competent job. I have to give them full credit for that.

Nobody knew whether the fact that I was dumping was of any significance. They could have decided that I knew something that other people didn't know – and the stock would have plummeted.

Or, as in fact happened, they could have decided that this was a tremendous buying opportunity. TWA had been virtually a privately-held corporation until then. I owned seventy-eight percent of the stock. Wall Street banged the drum that this was a great opportunity for the American public to have a share in a company that had previously been closed to them. The stockbuying public and the mutual funds liked that idea. They came running like chickens to a bag of corn. They bought. An example of mass stupidity.

They bought at $86 a share, which was just about the top, the all-time top, for the stock. The underwriters and Merrill Lynch got their cut out of it, you can be sure of that. They never lose. Merrill Lynch made more than $3 million, and there was another fifteen or sixteen million that went to other brokerage houses and all those other guys who dip their fingers in the pie. You know those gravestone ads – this was one of the longest in history, and some very fine firms were associated with it.

The check was placed in my hands for something like $566 million, which was the largest check ever issued to an individual, to my knowledge. I packed the bundles of cash in my suitcase and flew to Las Vegas.

You took that much cash with you?

No, no, that's just a figure of speech. I rarely have more than a five-dollar bill in my wallet. I didn't have enough money on me the other night to pay you that bet on the baseball game, did I? I'm cash-poor, I've told you that.

30

Howard invades Las Vegas, paces Hitler's carpet, insults Frank Sinatra, fights for the SST, and finds out that he's been kidnapped.

IN 1965, AS the TWA debacle was winding down, I moved my center of operations to Las Vegas, Nevada. For reasons I've never been able to understand, that move, and my residence there, captured the attention of the media more than anything else I've ever done, including breaking all those transcontinental and round-the-world air speed records. In the most recent years of my life I've received such an extraordinary amount of publicity that if you'd been reading the newspapers and watching television you would have thought I was setting up a separate kingdom in the state of Nevada with the Desert Inn Hotel as its capital.

When I bought a dinky little airline like Air West and changed it to Hughes Air, the business world behaved as though I were trying to take over Pan Am and United Airlines rolled into one. When I tried to get control of ABC you would have thought, if you subscribed to the *Wall Street Journal*, that the Russians and the Chinese were infiltrating the entire U.S. television industry.

And yet, paradoxically, my business life in recent years – and that includes the Nevada operation, which involved an expenditure of close to a billion dollars – was of little interest to me. Because these last years have been a period in my life when, for the first time – up to a point – I was able to let my business operations grow by themselves, so that I could do what I wanted to do, quietly and anonymously, in my private affairs.

I say 'up to a point' because of course I couldn't just abandon the habits of a lifetime and keep my hands off enterprises that had a far-reaching purpose – and into which, incidentally I'd sunk a good part of my fortune. And there were times, I'm sorry to say, when I got involved right up to my eyeballs and beyond. I tried to take over the American Broadcasting Company in 1968, with a tender offer through Toolco for a controlling interest in the stock, about two million shares, but ABC management opposed me. It was the same old story – I was going to do the company irreparable harm. Get the logic of this. The stock was selling for about $58 a share before I made the offer. I offered $74 a share. Naturally the stock jumped to over seventy. That's what they call 'irreparable harm.' They ran ads begging their stockholders to turn me down, and I came up 400,000 shares short.

With that, and other endeavors, I had to do a hell of a lot of organizing, because once I'd fired Noah Dietrich I was alone up there on the top of a pretty big heap. And then came the plunge into Las Vegas.

How did you manage to keep your affairs in order with your right-hand man gone?

Call him my left-hand man. I was always my own right-hand man. But I have to admit that it was a problem. The first person I turned to was Bob Gross. I tried to get him to take over the stewardship, I guess you'd call it, of the Hughes empire. He was still president of Lockheed. He didn't want to give that up.

And in 1961 he died, which was a terrible blow for me because he was the best friend I've ever had since my youth. I'm not being egoistic when I say it was a blow for me. For Bob it was simply a quick finish.

When you're alive you fear death, but when you're dead, you're dead and you don't know a goddamn thing about it. I never feel sorry for anyone who dies. I feel sorry for the ones they leave behind and, all too often, alone. I mourn, if I ever mourn, for the living. They suffer. The dead just decompose.

I was no stranger to Las Vegas. The first time I went there was just after I'd gone on a little riding trip in Death Valley with Ruth Elder, my pilot pal. That was around 1930. We'd been away for a long weekend and ridden out into the desert, under a blue sky without a single cloud, although it was baking hot. Then we had an accident. Ruth's horse was bitten by a rattlesnake, and panicked. Ruth held on, she was an excellent horsewoman, but the poison went through that horse like crap through a goose. He fell dead before he'd gone a hundred yards. Ruth landed clear, but that kind of took the bloom off the day, and we left Death Valley.

We spent the night in Las Vegas – my first sight of the town, which was just a pimple in the desert, with probably not more than five thousand people living there. Gambling was illegal. There were some tinhorn joints downtown but no one in his right mind would go in there.

Later I visited again, flying out from Hollywood. I flew over the whole state of Nevada ten or fifteen times. Every time I looked down I'd say, 'What the hell is that? That wasn't there before!' The towns seemed to be leaking out from the center – Las Vegas in particular. And I got interested in it. First of all, I liked clean, dry desert air. Germs can't live well, I thought, in that kind of air.

Later on I wanted to locate the avionics division of Hughes Aircraft there and I had business meetings in Nevada with Bob Gross and Zeckendorf and dozens of other men. In 1950 I rented a bungalow out there. By then the town was moving right along. But I still had no real interest in buying in. I did pick up a little real estate – fifty or sixty thousand acres here and there. I did that in Arizona, too, in Scottsdale, because I could see that area had the potential for tremendous development. I've still got that land in Arizona – I'm damned it I know what's happening to it.

Then, around 1960, I became seriously interested in Nevada. I looked into the future and I saw the tremendous pace with which the airline and the aircraft building industry was accelerating. The SST was an inevitability.

By the mid-1960s I was ready to move. What I lacked then was sufficient liquidity, and that was supplied when I dumped my block of TWA stock on the market. Then I had half a billion dollars ready cash to play around with.

I moved into a hotel, the Desert Inn, rented the top floor, the ninth floor, and set up headquarters. One day they announced to me that they needed part of the ninth floor for some big gamblers who were coming to Vegas for Christmas, and they always had those rooms, and would I mind giving them up? Well, I did mind, and I already had the Desert Inn on the list of properties I wanted to buy – but this business of their asking me to vacate some of the rooms on the ninth floor seemed to me like a golden opportunity to make one of those gestures that endear you to the hearts of the local citizenry and also throw a bit of a scare into the local politicos. So I said, in effect, 'No, I'm damned if I'll move. I'll buy the hotel before I do that.'

And I bought it for $13 million cash. But it took a while, because the place was owned by a syndicate, and I insulted the head man, some racketeer named Moe Dalitz. I had a private meeting with this guy Dalitz, who I disliked. The meeting took place a short time before Christmas, because he said to me, 'Mr. Hughes, it's my birthday in a few days, and I'd be honored for you to come to a little birthday party I'm having.'

I said I'd try to make it. Naturally, I had no intention of doing so. He said, 'It's going to be in your honor as well, Mr. Hughes, because I have the same birthday as you.' I felt a certain sense of revulsion at that idea. I said, 'I haven't celebrated my birthday since I was twenty-one years old. Birthday parties are for children,' and I walked out of the room.

I had the same set-up there in the Desert Inn that I've always had where I live. I'm indifferent to my surroundings as long as the basic comforts are there. My own apartment on the ninth floor was sparsely furnished, except that when I first arrived and started buying stuff I somehow acquired a huge Persian carpet that had belonged to Adolf Hitler. It was a beautiful old carpet and it cost thirty thousand dollars. It wasn't worth that much, of course, but someone in my organization no doubt got a fat kickback. Hitler had eight of them made for him back in the Thirties, woven by eight master weavers from the Arab countries. This one wound up on my bedroom floor in the Desert Inn. I used to pace back and forth on it and sometimes laugh like hell when I realized what I was doing. Good thing the newspapers didn't know about that. They would have had a field day.

Other than the extravagance of Hitler's carpet I had my amplifying equipment and closed-circuit television installed. I did have the drapes changed. They were too flimsy. I don't like the idea of the awareness of time passing, so I had very heavy drapes put in to keep out the light. That's something I've done all my life. I've refused to be a slave to time. And one way I've been able to get around it is to insulate myself against light from the outside so that, since I have no clocks and no watch, I don't know what time it is. I run by an internal clock. When I want to sleep, I sleep, and when I want to work, I work. And when I want to pick up the telephone and call somebody, I call them. I don't know if it's noon or five o'clock in the morning or what.

That inconveniences a lot of people, doesn't it? To be called at three and four o'clock in the morning?

I've discovered that when I call a man in the middle of the night, wake him out of sound sleep, I'm liable to find out precisely what I want to know, whereas if I ask him in the daytime when he's wide-awake and prepared, he'll be more guarded. I've got a lot of interesting answers out of people at four o'clock in the morning, much closer to the truth, because they're befuddled, and their defenses are not up to par. You may think that's unsympathetic and Machiavellian of me, but it's a fact that truth comes out more readily from a man's lips between the hours of midnight and dawn.

This also applies to some of my business deals which were concluded after long sessions in uncomfortable surroundings, when my opponent, I'll call him that, was exhausted and broken down and gave me concessions which I couldn't otherwise have obtained. I realized after several meetings with a man at three or four o'clock in the morning, the poor guy would be beat up and exhausted, and undoubtedly say to himself, 'I can't stand another one of these meetings with this Hughes guy, I've got to close this deal right now,' and he'd close it more or less on my terms to avoid another session and another series of phone calls. Men are slaves to sleep. It's a terrible weakness.

Please don't think I always plan it that way. I'm not cruel. I'm oblivious to time. And I never twist anyone's arm. Zeckendorf and

Rockefeller bitched forever about those meetings in Las Vegas, but nobody put a gun to their heads and forced them to come.

The idea of the Desert Inn hideaway was to live simply. I saw very few people. My apartment was stocked with food and medicines for a month's stay if I wanted to be alone, and there were many times that I did. Fresh foods and mail and books would come through the door in a special arrangement we had. Weeks would pass when I would refuse to see anybody or even answer memos. When I made telephone calls nobody knew where the hell I was telephoning from. I didn't need newspapers. If I want the news, if I want to know what a mess the world is in, I turn on the television.

What about the maids?

If you don't sleep in a bed, you don't need a maid. Anyway, I'm used to making the bed myself. I'm nearly sixty-six years old and I'm not an acrobat, but I'm not helpless. You think I want dirty hands touching my sheets? If anyone makes my bed other than me, it's someone I know very well. And he or she is wearing white gloves.

I've got no interest in gambling joints and gin palaces, except that they provide an interesting theater to observe human foolishness, but after the Desert Inn I bought a controlling interest in the Sands, and then the Castaways and the Silver Slipper, and eventually the Landmark, and one or two other places, including the Krupp Ranch, and a couple of little airlines around there, like Alamo Airways. Oh, sure – also Harold's Club in Reno. I also bought a few mining properties. I got my people well set up vis-a-vis the local officials in the gambling department of the state. Governor Laxalt made a public announcement that I was the greatest thing ever to happen to the great state of Nevada.

It was impossible to do this discreetly. In fact, it was not my purpose to do it discreetly. My decision was, if I was going to succeed in my overall purpose, the image of Las Vegas had to be changed. Now, it's totally impossible to root out all the corruption in a place like that. I didn't even try. But since the American people think almost entirely in images, and you can convince them that red is blue and black is white if you drum it at them hard enough, we worked at it diligently. We couldn't erase the idea that Las Vegas was the sin capital of the United States, but we could certainly erase the idea that it was Mafia-controlled. And it no longer is. It's Hughes-controlled.

Around that time, didn't you provoke Frank Sinatra into an argument, and have him thrown out of the Sands Hotel?

He got annoyed because I'd cut off his credit at the Sands.

You don't call that provocation?

We adopted a strict policy of cash on the line for the slow payers, of which Sinatra was definitely one. I didn't see myself in the role of a private loan institution for freeloaders and aging glamor boys. I had nothing against Sinatra personally, although he may have born a grudge against me from the time I helped Ava Gardner escape his clutches. I guess he did try to make peace – he once sent me a television set as a Christmas present, which astounded me, and I gave it to one of the Jamaican maids in the Beverly Hills Hotel. I had no relationship with the man. He was just a loudmouth blusterer, a crooner who liked to play tough guy. Lost his voice, which is why he retired. Now he pumps himself full of Jack Daniels sour mash and silicone. He has hair planted in his scalp, like grass on a lawn in a heat wave. What can you say about a man like that except that he's an idiot who can carry a tune?

To get back to my purchases: all of them were minor and preparatory.

My over-all purpose in Nevada had to do with the coming of the SST, the supersonic transport. I wanted Las Vegas to be the western port of entry to the United States for the SSTs. In order to accomplish that I had to have some clout in the state of Nevada. That's why I bought all those properties, the hotels and the mines, to establish myself and my people as a fixture and an asset before I set the wheels in motion on the major project. I saw the SST as an inevitability – and I still do – but I didn't believe, as most other people did, that the inevitable west coast port of entry was the Los Angeles area. When you're dealing with the size and speeds of aircraft like the Concorde and the Tupolev and the new Boeing – the three SSTs that are in various stages of manufacture and design at the moment – you're dealing with entirely new concepts, and it's fatal to think along conventional lines.

Los Angeles International Airport is already straining at its seams and they could never expand it to handle the traffic. They had more than 600,000 landings and takeoffs at L.A. International last year, which is nearly double what Kennedy Airport handled, and JFK has nearly twice as much acreage as LAX. All the other areas around the city are far too populated, because with the SST you've got the problem of sonic boom. The Department of Airports out there has been trying to develop an intercontinental airport at Palmdale, in the desert, but they're having problems with the ecologists.

On the West Coast the right place is Las Vegas, because the desert's for sale cheap, you've got no weather problems, and not many people care about the lizards as an endangered species.

Las Vegas is exactly one minute further by air from Tokyo, for example, than Los Angeles; so there was never any question, as some people tried to claim later, that it was 'too far to go.' I'd explored the whole problem thoroughly. I knew what I had to do. It was simply a matter of fitting the pieces together, like you assemble a child's building toy.

First of all it was necessary to get the state officials on my side. That's why I bought in. They knew I had something else in mind other than owning a few thousand slot machines, and since they were dying to broaden the industrial base of the area they went along with me.

Secondly it was necessary to have an airport, or at least a place to build it. I bought the North Las Vegas Air Terminal. I always like to own an airport near where I'm living.

Was your acquisition of Air West part of that SST plan?

It was a ripe plum – it cried out to be plucked. The airline was over its ears in debts with disastrous management problems. It was originally formed from a merger of three peanut lines – Pacific, West Coast, and Bonanza – and they were having a hard time integrating their schedules and facilities. The combined airline, which operated all over the Western

United States, up into Canada and down to Mexico, would have fitted right into the scheme – a perfect feeder line. I offered $90 million and said I'd pick up their debt, which was another sixty million.

But you'd have thought Khrushchev and Mao were putting in a bid for TWA and Pan Am the way some people reacted. The Air West board of directors started to scream. I could never quite figure it out, except that maybe they didn't want the heavy hand of Howard Hughes pushing the buttons and making them jump. The excuse they gave was that they didn't think the CAB would give me permission to own another airline after the TWA-Northeast fiasco, but they were wrong. They might have stopped me if the airline hadn't been so close to bankruptcy, but, in the end, the power of the dollar won out. They said, 'Okay, Mr. Hughes if you insist. We'll let you save our skins.' The preliminary vote had been thirteen to eleven against selling to me. The board waited until exactly three minutes before my offer officially expired – then they voted seventeen to seven to sell.

Then, with all the effort you put into it, why didn't the SST scheme work out?

There are two basic reasons. The first one's not so important, but it had to do with the failure, at least for the moment, of Boeing's development of the plane itself. I spent so many hours of my time working to implement that vision, only to have those shortsighted politicians in Washington cut the ground out from under the project's feet. Once that happened there was a general lack of enthusiasm for any concrete plans for super-airports. You don't need an SST airport if you haven't got any SSTs to land on it. Well, you do, of course, because the Concorde and the Tupolev will be operational eventually, but the United States government has never been keen to sink billions of dollars into projects that will only benefit foreign manufacturers.

But that wasn't the chief reason that I struck out swinging, at least for the moment. Lyndon Johnson was President when I started things going in Las Vegas. I've never met the man but we'd spoken many times on the telephone, and we were pretty much in accord on things, except for the way he so sneakily got us up to our eyeballs in trouble in that Vietnam adventure – and also, I might add, for the fact that he gave the go-ahead to the Atomic Energy Commission to blow up half of Nevada. Other than those two disagreements I had good reason to believe that Johnson would swing his weight behind me when it got down to the nitty-gritty as to where the western SST port of entry would be. You could even say I was counting on him.

However, this was 1966 and 1967 when I got deep into this thing, and if you'll recall it looked like Johnson was going to run again for reelection and probably win. Then he backed out, which few people, and certainly not I, had foreseen, and Mr. Richard Nixon was elected President in 1968.

His election was one of the great disasters, not only to the best interests of the American public, but to me personally. It was known by then that I was lobbying for Las Vegas against Los Angeles for the SST port, and the California politicians and industrialists naturally yelled bloody blue murder against me. Dick Nixon is from California, and when he gets his ass booted out of the White House eventually he'll undoubtedly go back to California. He's the one who, behind the scenes, did his best to stab me in the back on the Las Vegas vision. I'm sure it's partly revenge for what happened in 1960 when the details of the loan to his brother came out, and it cost him the election.

I'm a patient man, and we'll see what happens in the future in Nevada.

What sort of life did you live for five years on the ninth floor of the Desert Inn?

Behind steel doors and drawn curtains, tended by my five faithful Mormons, growing my fingernails and toenails eight inches long, shuffling around in Kleenex boxes, and watching old movies all night long. By the way, I've always wondered: if you had eight-inch toenails, how could you fit your foot inside a Kleenex box?

That's what I've read and I'm sure you've read it too. That's all so far from the truth that it's almost worth keeping up the pretence just to provide me with an occasional chuckle – but that's not why I'm sitting here telling you the story of my life. My purpose is to sweep away the myths and tell the unadorned and maybe not-so-glamorous truth.

I was in Las Vegas probably for a total accumulated time of eighteen months out of those whole five years, and I treated the ninth floor of the Desert Inn like one of my ten or twelve bungalows scattered around the western hemisphere. It was a convenience, a comfortable place to stay from time to time, and nothing more, I had a private elevator and a private exit. Only I had the key. I had to do that because there was always the sensation of panting hordes moving in the corridor outside, waiting for His Eminence to speak. If I ever pulled the drapes and looked out at the street, fifty cameras would go click. Several newspapers offered as much as $25,000 to anyone who could get a photograph of me. Can you imagine?

Why did you hire so many Mormons as close associates during that period?

I had a fellow named Bill Gay as my chief executive assistant. He had been a vice-president at Toolco. He was a Mormon and he wanted his own kind around, no more profound reason than that. I personally had nothing to do with it. I couldn't have cared less. The newspapers have often referred to them, in connection with me, as the Mormon Mafia. Well, they're Bill Gay's Mormon Mafia, not mine. I just found that in general the guys he hired were reasonably competent and discreet and didn't ask too many questions, probably because they don't have the imagination to ask too many questions. They don't drink or smoke. They're some of the dullest people I ever met, and that suits me fine.

The other significant lieutenant I had was Bob Maheu, an ex-FBI agent who ran the Nevada operation. In all the five years he worked for me I wrote him a lot of letters and talked to him often on the phone, but I never met him face-to-face. That suited me too.

Of course you can get into some peculiar situations living the way I lived then, and something happened once that could have been a minor disaster. It turned out to be a fiasco but not such a funny one when you think what might have happened. There was a kidnapping.

This was in 1967, and it's one of the most bizarre things that's ever happened in my life. First I have to tell you that I employed doubles from time to time. Not one but several. They made it easier for me to leave the hotel and travel.

This time I went away to meet Helga in Mexico, at Zihuatanejo, that Pacific coast fishing village. I'd bought a cottage there on the beach, in another name. People had no idea where I was going. My normal practice when I went on such trips was to tell my people: 'I'm going into a period of total seclusion. I'm not to be bothered, to be phoned, to receive any communications, under any circumstances, unless *I* communicate.' They usually thought I was on the premises because one of my doubles – in this instance his name was Jerry Alberts – took my place, ate my food, read the books and watched the movies I had ordered.

I wasn't feeling too well down in Zihuatanejo, and Helga had to leave earlier than planned, so I left. I made a stop in Houston on the way back. I went back there with some sentimental idea of catching a glimpse of Sonny. But Sonny was swallowed up in that mass of fifty-story buildings that had gone up since I left there.

You didn't contact anybody there?

Who? I didn't know anybody. I took a cab out to Yoakum Boulevard, to have a look at the old house, but the old house was long gone, which I should have known it would be. Some school, St. Thomas's, had been built on the lot.

Thomas Wolfe was right. You can't go home again. Not because home has changed so much, but because home's not there anymore. So I came back to Las Vegas and the Desert Inn sooner than expected.

And the place was in a turmoil. Jerry Alberts had been kidnapped.

I couldn't understand how this had happened. Jerry was under strict orders not to leave the ninth floor. Maybe, I thought, he got bored. Maybe he went out to see to some woman. No one knew. This, of course, was the thinking that was going on when I came back, when it was discovered that *he* had been kidnapped. You see, until then, Bill Gay and the Mormons thought *I* had been kidnapped. They had no way of knowing it was really Jerry. They only had the vaguest idea that I employed doubles. That was my private system of checks and balances.

What had happened was that about three days after I had left for

Mexico, my people received a ransom note asking for a million dollars. This situation had never arisen before, but the men had their instructions. First they tried to establish contact with me in my apartment – an emergency signal – but there was no answer to it. The protocol then was to break in, and they discovered that I was missing.

Now I'll jump ahead a little bit and tell you this from my point of view. I returned, as I said, considerably earlier than I had planned. I probably was away ten days in all. When I walked in, that is, when I established communication with my people again, their mouths hung open and they said, 'But, Mr. Hughes, how did you escape?'

I misunderstood. I said, 'How I left is none of your business – I've told you that before.'

They yelled: 'But, Mr. Hughes, you've been kidnapped!'

I said, 'Is that so? Tell me about it.'

The story came out about the ransom note.

But this was six days after they had received the note. I said, 'Why haven't you paid the ransom?'

You can believe there were some red faces. They had all sorts of excuses for that. First of all they weren't sure it was me.

Did you still use the 'Pay Damn Quick' code?

Yes, and the note that was supposed to have come from me, accompanying the ransom letter – while it was a good forgery of my handwriting, nevertheless it didn't have in it the letters 'PDQ.' That was one reason they gave. Also they said they were trying to negotiate with the kidnappers, to get some proof that they really had me.

I said, 'For Christ's sake, I could have had my throat slit by now.'

My point was that despite the code we had arranged, I wasn't satisfied with the reaction I had got from my people, because for all they knew I might have been given drugs by these kidnappers and unable to remember what I was supposed to put down.

When I got back and explained that it was Jerry who had been kidnapped, each of these Mormons said to me: 'I wanted to pay, Mr. Hughes, but not the other – not him.'

We were faced with an extraordinary situation. The kidnappers had

Jerry, who they believed was Howard Hughes – at least that's what we assumed, even though I realized that Jerry would have told them he was a double – and they were demanding a million dollars for the wrong man.

Someone said, 'Don't pay, Mr. Hughes. After a while they're realize they have your double and they'll let him go.'

'They may not believe him,' I said. 'They may kill him if I don't pay.'

You met and discussed all this with your people?

I didn't meet them face to face. It was discussed on the telephone. But they knew damn well it was me, and they knew damn well I wasn't calling from some place up near Reno, where the kidnappers were supposed to be. They knew I was right there on the ninth floor on the other side of the wall.

Finally we worked it out. These people, whoever they were, got in touch with us and were told they had the wrong man. They believed it finally, because Jerry had insisted, and although he was my double he didn't look precisely like me – he had a little nervous tic which I don't have, thank God – and his voice was quite different, much deeper than mine. I spoke to one of them on the telephone. They realized they'd made a mistake, but they said, 'If you want this man back alive, it's going to cost you a hundred thousand dollars.' Why they selected that sum, I don't know, but they did.

It was paid in cash, twenties and hundreds left under a cactus bush outside of Reno. It was all done like a cheap Hollywood gangster thriller, and Jerry was delivered unharmed, a little bruised and dirty – he hadn't bathed in a week – and apparently very grateful that I had saved his skin.

That was the end of it, except that a few weeks later, Jerry quit working for me. He quit under peculiar circumstances. He was being well paid for doing damn little, but he gave some excuse that his wife was sick and he felt he should be with her in the East. And then, before we had time to discuss whatever his real problem might really be, he was gone.

It came out shortly after that – not from me, I wasn't the least bit suspicious – but from other people who did a little investigating – that

Jerry was starting to live pretty high on the hog in the Virgin Islands. Then I realized what had happened. I can't swear to it, but it looked like I'd been taken for $100,000. And if my people had been more diligent and more deeply concerned about me, I would have been taken for a cool million. There was no kidnapping mob, there was just Jerry and a confederate.

The funny thing is, I didn't try to track him down. Once I got over my first annoyance at having been bilked, I found I had a secret admiration for the man. He had guts, and it was a clever scheme. I told Helga and she agreed. I saved most of my annoyance for my Mormon bodyguards who would have let me rot.

Finally I decided to leave Nevada. I was too old to be disillusioned. Call it a disenchantment.

A number of things caused it. The Atomic Energy Commission, for one. The AEC put out a brochure about their Nevada test site in which they called it 'America's Outdoor Nuclear Explosives Laboratory.' They presented it like a handbill for tourists. Nevada is relatively uninhabited, so naturally it's fair game.

The first stage came about when they fired off a hydrogen bomb underground at a place called Paute Mesa, no more than a hundred miles from Las Vegas. Windows broke downtown, people heard it within a hundred miles, and the shock waves were felt in Los Angeles. It clocked well above five on the Richter scale. I left, of course – I slipped away to a safer place.

The other big negatives were the slow collapse of America's SST program and the fact that I lost the appeal on the original $137 million default judgment in the TWA litigation, which, with lawyers' fees and interest, had climbed up in the lofty neighborhood of $250 million. The government said, 'You've got to pay.' And just as I said when the United States Senate demanded I bring Johnny Meyer back to Washington from St. Tropez, I said, 'No, I don't think I will.'

But before I left Nevada for good, I decided to take another trip. Not to Mexico this time. Not for pleasure. This time the trip was for a measure of enlightenment, and to save what was left of my life.

31

Howard reads the Bhagavad-Gita, meets a guru, and begs by the banks of the Ganges.

DURING THOSE YEARS in Las Vegas I had been involved in a lot of reading. And before that too. Not long after my last visit to Ernest Hemingway, I began reading other things besides novels. I'd always read casually for diversion, but then for the first time in my life I began to read in order to learn. And I don't mean to learn engineering or anything like that. I got curious about Hindu and Buddhist philosophy. I had found very little satisfaction finally in the way I'd grown up, with all the things all American kids are supposed to be proud of being able to do, to repair things and to build things, and to make money. These had become, for me, dry, mechanical operations with no deeper value than practicality. They didn't answer any of the questions that were looming larger and larger for me.

I was no longer looking for a great teacher or a guru. I didn't believe in that any more. After my disappointing encounters with men of great reputation, I sort of put this down as a childish notion. In fact, I had concluded that any man whose name was a household word was either corrupted or had the seeds of corruption in him. I felt, for example, that any man who would allow himself to be put in a position like Ernest, where he was so publicized and lionized, was being false to himself. How could he be wise?

I decided that if there were any wise men in this world, their names were totally unknown to me and to you, and to anyone who was reading the newspapers or even reading books.

I read about Bertrand Russell and the peace marches. He seemed an impressive man. I tried to read some of his works and, I confess, they were a little over my head, except for the mathematics. But when I read of him marching down the streets in London, I thought, hell, this is show biz.

Then what should I seek? Should I just look inside myself? I didn't dare. I didn't really respect myself as much as I once had, or thought I had. And if I looked too deep, I was afraid of what I'd find.

I considered myself well into middle age at that time – on the cusp of being old, mostly because of the physical damage I had suffered in those various accidents and partly because of the mental pounding I was taking, the constant attacks by these businessmen who were out to strip me of all they could. And partly, I suppose, because when you reach your early forties, you start to feel you're not young any more, but you don't want to face it. Then when you get to your fifties, you've learned to face it. Unless you're an idiot, you have no choice. At first it's a bit of a shock. In the end, however, it's a good thing – in Asia, you know, they have a proverb: 'Whom the gods curse, they keep young.'

My first reaction was to say to myself, 'Well, soon I'll be an old man and I'd better start thinking like an old man.'

I don't mean I wanted to jump into my wheelchair. I meant I wanted to assess my life and latch on to some sort of self-understanding – the beginning of it, at least. It seemed absurd to me to have lived some fifty-odd years and have no answers to questions. It wasn't enough to have more money than anyone else in the world. Most rich people I knew were awful human beings, angry and paranoid and grasping. They can tell you how to steal a company or invest money safely, or what a van Gogh is worth at Sotheby's, or where you can buy the best bench-made shoes, but they know damn little else. They certainly can't tell you the meaning of life, except in terms of gross national product and stock splits.

I thought, if anything, a man growing old should have some answers. I didn't have a goddamn one. I hardly knew the questions any more. That was terrible. I knew that lions ate donkeys and I knew that wasn't enough to know.

With Helga as my tutor, I began to read more difficult books. I started to read Hindu and Buddhist philosophy. I tackled the Upanishads and the Bhagavad-gita, and Lao-Tse, and some Zen, and I tried the teachings of Buddha. I was put off by the imprecision of the language, the vague terms that were used, speaking of the Self and the One and the Absolute. These were the sort of terms I couldn't come to grips with. At the time I put the books away in disgust. I don't want to be irreligious, but a lot of it seemed crap. I've always disliked organized religion, and while this Eastern stuff wasn't organized, it had all the trappings of the junk the church was pouring down everybody's gullet day after day. All the churches, not just the Catholics, except that these happened to be Asian religious terms.

A period of time passed while I drove myself crazy with the TWA situation and then the SST scheme. I began to claw my way out of it, and I was still just as restless and dissatisfied and it occurred to me that there might, after all, be something to this Eastern philosophy because so many millions of people had learned from it, and it certainly had a following among intelligent people in the United States and Europe, by people you couldn't help but respect.

Someone in Japan had done a private survey on Hughes Aircraft, They sent me a copy of it in Japanese, which I had translated. And shortly thereafter, in the late summer of 1970, I was invited to Japan by a consortium of industrialists. I decided to go.

These Japanese industrialists needed a billion or so dollars capital for expansion and it seemed to me like a good opportunity to get into new fields that were beginning to interest me. I was in contact with the Mitsubishi people, Sony, Matsushita, the one or two others in the electronics and television industries out there. They were starting to develop computers. I knew that was the future. I just didn't know who to trust to build them right.

My business trip to Japan came to nothing, because the government there was, and still is, anti-foreign, and didn't want to allow foreign capital to come in with any measure of control – and I of course would not invest any significant capital without obtaining a significant measure of control. They should have known that, but, amazingly, they didn't.

I wanted Helga to come out with me, but she couldn't. She was having problems with her teenage daughter who had got involved with drugs. She said she'd tried to meet me in Kyoto, or maybe later in India.

I asked her, 'What makes you think I'm going to India?'

She said, 'Go to India, Howard. It's different from anything you know. Go, and you won't regret it.'

'But I hate the sight of horrible poverty.'

'We all do,' Helga said. 'Still, it doesn't hurt to see what you hate. You can always walk away from it.'

I had a little time to wander about Japan. I couldn't break the habits of a lifetime and I missed several appointments, ducked out, for which some of those grim Japanese bigwigs couldn't forgive me – I'd made them lose face. I didn't care. I went down to Kyoto, where they have a shrine, and took a walk in the gardens, watched the deer, sat on the steps of the monastery and looked at the monks in their yellow robes. I found it a beautiful country, but a toy country for a man of my size. None of the beds fit. I had to sleep on the floor on a mat with one of those wooden pillows. It gave me a crook in my neck that took weeks to go away. And I found Tokyo a disgusting city – totally polluted, overcrowded, a cheap, honky-tonk atmosphere. I wanted none of that.

So as soon as the business was over, I left. And I stopped in India on my way home.

Did you make the stop in India because of Helga?

Probably. I've never been totally sure. I wired my itinerary to Helga in Europe and asked her to meet me out there. Maybe it was written in the book of life and I had to go.

It certainly had nothing to do with business. In fact I had no specific aim in mind when I went there. I had a few names and addresses that Helga had given me, and I thought that since I was out in that part of the world, I might as well take a look around.

As far as my business associates back in the States were concerned, it was the same old game I had always played, which was that I had vanished, and nobody knew where. I was hiding out somewhere, probably Mexico or France, with some starlet, and that was that. When I went to Cuba to see Ernest, nobody knew I went, and when I went to Zihuatanejo with Helga on those trips, my people were close-mouthed at all times about anything and everything that concerned me.

And so I flew from Tokyo to India. I stayed in New Delhi briefly, but only because the plane landed there. It didn't interest me. Delhi struck me as just another filthy city with a lot of jerry-built modern buildings.

I went to Calcutta, and quickly left. There was a cholera epidemic, and I found out that this was an annual event. People were dying in the streets. It was hard to tell the dead from the living, mind you – these poor scrawny kids, women and children, living in a patch of gutter, sharing it with their sacred cows. Calcutta disgusted me even more than Tokyo, because there was such an extraordinary contrast between the few rich Indians and the fat tourists and the teeming masses. You can believe me, it took all my courage to walk through the streets. You know how I feel about filth and contamination. This was like plunging in a cesspool.

In that case, why did you do it?

Curiosity overcame my repugnance. They must have thought I was some apparition from outer space, because I walked through those streets wearing white gloves and spraying my throat with a special spray from time to time. I would have worn a surgical mask, but I knew it would have drawn a crowd.

I became a vegetarian during my stay there, too, because I thought there was less chance of getting poisoned from their vegetables than their meat.

After the experience in Calcutta I almost left the country. I said to myself, 'This country has nothing to offer except a few beautiful temples, poverty, filth, and superstition. I'm not learning anything, I'm just confirming my prejudices.'

But I decided it would be foolish, having come so far, to flee so quickly, and that's when I took a better look at the addresses Helga had given me. I remembered she had shown me a book about the holy city of Benares, where all the *fakirs* and *babas* worshipped by the banks of the Ganges. It had great meaning for the Indians, and it was on my way back to New Delhi. I wanted to please Helga, to show her that I was more broad-minded than she thought I was, and open to new experience. I hired an air-conditioned car and chauffeur and went to Benares – now they call it Varanasi, but then it was Benares. The chauffeur was a student, bright and friendly. He acted as a guide for me.

It's almost always been my habit to get up pretty early in the morning, so it was no problem for me when he wanted to get down to the river, the Ganges, at five o'clock in the morning, just when the action started.

That's a sight I'll never forget. I had read about Benares and it had a certain legendary quality for me, but you never believe that things will be as exotic as they really are. I visited the temples. I saw the burning ghats along the river, where they were cremating the bodies of their dead. The Ganges was just a stream of mud and crap. But it's holy. Boy, if that's holy! The people had come down to the river just as soon as the sun was up, before they had to go to work, and they were bathing in this brown soup, this slop, and drinking it.

I was so horrified that I was fascinated. I couldn't leave even though I knew I was in mortal danger.

I watched, and then we left the river and we marched up some steps to get back to the town. Our car was parked quite a way away, because the streets were narrow and it was impossible to drive a car through them. I was surrounded instantly by beggars. I had deliberately dressed in my oldest clothes, but it didn't matter, I was obviously an American, and therefore rich. The beggars were a collection such as I've never seen before in my life. I had seen beggars in Mexico – small children come up to you and beg, and you give them a few pesos and they go away. But in Benares there were dozens of filthy, horrible, maimed little children, on the verge of starvation. They maim them at birth so they'll do well in their begging career. The men and women importuned in such a way that I felt as if a mob was menacing me. They yelled and shrieked and whined, and waved stumps in my face –

the guide and I gave them what little money we had and managed to get out of there.

On the edge of this crowd, on the steps leading up from the Ganges, was an emaciated old man covered in dust and ashes. He wore nothing but a white loincloth. He was moving himself along the street, along the rough cobbles, on his knees. He wasn't a cripple – he could walk if he wanted to. But he didn't. And his knees were like a battlefield, scarred and bloody, and his skin was not only caked with dust but full of scabs. People were bowing down toward him when he crawled by.

I said, 'Who – what's that?'

The chauffeur said, 'That's a very holy man. He's crawled that way from some village many hundreds of miles away, and he's come to die in Benares, because to die in Benares is to be assured of liberation.'

I said, 'What do you mean, liberation?' I was astonished, and he looked at me with equal astonishment and said, 'Why, liberation means to have your soul freed, to join the One.'

I smirked. This was the kind of nonsense that made me put those books aside. But it did astonish me that an ordinary chauffeur, a guide, should speak this way. So I looked at the holy man again. He had terrible bloodshot eyes. He couldn't have been less than seventy, with short white hair, limbs just skin and bones. The crowd treated him with great respect – but I didn't get it. He looked like he belonged on Pershing Square in downtown Los Angeles. To me it was a man who had lost all dignity.

'That's enough of India for me,' I said to myself. 'I want to get out of here.'

We saw another holy man on the road, on the way back to the hotel. He was standing on one leg, staring up at the sun. That's what he did in life, stood on one leg and stared at the sun.

The guide said he was a guru. I thought, these people are in a bad way to think a masochist like that is a guru. I'd heard about Western boys and girls who go out to India on their pilgrimages, to discover the East and throw off the chains of their middle-class backgrounds and fill up their knapsacks with drugs. That appalled me. Not only the drugs, but the appointment of India as a place for the ultimate spiritual pilgrimage. India has had a good publicity agent for the last twenty-five years, since the British finished raping the country and pulled out. The young Americans, I decided, looked at the masses of poor people on the streets – perhaps starvation gave the Indians a kind of faraway look – and the kids said, 'How holy and beautiful these people are.' All I'd seen so far in India was the result of centuries of oppression followed by a few decades of hypocrisy, and the people were either pretentious or half-starved, depending on whether they were rich or poor.

I went back to the hotel in Benares and scrubbed myself from head to toe, soaked in the bath in cold water with a powerful antiseptic, closed the shutters against the sun and the heat, and then lay down on my bed under my mosquito netting and just sweated. There was no air-conditioning, just an overhead fan that rattled away like – well, like a broken fan. India's barely in the twentieth century.

I decided to leave the next day.

That night, when I slept, a strange thing happened to me. I dreamed of a dark-skinned bearded man who put his hand on my shoulder gently, and said, 'Come along with me, Sonny.'

Yes, he called me Sonny. No one had called me that since I was a kid. I didn't mind it at all. I didn't even mind his hand on my shoulder, touching me, and usually I mind that a lot. This bearded man exuded an aura of pleasantness, and smiled at me in a way that gave me confidence in him, made me feel he liked me and understood me.

In my dream, I asked him where we were going. He said, 'Nowhere. Are you ready for that?'

Then I woke up. The fan was still rattling away but the room was cool. It was dawn. Usually, you know, I can't remember my dreams. But this one was quite clear and fresh. In fact, there was an amazing reality to it. And I knew right away who the bearded man was.

Was it Ernest?

My God, no. Ernest had a suntan but he wasn't dark-skinned. No, it was a man I'd never met. But Helga had told me about him. It was a man named Sai Baba. His real name was Sathya Sai, but he was called Sai Baba by his disciples, and he lived near the city of Bangalore, in an ashram, a spiritual center where he taught.

Helga had said to me, 'When I catch up with you in India, Howard, I'd like to take you to meet a man named Sai Baba. He's a great man, a true guru. I went once to his ashram.'

I had said, 'Well, we'll see,' but of course what I meant was, 'Hell, no. Don't insult my intelligence and waste my time.'

Then I dreamed about the man, and he said, 'Come along with me.'

So I followed my instincts and decided to go.

Just like that? Immediately?

Those decisions have to be made immediately. If you think about them, juggle the pros and cons, you never act, or you run out of available time. I'd learned that lesson when I was designing airplanes and when I was flying. You had to follow your instincts if you wanted to achieve anything of significance or get somewhere in the fastest possible time.

I made my decision immediately. I packed my bag, sent Helga a cable telling her where I was headed, checked out of the hotel in Benares, took a limo to New Delhi and a plane down to Bangalore.

That's in the state of Andra Pradesh, in southern India, and it's dirt-poor down there – the Mississippi of India, if you like. The people are darker than up north. It's hot, dusty, and dangerous. But I felt I had to go, and somehow I convinced myself that the health risks were minimal. I spent a night in Bangalore in the comfort of the Taj Hotel and then early the next morning I hired a car and driver to get down to Puttaparti, which is the nearest village to the ashram. That trip took nine or ten hours. It was like driving through the worst parts of Nevada in the heat of summer, except that in Nevada you had paved roads. This was a dirt track. It passed through a bunch of hovels that were full of the most wretched poverty you can imagine. All transport was by ox and cart, and the oxen were so thin that sometimes they had no strength to pull the cart.

Finally, when I thought I might collapse from fatigue, we got to the

Chittravati River. The village of Puttaparti was on the other side. The river was barely a trickle – brown, sluggish, hardly moving – but the driver said he couldn't drive across it, it would ruin the transmission of his car.

'Then how am I going to get to Puttaparti?' I asked.

'Sahib,' he said, 'you will have to walk.'

I hired a boy to carry my luggage and I splashed across the river, through the brown muddy water, which at its deepest was about two feet. I felt like Moses.

It was evening by now, and dark. I was exhausted and I didn't really know where I was. I mean I was so worn out that I was disoriented. But I found the ashram, on the edge of the village, checked in, so to speak, asked for a single room, had to argue my way into getting one, succeeded by paying out a few extra rupees – money talks, even in a spiritual center, at least to the poor people who work there – and finally stretched my bones out on a narrow little cot in a room that was about the size of a prison cell. Someone who spoke English said to me, '*Darshan* is at six.' I didn't know what *darshan* was and I couldn't have cared less. I finished my supply of butter cookies that I'd bought at the airport in New Delhi and went to sleep.

When they woke me it wasn't light yet. I didn't wear a watch in those days but I've always been able to tell the time by the position of the sun, or just by instinct. I guessed that it was five o'clock in the morning. I was still disoriented, because I got up like a zombie, splashed some water in my face, put on a shirt and loose trousers, and let myself be herded out with everyone else into this big dusty square. Then I sank down into a heap.

Close to two hundred people were sitting out there with me, almost all of them Indians, with maybe half a dozen westerners. Everyone was silent. They were meditating, or, if they were like me, they were half-asleep and sitting in a kind of pre-dawn daze. It grew light, and I don't know how long we all sat there, or where I found the patience to do it, but I did.

Did you meditate at all?

I'm going to tell you the truth, even though it sounds awful. I meditated, in my way, about my problems in the TWA lawsuit, and how to slide out of that fine the court had levied on me, because the interest was being added to the fine every day and piling up like a dungheap. Treble damages, I kept thinking. Treble damages! Those bastards! I had to squirm out of those treble damages. I sat there for about two hours, trying to figure a way.

I didn't know then what meditation was all about. I learned later.

When it grew light I could see that there was a little Indian temple on the far side of this square, and we all sat facing it. When I say temple, that doesn't quite fit: it was a modest place, probably as big as a three-bedroom ranch house, and decorated with figures of various deities like Shiva and Krishna and such other bigwigs in the Indian lineup of gods. I found out later that Sai Baba lived in a back room. That was his home. The ashram was his home. He'd been born in a shack in Puttaparti and that shack became the ashram, it sort of grew up around the shack, until finally his disciples tore down the shack, or it collapsed one rainy season, and they built the temple for him and he took a room in the back as his living quarters.

I didn't see him come out, I just heard a murmur all around me, maybe two hours later, and I raised my head and there he was, right in front of us. He had a lot of curly dark hair with some gray in it – almost an Afro. His face was a little pudgy, and he had big brown eyes and a sweet smile. He wore an orange cotton robe and old sandals where you could see, if you had a sharp eye, that the straps had been repaired. He was a moderately large man, although not tall, and not at all skinny like the holy men I'd seen up north in Benares. I'd have to guess he was in his middle forties – I never did ask him his age. My main impression of him was his sweetness. I'm going to use a word you never heard come from my mouth: his *goodness.*

He wandered around in front of us, like he didn't quite know where to settle, and finally he picked a place in the dust to curl up. He made a speech. He had an ordinary voice, not too loud, and of course he spoke in Hindi. So I dozed off.

I woke up when someone kicked me, or, let's say, nudged me firmly in the butt with his foot. I opened my eyes and sat up. It was Sai Baba who had done it. He was barefoot. He was standing in front of me, smiling.

He said to me, in English, 'I'm glad you came.'

I said, 'I dreamed about you.'

'We'll talk later,' he said. 'Another day.'

'That's fine,' I said. 'I'm not in a hurry.'

I looked around me. It was late in the morning, maybe eleven o'clock. The point is, a number of hours had passed while I slept and while Sai Baba talked in Hindi.

When he walked away from me and I walked back to my room with the rest of the people -*darshan* was over, I realized – I found myself thinking about what he had said. Not the brief conversation we'd had when he came up and booted me in the bottom, but the words he'd spoken to all those two hundred people while I slept. I could remember them. And you've got to understand: he spoke in Hindi. But I remembered in English.

What did he say?

He talked about what he called 'the middle path.' He talked about what he called 'the seven internal foes of humankind.' They were Lust, Anger, Greed, Attachment, Conceit, Hatred, and Control. 'These nocturnal birds infest the tree of life and foul the heart where they build their nests.' He also said, 'What is required in life is an awareness of the vicious game that the mind plays. It presents before the attention one source after another of temporary pleasure. It doesn't allow any interval for you to weigh the pros and cons. When hunger for food is appeased, it holds before the eye the attraction of, for example, a new movie that everyone is talking about. Then it reminds the ear of the charm of building something, and then it makes the organs crave for the release of sexual tension, and then it requires us to get in touch with and chastise someone who hasn't behaved in a way that we expected him to behave. The yearning for comfort, for ownership, for various satisfactions, becomes subtly all-powerful. The burden of desires gradually becomes too heavy and man becomes dispirited and sad.'

I knew instantly what he meant. I knew that it was true. I understood that it wasn't original, that such things had been preached for centuries by various religious and spiritual leaders worldwide. That made no difference to me. *He* had said it. And he had said it at the right time and in the right tone of voice to the right person. He was talking to me. He was talking about me.

Of course he brought in a few Indian names and concepts like Dharma and Avatar and Krishna and the divine Atma, but I was able to filter them out and keep to the meat of the message.

I wandered around the rest of the day, found a primus stove, and managed to cook myself a little meal. Then came evening *darshan*. I went outside, curled up, and listened again. This time I stayed awake, and of course I couldn't understand a word. But Sai Baba's voice was friendly and soothing and for the most part I thought of what he had said that morning.

That went on for several days. During that time he also pulled a few tricks. He was a kind of magician, or sleight-of-hand artist. He would come up to some of the people, right after *darshan,* and pluck things out of the air. Not rabbits from a hat, although he did on one occasion produce a red silk handkerchief that he gave to a young Indian, and on another occasion he produced a ring with some semi-precious stone in it that he gave to a middle-aged German woman. Most of the time, what he produced, or manifested – 'manifested' is the word his followers used – was a powdery substance called *vibhuti*. It was supposed to be sacred ash. You could eat it, or rub it on your body. It was meant to be purifying.

Did you ever meet him and talk to him personally?

Not for a few days. Then, after evening *darshan,* he beckoned to me. He did this often, with various of his devotees, but I had been told that you had to hang out there a long time and have a certain seniority before your moment came. However, I had been there less than a week when he gave me the nod. I was pleased, and a little nervous. I followed him into the temple.

I knew by now that Sai Baba was a poor man, didn't want worldly goods other than what he needed to live in simple comfort. Some of his better-off Indian and Western followers gave him money, but he put almost all of that into the physical upkeep of the ashram or the construction of a little hospital he was setting up there, or he fed and clothed beggars and found little jobs for them at the construction site. For himself he kept just what he needed to eat and buy a new robe now and then. He was a very clean-looking man. He smelled of spices. I liked that.

So I wasn't surprised by the sparseness of the furnishings inside the temple. Sai Baba sat on a cane floor mat in the lotus position, in front of me. He offered me a stiffbacked cane chair - no way I could ever have got into the lotus position like he did. He knew that. I sat down. He made the sign of welcome by placing his palms together, smiled at me, and said, 'Is there anything you would like to ask me?'

'Yes. Why do you go through all that hocus-pocus,' I said, 'with the manifesting of ash and jewelry?'

His smile grew broader. 'You think that's hocus-pocus?'

'What else?'

'What's wrong with a little hocus-pocus?' he asked. 'Does it harm anyone?'

I laughed. 'I guess not. Maybe you need to do it to impress a certain kind of person. Means to an end. I can understand that.'

Still smiling, he reached out to my ear and pulled a handful of dark ash, what they called *vibhuti*, out of it, or out of the air, or out of his sleeve; who knows. 'Here,' he said. He pressed it into my palm. 'You keep this handful of "means to an end." Eat it, or anoint yourself with it, or throw it away. Do whatever you like with it.'

I laughed again, mumbled a kind of thank-you and put it in my pants pocket.

'Now may I ask *you* a question, sir?' Sai Baba said.

'Absolutely.'

'In the years left to you, if you knew beyond doubt that you wouldn't fail, what is the one thing that you would do?'

I was stunned into silence. I knew right away he had asked me the most intelligent question that you could ask any human being beyond the age of puberty. All the inessentials fell away. TWA, the various lawsuits, the default judgment, the SST, Las Vegas as the port of entry, Hughes Aircraft, Toolco – none of them rose to the mark. Not even life with Helga.

'You don't have to answer now,' Sai Baba said. He rose to his feet – not all that easily, I realized, because he was a bit overweight. I got up too. He made the sign of farewell by placing his palms together. I did the same. He had never asked me my name. He'd never asked who I was or what I did. He'd only asked that one question. At the door to the temple, as I was about to step outside into the hot evening, he placed a sweaty hand on my shoulder, and he said softly, 'Don't forget.'

I went to one more *darshan* before I left Puttaparti, but I realized that for the moment there was little more I could gain by being there. I also realized I didn't have to say goodbye to Sai Baba. He didn't expect it.

I hired another porter, waded across the Chittravati River in the other direction, found someone to drive me to Bangalore, and flew to New Delhi. There was a message from Helga waiting for me at my hotel. She said she was coming to India to spend a week with me, and if I left New Delhi I should leave a message for her where I'd be. She was due to arrive on Swissair from Geneva the following day.

I took a long hot bath to wash off the dirt of southern India, then a long cool shower to refresh myself, and then I sent for the maid to pick up my dirty clothes. Just before I handed my things to her I remembered what I had in the pocket of my old pants. I had all that *vibhuti* Sai Baba had 'manifested' and given to me. I poured it out into an ash tray before I stuffed the pants into the plastic laundry bag.

I decided to meditate for a while. By then I'd learned that meditation was a process to clear your mind, not to analyze what you thought were your problems, and you accomplished this by sitting still and silently saying a meaningless short word, which they called a mantra, over and over again. That way your mind became a blank receptacle, and if you were ready, good things entered in it. In the least, you were refreshed. It was like a fast, where you eat nothing and cleanse your guts – in meditation you cleansed your mind.

Then I remembered the *vibhuti*. What was I going to do with it? I could throw it out, but that troubled me, because he'd given it to me just before he'd asked me that big question. I could take it back with me to Nevada, but what was I supposed to do with it there? Put it in an urn and worship it? That seemed ridiculous. Or I could use it. How should I use it? I wasn't going to eat it; it was ash, and I might choke to death. The other thing I'd seen people do was rub it all over their bodies. I hesitated, because if I did that, I'd be dirty again. But what the hell, I thought, I could take another bath when I finished meditating. I had nothing else to do until Helga arrived.

I smeared the *vibhuti* all over my chest and forehead. It had a soft, powdery texture, not harsh at all. It smelled slightly of spice. Then I sat down in a chair to meditate.

What happened next is hard to explain. You probably won't believe it. Part of this is clear to me, but part is vague. Kind of shadowy.

I dimly remember leaving the hotel. I remember renting a chauffeured car. I hardly remember the journey at all. I must have slept on the way. I remember arriving again in Benares, where I spent the night, what was left of the night, I'm not sure. I had no luggage – I found that out later. I don't remember going down to the river, but it's clear that I must have done so, probably under my own steam – the car and driver definitely didn't take me – because I remember arriving there, by the Ganges, probably before dawn. I remember the darkness and the smells of incense, mud, and burning wood.

I sat down in the dirt by the river. Before that, as I told you, I couldn't get into the lotus position, but now I did it, or at least a fair approximation of it. My legs were crossed in front of me, and my hands were in what I'd have to describe as a cupped position, also in front of me.

I wore only my undershorts. They were white Jockey shorts. I didn't have another blessed thing on my body. No shirt, no socks and shoes, no pants, no hat. Just my white undershorts.

Do you see the picture I'm painting for you? I was thin, almost scrawny. I had long hair, even longer than it is now. It fell almost to my shoulders. I had a beard. And all my hair, of course, was gray, a pale shade of gray. I was not a thing of beauty.

I looked like a beggar. I was sitting there by the Ganges, in a trance, in beggar's clothes and in a beggar's position.

Now, as I may have told you, the riverside was full of beggars. They didn't do very well except when an occasional tourist gave them a dollar – they could eat for a day or two on a dollar – in the hope that they'd go away. I, on the other hand, was sitting there cross-legged in my Jockey shorts, with my hands forming a little cup in front of me. I didn't importune anyone, I didn't clutch at them, I didn't even ask. I just sat there, meditating. And I was deluged with money. With dollars, with rupees, with English pounds, with yen, with marks and francs. People couldn't pass by without giving me something. Indians, Asians, Europeans – everyone gave.

You see, money just gravitates to some people, whether they're accumulating TWA stock or sitting by the side of a muddy river in India. They're money magnets, and money is like metal shavings. I'm one of those people. I can't help it.

The coins and bills spilled over my cupped hands into a pile in the dust of the street. No one, not even the other beggars, dared take it from me. They must have thought I was a holy man come from afar, God knows where. I was thin enough, my hair was scraggly enough, my undershorts could have been taken for a loincloth, and I had the *vibhuti* rubbed into my chest and forehead. Anyone who stole from me would come back in the next life as a cockroach with backache.

I don't know how much time passed. I only know I was there and doing very well indeed.

I know this because suddenly Helga said, 'Howard! My God! Are you all right? What are you *doing?*'

She stood there in front of me wearing a lovely white silk dress from Chanel.

She had flown into New Delhi, gone to the hotel, found out I wasn't there, checked around and quickly learned that a car and driver had taken me to Benares. She hired another car.

I wasn't in any of the good hotels in Benares, but someone – she never knew who it was – said, 'Madam, I have seen the man you describe. He is down by the river near such-and-such a temple.'

So she came down with a guide and found me. She helped me to my feet and took me back to the hotel. I had tears in my eyes. I don't know why.

We took all the money with us in a sack. And outside of town, on the drive back to New Delhi, we passed a hospital for the poor. Helga took the sack inside and gave it one of the nursing nuns at the desk. It was a considerable amount of money – the driver had to help Helga carry it. I had done really well.

32

Howard flees Las Vegas for Paradise Island, claims he's the richest man in the world, reveals how he wrote his will, and admits his greatest ambition.

A GREAT PART of my experience in India – that last part, I mean, when I visited Sai Baba and ended up by the Ganges as a beggar – is of course difficult to explain. Most people wouldn't believe it, and so I haven't told it to anybody. They'd think I was cracked. They probably think it anyway, but if I told them about the *vibhuti* and the rest of it, they'd be absolutely certain.

Helga and I flew down to Rajastan: saw some temples, rode an elephant who tried to pickpocket me with his trunk, stayed in some palaces – played at being tourists.

While we were in Jaipur she said, 'Howard, my husband knows about us. He doesn't know it's you, but he knows it's someone. He begged me not to leave him for you.'

That made me nervous. I had never asked her to leave her husband.

She knew that. 'Don't worry,' she said. 'I told him I wouldn't. Then he asked me to give up seeing you so that he and I could try to make our marriage work again. I thought about it for a few days and then I agreed to do that, after this trip to India. He and I have a history, you see. History counts.'

'You and I have a history too,' I said.

'I know. Well, maybe we'll see each other again. Just give me time.'

I told her I understood. We flew back to California, I said goodbye to her at LAX, and then I took off for Las Vegas.

I didn't feel good about that parting, but nevertheless, in a way, I felt liberated. I didn't own her. I had fine memories. I still do. We talk now and then, but I haven't seen her since. Sometimes that saddens me. But I've learned to accept it. What can I do? She made a choice. It was the right choice for her and the wrong choice for me. The Mexicans say, '*Ni modo*' – so it goes. It implies the acceptance of suffering as part of life.

As soon as I reached Nevada, I thought, my time here is up. I'm leaving. This is not how I want to live. Let them take their treble damages, I no longer cared. My health was failing, and I had the feeling that there were greener pastures elsewhere, in the Bahamas, where the government was friendly to me, and malleable.

Did you try to buy the Bahamian government?

I didn't have to go that far. I could just rent it, so to speak, for as long as it was convenient.

I flew out to the Bahamas on Thanksgiving Day of 1970. But that wasn't a snap decision. In fact it was a decision I had made at least a year before that. I contacted the people I know on Paradise Island and they set it up within two weeks. I took over the top floor of the Britannia Beach Hotel.

Do you like the view better than the one from the ninth floor of the Desert Inn in Las Vegas?

There is no view. I had light-proof curtains put up before I moved in. I don't need a view. The view is in my mind.

Regarding my getaway from Las Vegas, the newspaper accounts, as always, were partly cockeyed and partly accurate. I did contact the people I knew at Lockheed and borrowed one of their Jetstars to fly out of Nevada. But I never got carried down nine flights of stairs and put on any stretcher, and I never will – unless they're carrying me out feet first to the graveyard, or I'm too sick to walk, or they've drugged me and are taking me away to dump me down an abandoned mine shaft. That last carries the highest probability rating, and if you ever hear that I've been carried away flat on my back you can tell the world that it undoubtedly wasn't of my own free will.

I left the hotel in the back of a panel truck and drove out to the airport and flew down to Nassau. I had done that twenty times in the previous five years, although not to Nassau. Only this time the newspapers found out because my people moved out too. And they made a fuss beyond belief.

You wonder why I've cut myself off from people? Why I live the way I live? There's your answer. I fear people because they're empty-headed and therefore dangerous. How is it possible that I've become like a specimen in the zoo when I'm deliberately not living in the zoo? That intrigues me. What an age we live in. I can tell you, I wouldn't mind getting out of it for awhile, and I'm not talking about using the cryogenic process to deep-freeze my body. With all the fine research facilities I've had at my command I should have stolen a page from H.G. Wells and had my people develop a time machine, a time traveler. I suppose if I sunk my entire fortune into it they'd be bound to come up with something that worked.

Where would you go if you had your choice?

I'd go back to China when they were building the Great Wall, and I'd be an engineer and help to build it, and I'd live a quiet life and die in my sleep. Have my Chinese sons bury me. Or out of curiosity I'd go back to America in 1870, to Texas, to see what the real West was like. That would fascinate me. Two-gun Howard, the Yoakum Kid.

But if I had just one choice, one trip, I'd go forward to the year 3000 and see what was going on then. See if there's anything left.

You don't regret your life, do you?

No, that would be a useless emotion. All that I really regret is that I was orphaned young, that I was rich much too soon to be able to deal with it properly, and that I couldn't have lived a more simple life among simpler people.

And what does it mean to you now to be one of the three richest men in the world?

I'll bet you or anyone else, including Paul Getty, that I'm not one of the three richest men in the world – I'm the richest. Every one of those Nevada properties which everyone thinks are such a bust is going to pay – and what do you think is going to happen when the United States, as it absolutely must, within the next five years, devalues the dollar by letting the price of gold float to its proper level? Do you know how much gold I've got, in the ground and out of it?

You have no idea. Well, plenty. And nobody knows how much real estate I've got. Not even me. But I can tell you it's worth a fortune. I have other investments where nobody knows I've got them. I put money into Indonesian oil a few years ago. I'm riding that one out, but it's a handsome profit so far. Getty's got an oil company and a collection of paintings. Big deal. The Sultan of Brunei is an out-and-out liar about what he owns. I can tell you, the most conservative estimate I can make of what I own – right now, this minute – is two billion nine hundred million dollars. That's conservative, that's on the shallow side.

What's the top?

Three billion one. And if I wanted to use an optimum figure, including my Indonesian oil, it's pushing three and a half billion. That makes me nearly twice as rich as Getty. The others, Hunt and the Mellons and Bob Smith, don't even come close. The one who's creeping up is Ludwig, the shipping guy. And of course one day someone's going to invent a computer that the average citizen can use in his home, and a way to write and pay your bills with it and communicate with other computers, and that man or woman will automatically make $10 billion and be on top of the heap. And it will be some twenty-five-year old whiz kid, because the computer industry is a young man's game.

I'll change my question. What does it mean to you to be the richest man in the world?

Not a damned thing. Money is of no interest to me anymore. All I care about is that I have a little peace in the rest of my days, and freedom from the seven internal foes of humankind. You remember?

Not offhand, but I'll look it up. Who are you leaving all that money to that doesn't interest you anymore?

That's in my will. Of course I won't have it published before I die. Nobody knows the contents of my will but me, not even the people who helped me draw it up.

I worked out all the variations, the ways in which I planned to divide my property on my death, and had a dozen typists type them up. I've done this several times. I had different sets of different bequests, all sorts of possibilities – I threw in a batch of red herrings. I had each of the secretaries type up a different version of the will, with each clause on a separate page. It was like taking a deck of cards and shuffling them. They couldn't possibly know the eventual outcome. In one paragraph I'd leave Toolco to the Hughes Medical Institute. In another I'd leave Hughes Aircraft to the United States government, ha ha ha. And in another to my cousins in Houston, or a dog pound in Las Vegas, or a guy who once gave me a lift in the desert when I ran out of gas. When I got all these pages back I threw out what I didn't want and arranged the right ones in the correct final order, and I had the last page, with my signature, witnessed by people in my organization. They saw only the last page.

The secretaries couldn't figure it out by seeing which pages were discarded, because I personally burned them and flushed the ashes down the toilet. You can reconstruct the writing on paper that's been burned, you know. But I doubted that anyone was going to climb down into the cesspools under Los Angeles or Las Vegas to find the ashes.

And I have one more question, if you don't mind. A naive one.

I know your naive questions pretty well by now. What's this one: how many people have I murdered in my lifetime?

I just wanted to ask you, after all you've gone through, in a long life with many achievements and many sorrows, what you believe in. Do you have a philosophy of life now? A guiding principle?

That certainly is a naive question, but I'll answer it. I can put it in one sentence. *Live and let live.* Privacy is all we've got – you, me, anybody. You can take any road in this world and if there are other people on it, no matter how crooked that road is, no one will pay serious attention to you except to flatter you and get things they want from you. But people will think you're 'normal.'

If you cut your own road, go your own way without inviting anyone along, then everyone in the world will say you're crazy, you took the wrong road. Because it *is* your own. You made it. People can't stand that, unless of course you invite them along – in which case it's not yours anymore and you might as well cut your losses and start all over again.

Did it ever occur to you that it doesn't make any difference what road you take, even if there are other people on it, as long as you're independent? 'If you are alone, you are your own man' – according to Leonardo da Vinci.

I like that. It could serve as a motto on my nonexistent family crest. You've said something intelligent. Now, why don't you ask me an intelligent question instead of things like, 'What's your philosophy of life?' and 'How does it feel to be the richest man in the world?'

What would you consider an intelligent question?

Why don't you ask, 'Did you enjoy your breakfast today?' That's a question that makes sense.

Did you enjoy your breakfast?

Yes, I did. Fresh fruit is a gift from the planet. And since I've reached what's undoubtedly the final decade of my life, you could also ask me what is my greatest ambition at this point.

What is your greatest ambition, Howard?

To enjoy my breakfast tomorrow.

What about Sai Baba's question? 'In the years remaining, if you knew beyond doubt that you wouldn't fail, what is the one thing that you would do?' What is that one thing?

Don't you know?

Not really. Unless it would be to seek enlightenment.

That would have been a magnificent task, but beyond my spiritual capability and the years I had left to me. What I chose to do was tell the story of my life, warts and all. And I've just finished.

Afterword

IN FEBRUARY 1972 Howard Hughes fled Paradise Island in the Bahamas to take up residence on the top floor in yet another hotel, the Intercontinental Managua in Nicaragua. During the four remaining years of his life, he never returned to live in the United States. In December 1972 he moved to England, to London's Inn on the Park; a year later he was back in the Caribbean in the Xanadu Princess Hotel on Grand Bahama Island; and two years later he flew to Mexico, to a hospital bed in the penthouse of the Acapulco Princess Hotel.

In 1972 Hughes finally relinquished control of Toolco and allowed it to become a public company; he soon sold all his shares. A holding company, Summa Corporation, was created, and all of Hughes's property except for Hughes Aircraft was placed under its umbrella.

Many witnesses, including a four-man medical team, later testified that by 1973 Hughes had become a hopeless drug addict, and that the chief purpose of his move from the Bahamas to Mexico was to insure a steady supply of codeine for his habit. (One of his doctors said under oath that Hughes's drug usage had risen to between 25 to 45 grains of codeine and seven to fifteen ten-milligram Valium tablets per day.) In the last year of his life he shrank three inches, a tumor protruded from the side of his head, his teeth were almost destroyed, his arms and thighs were a maze of needle tracks, his prostate was radically enlarged, and he weighed less than one hundred pounds. He was starving.

On April 3, 1976, after a period of delirium, he lapsed into a virtual coma. On April 5 he was flown in a private plane from Acapulco to a hospital in Houston, the city where he had been born. He died before the plane crossed the border.

In 1983 the wooden flying boat – the Hercules, or Spruce Goose: 750 feet long with a wingspan of 330 feet – was moved from its hidden hangar by the City of Long Beach, California, and placed on exhibit in the world's largest geodesic dome as a tourist attraction. A decade later it was disassembled and moved to McMinnville, Oregon by the Evergreen Aviation Educational Center. There she still sits.

The original H-1 racer is on exhibit at the National Air and Space Museum in Washington D.C.

About the Author

FOR PERPETRATING the hoax, Clifford Irving was sentenced to 2½ years in federal prison. Richard Suskind, his researcher and co-author, served five months, and Edith Irving, as a co-conspirator, was sentenced to sixty days by the U.S. courts and to one year by a Swiss tribunal.

Irving was twice transferred from prison to prison on charges of possession of contraband; at the final stop, Danbury Federal Correctional Institution in Connecticut, where he was co-chairman of the Inmate Committee, he was placed in solitary confinement and formally accused of organizing a work-stoppage and riot. When Irving demanded that lie-detector tests be given to him and his accusers, the charges against him were dropped. Twice denied parole by the Nixon administration, he finally achieved it by filing a writ in federal court against the prison authorities. He kept a prison journal; an excerpt was published in *Playboy*.

Freed, Irving resumed his career as a novelist, and he has since published ten books. The *New York Times Book Review* has called him 'a born storyteller.' Ernest Lehman wrote: 'With *Tom Mix and Pancho Villa*, Clifford Irving takes his place among the giants of contemporary literature.' In the *Los Angeles Times*, Caroline See lauded Irving as 'a master,' and William Safire in the *New York Times* called Irving's *Trial* 'the novel of the year.' Thomas Keneally wrote: 'In *The Angel of Zin*, Irving has given the concept of murder an enlarged dimension... a totally engrossing thriller.' Donald Westlake said of *Final Argument*: 'Every part of it is terrific. What a wonderful piece of storytelling.' *Booklist* called *The Spring* 'extraordinarily entertaining and thoughtful.'

Joseph Persico, Colin Powell's biographer, wrote: 'No writer today surpasses Clifford Irving in making fiction ring like truth.' Portrayed by Richard Gere, he is the subject of the 2007 Miramax film, *The Hoax*; but Irving maintains that 'The movie is itself a hoax'.

With his Australian wife he lives in Colorado and Mexico, writing and painting, although his chief preoccupation, he says, 'is to understand some small part of the nature of existence'.